ORIENTAL RUGS in The Metropolitan Museum of Art

ORIENTAL RUGS IN THE METROPOLITAN MUSEUM OF ART

by **M. S. Dimand** CURATOR EMERITUS OF ISLAMIC ART

WITH A CHAPTER AND CATALOGUE OF RUGS OF CHINA AND CHINESE TURKESTAN

by Jean Mailey ASSOCIATE CURATOR OF THE TEXTILE STUDY ROOM

The Metropolitan Museum of Art

DISTRIBUTED BY New York Graphic Society

Color photography by O. E. Nelson (pages 146, 158),
Taylor and Dull (page 154),
and William F. Pons (all other photographs).
Black and white photography, unless otherwise
specified, by the Museum's Photography Studio.
Designed by Peter Oldenburg
Composed by Lund Humphries, Bradford, England
Printed by The Meriden Gravure Company,
Meriden, Connecticut
Color printing by Imprimeries Réunies,
Lausanne, Switzerland
Bound by A. Horowitz & Son, Clifton, New Jersey

LIBRARY OF CONGRESS CATALOGING IN PUBLICATION DATA
New York (City). Metropolitan Museum of Art.
  Oriental rugs in the Metropolitan Museum of Art.
  Bibliography: p.
  1. Rugs, Oriental—Catalogs. 2. Rugs—New York (City)—
Catalogs. I. Dimand, Maurice Sven. II. Mailey, Jean. III. Title.
NK2808.N37   746.7'5   73-2846
ISBN 0-87099-124-8

CONTENTS

INTRODUCTION   Thomas Hoving   vii

PREFACE   ix

1   Techniques of Oriental Rugs   1

2   Rug Weaving and Knotting from Antiquity
to the Twelfth Century   5

3   Seljuk Rugs of Asia Minor:
Thirteenth Century   15

4   Representations of Mongol Rugs in
Chinese Paintings   21

5   Rugs of Persia   27
     CATALOGUE   96

6   Rugs of India   117
     CATALOGUE   129

     Color Plates   133

7   Rugs of Ottoman Turkey   173
     CATALOGUE   220

8   Rugs of Spain   251
     CATALOGUE   262

9   Rugs of the Caucasus   265
     CATALOGUE   277

10   Rugs of Western Turkestan   286
     CATALOGUE   291

11   Rugs of China and Chinese Turkestan   296
     CATALOGUE   337

     BIBLIOGRAPHY   350

INTRODUCTION

It has often been stated that only prolonged study of a complex work of art will establish its identity or elucidate the final mystery surrounding its creation. To express this truism in more colloquial terms, one can say that if one has not "lived" with a work of art, one cannot expect to understand it fully. No such reproach can be leveled at Maurice S. Dimand with regard to the objects he deals with in the present book.

Dr. Dimand came to the Museum in 1923 as a research assistant in the Egyptian Department, where he was asked to write a catalogue of its Coptic textiles. He had worked on such material during his studies at the University of Vienna, where he had been a student of the celebrated Josef Strzygowski. His Ph.D. thesis, *Die Ornamentik der koptischen Woll-wirkereien*, published in Leipzig, 1921, was written on Coptic tapestries, particularly on those in the Museum of the University of Lund, Sweden. In 1921, a subdepartment of the Metropolitan's Department of Decorative Arts was created to deal with Near Eastern, particularly Islamic, art, and Dimand was put in charge of this section. He rose in the Museum hierarchy in charge of both the collection of Ancient Near Eastern Art and Islamic Art, until he retired in 1960 to become Curator Emeritus.

During his long Museum service Dimand was, of course, concerned with many media, but he always retained a special love for the textile arts, particularly for the vast field of oriental rugs, in which he organized two memorable exhibitions. First, in 1930, there was a show of Persian rugs of the so-called Polish type, in which many of the fine examples were from the Museum's collection. Five years later Dimand produced a more general exhibition of oriental rugs and textiles. In both instances he published a general guide combined with an illustrated catalogue of the exhibited pieces.

When Dimand joined the Metropolitan, we had already been given a splendid assembly of rugs, presented by James F. Ballard of St. Louis, a catalogue of which was published in 1923 by Joseph Breck, Curator of the Department of Decorative Arts and Assistant Director of the Museum, and by Frances Morris, Head of the Textile Study Room. Having arrived too late to deal with the Metropolitan's share of the Ballard Collection, Dimand proceeded to catalogue the second part of the collection, which was given in 1929 to the City Art Museum of St. Louis. The beautifully produced publication proved to be one of *the* rug books both here and abroad, and it is still highly esteemed by scholars. Dimand's special day in rug history at the Metropolitan arrived somewhat later when he, together with the then Director, James J. Rorimer, negotiated another splendid gift: oriental rugs belonging to Joseph V. McMullan. Many of these were selected by Dimand and then given outright to us. Others remained with the collector but were earmarked to come to us eventually in a succession of gifts. This is by no means all. Dimand was also the happy recipient of gifts of rugs of outstanding quality, notably those belonging to J. Pierpont Morgan, George Blumenthal, Horace Havemeyer, and John D. Rockefeller, Jr., as well as to the Kress Foundation.

During his curatorship Dimand wrote many articles on rugs and textiles, especially studies of pieces newly acquired by the Museum. If one were to mention but one of his outstanding research contributions, it would doubtless be "An Early Cut-Pile Rug from Egypt," which appeared in the *Metropolitan Museum Studies*, Volume IV (1932–1933). As a scholar-writer Dimand continued to produce, even after his retirement. I point merely to his article "The 17th Century Isfahan School of Rug Weaving" in our 1972 book *Islamic Art in The Metropolitan Museum of Art*.

Having long presided over an outstanding collection of rugs in which he took special pride, Dimand eventually conceived the idea of writing the present volume. Our extensive collection, as the book shows, is of the first order and ranks with those in the Museum of Decorative Arts, Vienna, the Victoria and Albert Museum, and the Museum of Turkish and Islamic Art, Istanbul. However, not all the rugs in our collection are masterpieces. Certain less interesting ones have been excluded from the book, notably, near duplicates and the more common types of the eighteenth and nineteenth centuries such as the Ghiordes Kula and Ladik varieties. Also absent are doubtful pieces, fragmentary copies of earlier types, and the common types of modern production. A group of high quality, the rugs given to the Museum by Joseph V. McMullan, our long-term friend and benefactor, is only partly catalogued here; inasmuch as this collector has published his own catalogue, it did not seem necessary to repeat his entire data.

While June 1, 1970, was set as the cut-off date for late additions to the catalogue, exceptions were made for two outstanding rugs. One, the so-called Simonetti rug (figure 181, catalogue number 97), is considered one of the finest examples of the rare group of Mamluk Egyptian rugs of the early sixteenth century. Since this rug has not been seen in public since it was first exhibited in Munich in 1910, its last-minute inclusion in this book should be regarded as a happy omen for the publication. The other, a Mughal Indian floral rug (figure 134, catalogue number 59), is too well known not to find its place in this distinguished assembly of rugs.

Both the Museum and Dimand are pleased that Jean Mailey, Associate Curator of the Textile Study Room, has contributed a chapter and catalogue on our Chinese and Chinese Turkestan rugs. In combination with Far Eastern textiles, she has been studying this little-known material for years, and its inclusion makes our book all the more valuable.

Two persons have been especially helpful in bringing this ambitious work to publication: Madeline Hart, who checked and re-checked the factual matter, and Toby Volkman, who did the final editorial work on the manuscript. The Museum and all other friends of oriental rugs are thankful for their help, and thankful above all to the achievement of Dimand, whom we shall now call the *Altmeister* in this particular field.

Thomas Hoving
Director

viii

PREFACE

The appreciation of oriental rugs in America has a distinguished tradition. Names of such collectors as Charles T. Yerkes, Joseph L. Williams, James F. Ballard, Benjamin Altman, John D. Rockefeller, Jr., George H. Myers, and Joseph V. McMullan are well known the world over. Thanks to these collectors some of the finest oriental rugs in existence today are in this country. The importance of American collections became especially apparent after the Second World War, when many rugs either disappeared or were destroyed by bombing, as in the case of the twenty great rugs of the Berlin Museum.

The Metropolitan Museum's rug collection has been built up over the years through generous bequests and gifts and also through fortunate purchases. Many of the outstanding rugs in the Museum have come from the collections of Altman, Ballard, Rockefeller, and McMullan, as well as other notable sources: Isaac D. Fletcher, J. Pierpont Morgan, George F. Baker, George Blumenthal, Horace Havemeyer, and the Kress Foundation. As a result, the Museum's collection has become, according to Dr. Erdmann and others, one of the most important in the world.

In this book I have endeavored to give a history of rugs in the Near and Middle East, including Moorish Spain, illustrating it mainly with the material in the Metropolitan, complemented by significant rugs in other collections. To complete this history for the whole of Asia, Jean Mailey has contributed a chapter, with catalogue, on the rugs of China and Chinese Turkestan.

I would also like to thank many of my colleagues for their assistance in the preparation of this book, which was first suggested by the late Director James J. Rorimer. The late Hannah McAllister, Associate Curator of Ancient Near Eastern Art, was responsible for many of the catalogue descriptions and technical analyses.

M. S. Dimand

One:

TECHNIQUES OF ORIENTAL RUGS

Oriental rugs can be divided into two main groups, those with a flat surface—without a pile—and those with a pile. The flat-woven rugs are produced by a number of methods. Most of the pile rugs are knotted, with the individual knots tied by hand. (Some early pile examples from Egypt, made by another method, will be described in chapter 2). Since rugs with a pile are the ones most frequently encountered, we may begin with a brief account of the techniques used in making them.[1]

The structure consists of warp, weft, and pile, and in the making of the rug two processes are combined, weaving and knotting. The rug is made on a loom, usually vertical (horizontal looms are used by certain nomad weavers) and ordinarily consisting of two horizontal rotating beams of wood attached to upright side pieces. On this frame the warp threads are stretched from beam to beam. Cotton, wool, or silk is used for the warp. In general, the rugmakers of Persia prefer cotton, and the Turkish weavers of Anatolia and the weavers of the Caucasus prefer wool. The loom is equipped with a heddle, a device that divides the warp threads into two groups to produce the openings (sheds) for the weft threads. The material of the pile is usually wool (sheep or goat) or silk. However, in certain rugs cotton and camel hair appear. Balls of colored yarn hang conveniently from the loom's upper beam. To produce the pile, the weaver, seated before the loom, inserts a short length of yarn of the desired color and ties it

in a particular way around a pair of warp threads, or, in a less common procedure, around a single warp thread. After the knot is in place it is trimmed to the desired level. The length or height of the pile varies from country to country. In some rugs the pile is clipped short; in others, such as the nomad-woven rugs of the Caucasus and of Kurdistan, in northwest Persia, the pile is left quite long. Several weavers work together, tying the knots in rows across the rug; they follow cartoons divided into small squares, with each square representing an individual knot. After a row of knots is tied, two, three, or even four weft threads are shot through alternate sheds and beaten into place with a heavy comb to tighten the structure of the rug.

The knots used in oriental rugs are three: the Ghiordes, often called the Turkish knot; the Senna, often called the Persian knot; and the single-warp or Spanish knot. The last is used mostly in Spanish rugs.

The Ghiordes knot, named after the town of Ghiordes in western Anatolia, is tied around each successive pair of warp threads, encircling each warp, the ends coming together between the warps (figure 1). In rugs tied with the Ghiordes knot the warps usually all lie in one plane. When, in certain rugs, alternate warps are set on a lower plane, the pile may incline toward one or the other side of the rug.

The Senna knot, named for the town of Senna in Kurdistan, is also tied around a pair of warps. One end encircles one of the warps, as in the Ghiordes

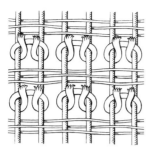

FIGURE 1
Ghiordes knot

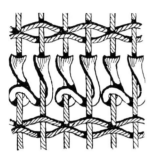

FIGURE 2   Senna knot.
From Erdmann, *Oriental
Carpets*

knot, the other passes beneath the second warp and comes to the front beyond it (figure 2). This knot may be made in either direction; that is, the encircled warp may be either the right or left one of the pair. The first, which is commoner, produces a pile that inclines to the weaver's left, the second, to his right. The Senna knot, used in most antique Persian rugs, is also the knot of Indian and Chinese rugs, some Turkoman rugs, and Turkish court rugs.

In some Persian rugs, usually of silk but sometimes of wool, a brocading with metal threads is used in conjunction with the knotting. In this technique the brocade shoots pass alternately over and under each warp thread, or, when the warps are set on two levels, the brocading may be on the upper level only, in which case the metal threads pass under one and over three or under two and over two.[2] The brocading technique was practiced as early as the sixteenth century, since it is found in a famous silk hunting rug of this period (figure 78). In the so-called "Polish" or "Polonaise" rugs of the first half of the seventeenth century (page 59), with their large areas of glittering metal, there are, to every row of knots, five brocade shoots woven on the warps of the upper level. The threads consist of a silk core closely wound with strips of silver or silver gilt. The metal covering often wears away, and now, in many of these rugs, only the silk core remains.

The third of the pile knots, the single-warp or Spanish, is found chiefly in oriental rugs made in Spain. (It is also known in some medieval rugs of

western Europe.) Simpler in structure than the Ghiordes and Senna knots, and by some authorities not regarded as a true knot, it is tied around a single warp thread, the ends crossing at the back and coming to the front on either side of the warp (figure 3). A further difference in the technique is that the Spanish knot is placed on every other warp only, shifting to the adjacent warps in the succeeding row of knots, while the Ghiordes and Senna knots are tied on each pair of warps in a given row.

A rug needs selvages and ends to prevent it from raveling. Oriental weavers formed their selvages in various ways.[3] In some rugs the weft threads are wound around one or two double warps, forming so-called cords. Sometimes such cords are strengthened with an overcasting of wool or silk. The ends of rugs were finished in different ways, according to the region. Many Caucasian rugs, for example, have a band woven in tapestry technique, beyond which fringes are formed from the warp ends. Such fringes are often twisted or knotted together in groups. In other rugs the warp ends form a series of loops, sometimes two or three rows of loops; in still others the warp may be braided.

Among the flat-woven oriental rugs the tapestry-woven one known in Turkey as a *kilim* (this Turkish term is now in general use throughout the Near East) is the most popular. The tapestry technique, one of the simplest methods for producing a decorated fabric, is also one of the oldest, for it was known in ancient Egypt. Fine linen fabrics found in the tomb of Tuthmosis IV of the XVIII Dynasty (died 1417 B.C.) show a tapestry decoration.[4] The kilims have warps and wefts of wool, silk, or sometimes cotton, and occasionally wefts of metal thread. The wefts of

FIGURE 3   Spanish or single-warp knot. From Tattersall, *Notes on Carpet-Knotting and Weaving*, with permission of the Victoria and Albert Museum

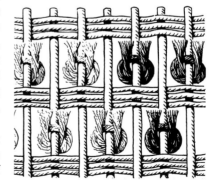

FIGURE 4
Tapestry with slit.
From Tattersall,
Notes, with permission
of the Victoria and
Albert Museum

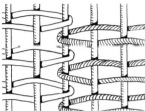

FIGURE 5 Persian
tapestry without slits

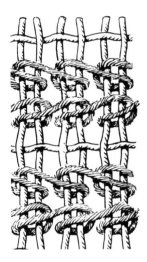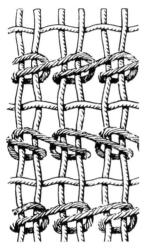

FIGURE 6 Sumak weaving. From Tattersall, *Notes*,
with permission of the Victoria and Albert Museum

centers, particularly Kashan. Here fine kilims were made of silk and metal thread, the multicolored silk wefts numbering from forty-five to eighty to the inch.

Another flat-woven technique is known as Sumak, the name supposedly derived from Shemakha, a town in the Caucasus. In the Sumak technique, found in several types of Caucasian rugs, the pattern-forming threads are carried in front of four warps and then back, encircling two of the warps (figure 6), or, in some rugs they go forward over only two warps and back under one. The "stitches" overlap, making a herringbone effect when their direction is reversed in successive rows. After every row or two of pattern stitches a weft thread is shot through to give the fabric strength. In many Sumak rugs the ends of the pattern wefts are left dangling on the back, to act as a pad when the rug is placed on the floor.

Some flat-woven rugs, chiefly Caucasian, show still other methods. In one type the pattern wefts, when not visible on the surface of the rug, float free on the back. This technique recalls the so-called lancé weaves that the Coptic weavers of Egypt, early in the Christian era, used in decorating narrow bands.[5] Other flat-woven Caucasian rugs, particularly the so-called Verné rugs (page 275), show several techniques combined, with some sections in plain or tapestry weave, others in Sumak or even needlework. Embroidery, as a technique for producing rugs, was known in antiquity. The making of embroidered rugs of wool or silk continued in the Islamic era, with this use of pictorial needlework reaching its height in Persia in the time of Shah Abbas (page 67).

The fineness of an oriental rug depends on a number of factors. An important one in wool rugs is the quality of the wool.[6] The wool of sheep, the preferred material for the pile, was carefully chosen, with the different qualities from the back, belly, and legs being kept separate. The very fine white wool of Persian rugs that was supplied to the workshops of Tabriz is said to have come from the Salmas and Maku districts of the Azerbaijan Mountains. Other districts that produced excellent wool were that of which Kermanshah is the center, and the province of Khurasan. To the expert's hand, rugs made of the best Khurasan wool have a soft, silky feel, as opposed to those made of Tabriz wool, which have a certain dryness. Goat hair was used for the pile in a few regions. It occurs in some Turkish rugs but is rare in old Persian rugs. A more common practice was to mix goat hair with sheep wool.

Other important technical factors in the quality of a rug include the spacing of the warp, the number of

various colors pass over and under alternate warps, carried by a bobbin as far as the pattern requires. As the weaving progresses, the wefts are beaten tightly into place, concealing the warp. In this technique, unlike that of pile rugs, the front and back surfaces of the rug usually look alike.

Two principal variations in the tapestry technique may be mentioned. In the group of kilims made by nomad and peasant weavers there are slits through the fabric where the areas of different color meet but do not join, the pattern wefts turning back on adjacent warps (figure 4). In the group of kilims made in Persian court manufactories the pattern threads turn back on the same warp, obviating the slits (figure 5). In Persia in the time of Shah Abbas (1587–1628) the tapestry technique was highly developed in several weft threads inserted between the rows of knots, and the type of knot. Rugs tied with the Senna knot are generally finer in texture than those with the Ghiordes. The early Anatolian rugs show about 70 to 80 Ghiordes knots to the square inch. On the other hand, Persian rugs tied with the Senna knot show from about 200 to 575 knots per square inch in wool rugs, with the count still higher in silk rugs—for example, about 728 knots per square inch in the Vienna silk hunting rug (figure 78). Some seventeenth-century Mughal rugs of India, made of very fine wool, have as many as 800 Senna knots to the square inch, and one fragment (figure 136) has 1258. An Indian silk rug of this period, tied with the Senna knot (figure 140), has about 2552 knots to the square inch. A further significant point about the Senna knot is that it surpasses the Ghiordes in its ability to define details.

Until the importation of European aniline dyes began in the second half of the nineteenth century, the oriental craftsmen colored their yarns with a great variety of natural dyes.[7] Most of these, together with their mordants, were obtained from vegetable sources. A popular mordant, tartaric acid, was extracted from grapes. In the classic period the dyemaster procured various shades of blue from the leaves of the indigo plant, which was native to Persia but was also imported by Persian dyers from India. Yellow was obtained from a number of sources, notably vine leaves, turmeric blossoms, the rinds of pomegranates, and the crocus or saffron flower. In Anatolia and the Caucasus, yellow, and green as well, were obtained from buckthorn berries. Browns came from oak bark, walnut husks, and from catechu, a substance produced by an acacia tree. The roots of the madder plant, grown in Persia and other countries, yielded many shades of red. Another source of red was the dried body of the female *kermes* insect, as it is known in Persia. Used by itself, this dye produced a dark red;

in various combinations it gave a salmon pink or a deep blue red. To obtain their secondary colors, the dyers employed double-dipping. A green, for instance, was made from indigo and a yellow dye. Violet tones were made from indigo and a red dye. Black and dark brown were obtained from a chemical substance, sulphate of iron, produced from filings dissolved in citric acid. This black is an impermanent color and in addition the dye, through oxidation, has a corrosive effect. Consequently, old rugs frequently show a loss of pile in black areas. When it was available, the natural wool of black sheep was used instead. The weaver's white or near white was in most cases the natural undyed wool.

The type and condition of the yarn could have a perceptible effect on the taking of the dye. Often to be seen in old rugs is an effect known in the Near East as *abrash*: a change of hue within an area of color, producing streaks of various widths. Far from being considered a defect, abrash is regarded by many connoisseurs as a decorative effect and a proof of handwork.

As early as the sixteenth century the Persians were renowned in Europe for the quality of their dyes. Attempts were made to copy their methods. In 1579 the English dyer Morgan Hubblethorne was sent to Persia by the Right Worshipfull Societie of Merchant Adventurers, charged by Richard Hakluyt with these instructions: "In Persia you shall finde carpets of course thrummed wooll, the best of the world, and excellently coloured: those cities & townes you must repaire to, and you must use meanes to learne all the order of the dying of those thrummes, which are so died as neither raine, wine, nor yet vinegar can staine: and it you may attaine to that cunning, you shall not need to feare dying of cloth: For if the colour holde in yarne and thrumme, it will holde much better in cloth."

Notes to Chapter One

1 Recommended sources for further details on weaving and knotting techniques in oriental rugs are: Irene Emery, *The Primary Structures of Fabrics*; Arthur Upham Pope, "The Technique of Persian Carpet Weaving," in *A Survey of Persian Art*, ed. Arthur Upham Pope, III, pp. 2437–55; C. E. C. Tattersall, *Notes on Carpet-Knotting and Weaving*.

2 Pope, in Pope, *Survey*, III, figs. 799, 800.

3 Tattersall, *Notes*, pl. IV.

4 Howard Carter and Percy E. Newberry, *The Tomb of Thoutmôsis IV*, Catalogue général des antiquités égyp-

tiennes du Musée du Caire (Westminster, 1904), pl. XXVIII.

5 A. F. Kendrick, *Catalogue of Textiles from Burying-Grounds in Egypt*, II, *Period of Transition and of Christian Emblems*, Victoria and Albert Museum (London, 1921), pls. XXVIII, XXIX.

6 Information in this paragraph comes from Heinrich Jacoby, "Materials Used in the Making of Carpets," in Pope, *Survey*, III, p. 2456.

7 Information on dyes comes in part from Jacoby, in Pope, *Survey*, III, pp. 2459–62.

Two:

RUG WEAVING AND KNOTTING FROM ANTIQUITY TO THE TWELFTH CENTURY

The use of rugs as floor coverings or wall hangings can be traced back to the ancient Near East. The Greeks, according to literary sources, were familiar with rugs from Babylonia and Persia and admired them greatly. Several alabaster slabs from the palaces of Sennacherib (705–681 B.C.) and Assurbanipal (668–626 B.C.) at Nineveh show ruglike designs. The surfaces of these slabs, which once paved doorways, are divided into a field and a border, as are later oriental rugs. The field of one of the Assurbanipal slabs is divided into squares containing large rosettes of stylized lotus blossoms and pine cones (figure 7). The double border has a row of alternating lotus blossoms and buds, connected with one another, and a row of linked palmettes; both borders are edged with bands of circular rosettes.

Whether the prototypes of these rugs represented in stone were pile or flat-woven rugs is impossible to tell from the stones themselves. However, the technique of rug knotting was certainly known in the ancient world, as is evident from the Russian excavations conducted by S. I. Rudenko at Pazyryk in the Altai mountains of Central Asia.[1] Here Rudenko brought to light a Scythian burial ground of the fifth century B.C. In its forty mounds, preserved by a thick

FIGURE 7 Alabaster slab from the palace of Assurbanipal (668–626 B.C.) at Nineveh. Courtesy of the Trustees of the British Museum

FIGURE 8   Wool pile rug (detail) from Pazyryk, v
century B.C. State Hermitage Museum, Leningrad

layer of permanent ice, was found a veritable treasure
of Scythian art in leather appliqué, felt appliqué, textiles, and rugs. One of the mounds yielded a well-
preserved wool rug measuring 6 feet 3 inches by 6
feet 4½ inches (figure 8). Students of oriental rugs
were astonished when Rudenko announced this as a
true knotted-pile rug. Rug and textile experts, exam-
ining it in the Hermitage Museum, confirmed that it
is tied with the Ghiordes knot and has about 240
knots to the square inch. The deep red field has rows
of large rosettes in squares, as do the stones from
Nineveh just discussed. Like the illustrated slab, the
Pazyryk rug has a double border. The outer one contains a row of horses, some with riders, some with
walking grooms, known from Achaemenian sculpture of Persepolis; the inner one contains a frieze of
elk. The rug shows a mixture of Assyrian, Achaemenian, and Scythian motifs. Although some writers
—I am one of them—regard the rug as a Persian product, others regard it as Scythian, with a strong Persian and Assyrian influence. While this ancient rug
shows the Ghiordes knot, a fragment of a rug found
by Rudenko in a Scythian tomb at Bashadar, near
Pazyryk, shows the Senna knot. Thus it is clear that
the art of rug knotting was practiced as early as the
fifth century B.C. Consequently, it is not impossible
that the rugs represented on the Assyrian stone slabs
may have been pile rugs.

The manufacture of pile and flat-woven rugs continued in the Christian era in various parts of Central

Asia and the Middle East. Fragments of wool pile
rugs dating from the beginning of the first millennium have been found in Chinese Turkestan, Syria,
and Egypt. In the dwellings, refuse heaps, and grave
pits of Lou-lan, a station in Chinese Turkestan on the
Chinese trade route to the West, Sir Aurel Stein found
fragments of pile rugs that can be dated to the second
or third century.[2] Tied with either the Ghiordes knot
or a single-warp knot similar to the Spanish knot,
these fragments have rows of long woolen tufts. A
fragment of a rug found by Albert von Le Coq in
Kyzyl, Chinese Turkestan, dates from the fifth or
sixth century and has a knot tied around a single
warp.[3] Where this rug and those of Lou-lan were
made is not known. Perhaps they were made locally,
perhaps they were imported from the west, possibly
from eastern Persia, particularly the province of
Sogdiana. Eastern Persia was under Sasanian rule
during the centuries mentioned, and it had active
trade relations with Chinese Turkestan.

Rivaling Rome and Byzantium, the Sasanian dynasty (226–637) ruled not only in Persia and Mesopotamia but in parts of Syria. Under the Sasanians
the great Achaemenian traditions of Persian art were
revived, and the arts and crafts were highly developed. Holding a monopoly on the silk trade between China and the West, the Sasanians established
their own looms for the manufacture of silk stuffs.[4]
Important centers of their silk weaving were in the
provinces of Khuzistan (ancient Susiana), bordering
Mesopotamia; fine silks were made here not only for
home consumption but export. Sasanian silk textiles
of the third to seventh century have been found in
Egypt, chiefly in the cemeteries of Akhmim and
Antinoë.[5] The Persian artists of this period created
a new style of abstract pseudofloral ornament with the
palmette as the principal motif. This ornament,
known in stucco decoration (figure 9), greatly influenced the formation of the Islamic arabesque.

It is known that the Persians of the Sasanian period
manufactured rugs. From literary sources we learn
that both flat-woven and pile rugs were made. When
the Sasanian king Khusrau II was defeated in 638 by
the Byzantine emperor Heraklius, his favorite residence, Dastagird, north of Baghdad, was looted of its
treasures. Found in the king's palace was a great
quantity of silk weavings, silk garments, pile rugs,
and rugs embroidered with a needle or tapestry-
woven. Arab sources also mention a famous garden
rug, called the Spring of Khusrau, that was kept in
the palace at Ctesiphon. This rug, which can be regarded as a predecessor of the seventeenth-century

FIGURE 9 Stucco relief from Ctesiphon, Sasanian,
v–vi century. The Metropolitan Museum of Art,
Rogers Fund, 32.150.1

pile—fabrics that must have been used as wall hangings and floor coverings. These were woven on a
special loom that permitted great refinements in the
control of warp and weft—the draw loom.[8] A feature
of these early draw-loom textiles is their two sets of
warps: a set that binds the wefts and an inner set that
appears neither on the face nor the back of the fabric.
There are two sets of wefts also, one of the pattern
color and one of the ground color, and these appear
either on the face or the back of the fabric according
to the changes in the pattern. The face and back are
thus identical as to image but reversed as to color.
The draw-loom technique was known in the Roman
empire as early as the first century B.C.; draw-loom
fabrics are mentioned by Pliny the younger (A.D.
62–113) as products of Alexandria and called *polymita*.
Neither Egypt nor Rome knew this technique before
the first century B.C. On the other hand, Chinese silks
of about the first century B.C. found in Tunhwang
and Lou-lan in Central Asia indicate that the technique was known earlier in China. The technique,
then, was probably introduced from China, passing
through Central Asia, Persia, and Syria to the West.
To Syrian looms may be assigned a fragmentary
draw-loom band or border of the fifth or sixth century, showing scenes from the life of Christ (figure 10).
Other early Christian draw-loom weavings found in
Egypt were either of local origin or imported from
Syria, Mesopotamia, or Persia. Their decoration,
either in monochrome or polychrome, consists of
an allover geometrical pattern or a repeat geometrical
pattern with animals, birds, or human figures. A
number of these pieces, consisting of complete hangings, are in the Victoria and Albert Museum,[9] and
the Textile Museum, Washington (unpublished).
Several of them have large circular medallions with
birds in imitation of Sasanian silks. One example,
found with other Coptic textiles in Akhmim, Egypt,
is divided into bands with a checkerboard pattern in
various colors, the colors changing from band to
band (figure 11). This pattern, popular in ancient
Egyptian decorations, continued in the Coptic period
in tapestries and survived in some Kurdish rugs of
the early nineteenth century.

Safavid garden rugs (page 77), was made of gold
threads and embroidered with gems and pearls. A
Sasanian rug is represented in a seventh-century
carved relief depicting a boar hunt, at Taq-i-Bustan,
near Kermanshah.[6] It is quite probable that some of
the rug fragments, particularly those tied with the
Senna knot, that were found at Dura Europas by the
Yale University Expedition, were of Sasanian manufacture. As no dated monuments were found in the
city that were later than 256, the rug fragments can
be dated to the first half of the third century.[7] One
of them, tied with the Senna knot, has a thick pile on
the face and loops woven on the back. Other fragments show the Ghiordes knot or the cut-loop pile
to be discussed further on.

The Christian East, particularly Egypt and Syria,
has given us important early material for the study of
rugs and textiles. Most of the textiles produced by the
Copts of Egypt were tapestry-woven. Their garments
and wall hangings of linen were decorated with
tapestry bands and panels in wool, rather than in
linen as in ancient Egypt. Some of the hangings,
especially those of the developed Coptic style of the
sixth and seventh centuries, were entirely tapestry-
woven, including the background.

Egypt, as well as Syria and Persia, produced in the
early Christian era not only tapestry-woven textiles
but thick, intricately patterned fabrics without a

The production of fabrics with a pile, first of linen
and then of wool, began in the Middle East in antiquity. In the Metropolitan's excavations at Deir el
Bahri, Egypt, linen towels of about 2000 B.C. were
found, their surfaces having long weft loops.[10] These
are the earliest known examples of loop fabrics.
Shaggy tunics were known in Rome in the time of
Pliny the younger, who mentioned fabrics shaggy on

FIGURE 10   Fragments of a draw-loom weave, Syrian, v–vi century. The Metropolitan Museum of Art,
Gift of George F. Baker, 90.5.11 a–e

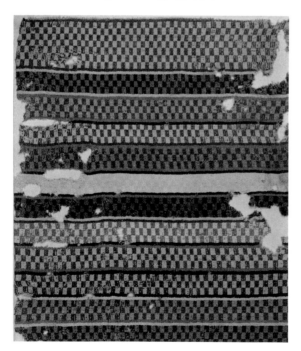

FIGURE 11   Fragment of a woven cloth, Coptic,
v–viii century. The Metropolitan Museum of Art,
Gift of Miss Lily S. Place, 21.6.3

both sides, called *amphimalla*. The technique continued in the Coptic period, tunics and shawls often
showing long or short linen loops. Their mass gives
the fabric substance and warmth. For the decoration
of these tunics and hangings with figure subjects and
floral and geometrical patterns, the Copts used loop
weaving in either purple or polychrome wool with
linen details. According to Ernst Fleming and Louisa
Bellinger there are several types of loop weaving.[11]
The loop weavings just described are regarded by
Bellinger as weft loop fabrics. Another process of
loop weaving recognized by Bellinger is called the
Senna loop techniques; this is found in Dura and
Auja el-Hafir in Syria as well as in Egypt.

By cutting through the loops, which entirely
covered the ground weave, the Copts and Syrians of
the Christian era produced cut-pile rugs. From Egypt,
probably from Antinoë, comes a fragment of a
fifth-century Coptic cut-loop pile rug (figure 12),
large enough to allow construction of the whole
pattern. Originally the rug had a field of four or
six rectangles with a pattern derived from Roman
and early Christian mosaic pavements. The ornament
of the double border and the rich polychromy are

those of Coptic textiles from the fifth to the seventh century. The meander of the inner border encloses squares and rosettes, overlaid with Coptic crosses. The outer border consists of an angular vinescroll with leaves and bunches of grapes, treated in the decorative fashion characteristic of Coptic ornament of the fifth and sixth centuries. The warps and wefts of this rug are of wool. The pile yarn, consisting of two strands of wool, loops between two warps, encircles the first warp as it is brought back to the surface, passes over this warp and a second warp and behind a third (figure 13). This is the process that Bellinger calls the Senna loop technique. After the yarn of the required color was inserted, the loops were cut, the free ends forming the pile coming out between every other pair of warps. There are about 63 "knots" to the square inch. After each row of cut loops the weft was inserted, consisting of two shoots of three strands of pale green and pink wool. The cut-loop process was most probably an imitation of the true knotting technique known at that time in both Egypt and Syria.

That true knotting was also known to the Copts is evident from at least two fragments of wool rugs found in Egypt. One of them, which came from Karanis in the Fayyum and can be dated to the fourth or fifth century, is in the Museum of the University of

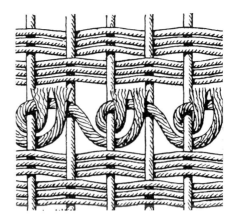

FIGURE 13 Cut Senna loop of rug in figure 12

FIGURE 14 Fragment of a wool pile rug, Coptic, VII–VIII century. The Metropolitan Museum of Art, Rogers Fund, 49.97a

FIGURE 12 Fragment of a wool pile rug, Coptic, v century. The Metropolitan Museum of Art, Rogers Fund, 31.1.1

Michigan.[12] The knots of this piece are attached to every other warp. The second piece, which comes from Fustat, shows, on a red ground, the figure of a saint with a halo standing between two trees (figure 14). The vivid colors of the pattern—yellow, dark blue, green, and brown—are typical of late Coptic textiles, and the fragment can be assigned to the seventh or eighth century. As in the preceding piece the pile was produced with the single-warp knot—the technique that was to be adopted by the rug weavers of Spain, beginning in the twelfth century.

Rugs were made elsewhere in the Christian East at an early period, as we know from literary sources. In the sixth century rugs covered the floors of the church of Santa Sophia in Constantinople and of the great halls of the palace of Justinian. The manufactories of Constantinople produced wool rugs whose patterns resembled floor mosaics.[13] These patterns were probably not unlike that of the Coptic rug of figure 12. It is recorded that in the ninth century, a lady from Peleponnesos ordered large soft rugs—

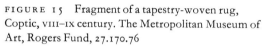

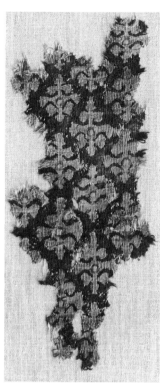

FIGURE 15   Fragment of a tapestry-woven rug, Coptic, VIII–IX century. The Metropolitan Museum of Art, Rogers Fund, 27.170.76

FIGURES 16, 17   Fragments of tapestry-woven rugs, Arabic, VIII–IX century. The Metropolitan Museum of Art, Rogers Fund, 27.170.73, 27.170.81

that is, pile rugs—and sent them as a gift to the newly built church of Basil I in Constantinople.[14]

With the advent of Islam, early in the seventh century, there began a new period in the art of the Near East. In the early years of the Islamic era the Arabs had little art of their own, but with the rapid expansion of their dominion they adopted the highly developed arts of the conquered countries of Syria, Mesopotamia, Egypt, and Persia. The Islamic style that now evolved derived chiefly from two artistic sources, the Sasanian and the Eastern Christian.

In the early Islamic period the weaving and knotting techniques of the Copts continued in Egypt and Syria and were known in Mesopotamia and Persia as well. During the reign of the Abbasid caliphs (749–1258) many Coptic weavers were employed in Arabic *tiraz* (manufactories). Several Egyptian weaving centers of this period are mentioned in the Arabic inscriptions of textiles found in Egypt. Tinnis, for example, had five thousand looms, renowned for their production of *kasab*, a fabric used for turbans, *badana,* a fabric for the caliphs' garments, and *bukali-mun,* a fabric with changing colors, used for saddle

cloths and covers for royal litters. Other famous centers were Tuna, known for its fine linen cloth and its *kiswas*, coverings for the Kaaba in Mecca; Dabik, known for its silks; and Damietta, noted for its fine white linen cloth. Still other known weaving centers were Alexandria, Fustat, the Fayyum, Ashmunain, and Bahnasa and Akhmim in Upper Egypt.

Among the Islamic wool tapestries found in Fustat and other Egyptian sites are heavy fabrics that were undoubtedly used as floor coverings, hangings, or cushion covers. Fragments of these tapestries are in the Textile Museum, Washington, and the Metropolitan. Their decoration is usually either geometrical or floral, combined with Arabic inscriptions, but sometimes consists of birds and animals. Some show Arabic adaptations of Coptic designs, others are entirely Arabic in style. One piece utilizes a Coptic cross for an allover pattern in light blue on a dark blue background (figure 15). Another shows large stylized peacocks in dark brown, arranged in rows and forming a repeat pattern (figure 16). Diapers forming compartments of hexagons were popular.

In one example the compartments contain pomegranates (figure 17); in another the hexagons contain a geometrical design of arabesques with trefoil palmettes in light blue on dark blue, with a bird appearing in the border (figure 18). In some of the fabrics the Sasanian tradition of circular medallions is apparent. Arabic inscriptions in the angular lettering known as Kufic (figure 19) are not uncommon. One fragment shows hook motifs in various colors and lozenges with double T-motifs, forming an allover pattern (figure 20). This piece may be regarded as a prototype of later Turkish and Caucasian kilims.

The Arabs of Egypt continued the manufacture of heavy draw-loom fabrics, begun early in the Christian era. Fragments of such fabrics, originally rugs or hangings, are in the Textile Museum, Washington, and the Metropolitan. A number of them have Kufic inscriptions dating them to the eighth or ninth

century. The background is usually red, with the decoration frequently in white, yellow, and dark blue. An interesting piece, perhaps a pillow cover, has a field divided into rectangular compartments containing geometrically stylized horses with Sasanian ribbons (figure 21). Here we probably have an early Islamic predecessor of the Turkish animal rugs of Asia Minor (page 173). As in the pre-Islamic era, such draw-loom weaves were made not only in Egypt but in Syria, Mesopotamia, and Persia.

Cut-loop weaving was another technique that continued in Egypt under the Arabs. In the Textile Museum, Washington, is a fragment in the weft-loop technique with a floral motif, probably a palmette tree, on a red field (figure 22). Its Kufic inscription in yellow tan in the red border reads, "In the name of God. Benediction from God. From what has been made in the factory of Akhmim. Year two hundred

FIGURES 18, 19, 20   Fragments of tapestry-woven rugs, Arabic, VIII–IX century. The Metropolitan Museum of Art, Rogers Fund, 27.170.74, 75; 27.170.79; 27.170.82

FIGURE 21 Fragment of a draw-loom weave, Arabic, VIII–IX century. The Metropolitan Museum of Art, Rogers Fund, 48.43

and three."[15] We are thus given not only its date, 203, corresponding to 818/819 in the Gregorian calendar, but the place of manufacture, a town in Upper Egypt that has been the source of many Coptic and early Islamic textiles. The existence of a tiraz in Akhmim in the Islamic period is certified by two Arab authors, Masudi, who died in Fustat in 956, and Yaqubi, who died in 891. The latter writes in his *Kitab al-Buldan* (*Book of Countries*), "There are made cut rugs and Akhmim leatherware." Ernst Kühnel rightly identifies these "cut rugs" as rugs made with a pile of cut loops. Two other fragments in the Textile Museum are related to the cushion cover just described. One of them contains the word *Misr*, which could mean either the city of Cairo or all of Egypt; in both these fragments the white Kufic letters are formed of bundles of undyed cotton fibers. In the Museum of Islamic Art, Cairo, are several fragments of Abbasid rugs. One of these pieces shows a lozenge design and a Kufic inscription that includes the Muhammadan date 206 (821/822).[16] Some authors consider this rug to be knotted, and others believe it to be woven in the cut-loop technique. Another fragment in the Museum of Islamic Art, found in Fustat, is decorated with a bird and a Kufic inscription. M. Mostafa, who published it,[17] believes that its pile was produced by knots rather than cut loops, but he does not say what kind of knot was employed. Two fragments found by Carl Johan Lamm in Fustat are regarded by him as Abbasid and dated to the first half of the ninth century.[18] One of these, in the Röhss Museum of Arts and Crafts, Gothenburg, Sweden, has an allover lozenge diaper; the other, in the National Museum, Stockholm, has a diaper of octagons bordered by a lozenge diaper. The pile of both these pieces is formed of what has been called "open single-warp knots," meaning that the yarn was simply placed around alternate warps, without being actually tied. In the Victoria and Albert Museum is a fragment showing a bird within a medallion with Abbasid palmettes. According to Bellinger,[19] this piece has a cut-loop pile.

The use of rugs as floor coverings elsewhere in the Middle East in the eighth and ninth centuries is

FIGURE 22 Fragment of a cushion cover, Akhmim, 818/819. Textile Museum Collection, Washington, D.C.

documented by pictorial representations. Wall paintings and miniatures from Khocho, the capital of the Turkish Uigurs in Chinese Turkestan, show rugs decorated with geometrical scrollwork or lotus palmettes.[20] Some of these paintings depict the Uigurs seated upon their rugs. This is the earliest pictorial evidence we have of a custom later in evidence among the Mongols (page 21) as well as the Arabs and Persians. Although some of the Uigur rugs, judging by their colors and designs, seem to have been pile rugs, most of them appear to have been made of felt appliqué. Felt rugs were made in Central Asia in antiquity, as confirmed by the finds at Pazyryk (page 6), and they were made there until modern times.

An eighth- or ninth-century silver plate in the Hermitage Museum,[21] attributable to Central Asia, depicts a seated ruler with a rug covering his throne. The rug is decorated with an elaborate floral pattern suggesting a Chinese design of the T'ang period. The character of the design suggests that the original rug was probably made of silk, and woven rather than knotted.

In the period from the tenth century to the twelfth there is considerable evidence of rugmaking in the Islamic world. In Egypt during the Fatimid period (969–1171), and also in Iraq and Persia, rugs were made for export. The historian Makrizi (1364–1442), speaking of the rugs used in the Fatimid palace in Cairo in the eleventh century, mentions Kalimun rugs and a type made of reeds, embroidered in silver and gold. Two such reed mats, both dating from the first half of the tenth century, are known today; one is in the Benaki Museum, Athens, the other in the Metropolitan (figure 23). According to the Kufic inscription on the first of these pieces, such mats were made in Tiberias, Palestine.

From texts of the tenth and eleventh century[22] we learn about rug manufacturing in Persia. Rugs were made by both men and women in the western province of Khuzistan, and exported from Tustar in the same province. Rugs of good workmanship were also made in the southern province of Fars, where those made at Jahram were particularly famous. In central

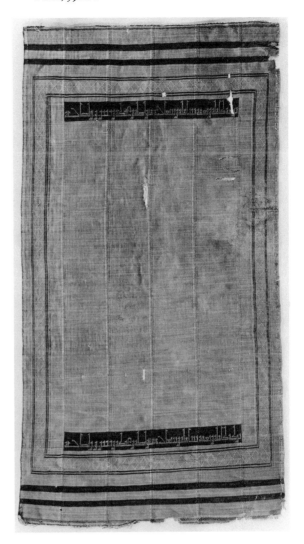

FIGURE 23 Reed mat made in Tiberias, Arabic, x century. The Metropolitan Museum of Art, Pulitzer Fund, 39.111

Persia, in the province of Kuhistan, beautiful prayer rugs were made. In Tun, four hundred looms for the making of rugs existed in the eleventh century. Other looms were at Amul, in northern Persia, famous for its prayer rugs.

Notes to Chapter Two

1 S. I. Rudenko, *Kul'tura naseleniia Gornogo Altaia v skifskoe vremia*, pp. 342–61; R. D. Barnett and W. Watson, *Illustrated London News*, July 11, 1953, pp. 69–71.

2 Aurel Stein, *Serindia*, IV (Oxford, 1921), pl. xxxvii; idem, *Innermost Asia*, III (Oxford, 1928), pls. xliv, lxxxvii.

3 Friedrich Sarre and Th. Falkenberg, *Berliner Museen*, XLII, pp. 110–14.

4 R. Pfister, "Les Premières Soies sassanides," in *Études d'orientalisme, publiées par le Musée Guimet à la mémoire de Raymonde Linossier* (Paris, 1932), pp. 461–79.

5 E. Guimet, *Les Portraits d'Antinoé au Musée Guimet* (Paris, n.d.), pls. v–viii, xi.

6 Ernst Herzfeld, *Am Tor von Asien* (Berlin, 1920), fig. 44.

7 R. Pfister and Louisa Bellinger, *The Excavations at Dura-Europos. Final Report IV, Part II: The Textiles*, pls. iv, xxiv.

8 Maurice S. Dimand, "Early Christian Weavings from Egypt," *Bulletin of The Metropolitan Museum of Art*, XX (1925), pp. 55–58; J. F. Flanagan, "The Origin of the Drawloom Used in the Making of Early Byzantine Silks," *Burlington Magazine*, XXXV (1919), fig. 2.

9 A. F. Kendrick, *Catalogue of Textiles from Burying-Grounds in Egypt*, II, *Period of Transition and of Christian Emblems*, Victoria and Albert Museum (London, 1921), pl. xxv.

10 H. E. Winlock, "The Egyptian Expedition, 1930–1931," *Bulletin of The Metropolitan Museum of Art*, XXVII (March, 1932), section ii, p. 31, fig. 33.

11 Louisa Bellinger, *The Textile Museum: Workshop Notes*, paper no. 12; Ernst Flemming, *Textile Künste* (Berlin, n.d.), pp. 44–46.

12 Lillian M. Wilson, *Ancient Textiles from Egypt in the University of Michigan Collection*, pl. 1, no. 5.

13 Jean Ebersolt, *Les Arts somptuaires de Byzance* (Paris, 1923), p. 147.

14 Ibid., p. 14.

15 Ernst Kühnel, *The Textile Museum: Workshop Notes*, paper no. 22, pl. 1.

16 Ali Ibrahim Pasha, *Bulletin de l'institut d'Égypt*, XVII, pls. iii, iv.

17 Mohamed Mostafa, in *Aus der Welt der islamischen Kunst*, pp. 89–90.

18 Carl Johan Lamm, "The Marby Rug and Some Fragments of Carpets Found in Egypt," *Svenska Orientsällskapets Årsbok* (1937), pp. 54–56, pl. 1.

19 Bellinger, *Workshop Notes*, paper no. 12, figs. 21, 22.

20 Albert von Le Coq, *Die Buddhistische Spätantike in Mittelasien*, vol. II, *Die Manichaeischen Miniaturen* (Berlin, 1923), pls. 7–8 b.

21 Arthur Upham Pope (ed.), *A Survey of Persian Art*, IV, pl. 208 A.

22 Gaston Wiet, *L'Exposition persane de 1931* (Cairo, 1933), pp. 93–129.

Three:

SELJUK RUGS OF ASIA MINOR
THIRTEENTH CENTURY

A brilliant new period in Islamic art began in the eleventh century with the ascendancy of the Seljuks, a Turkish tribe whose homeland was the Kirghiz steppes of Western Turkestan. Their name was that of a progenitor, Seljuk ibn Dakak, once a subject of the Turkish Uigurs of Central Asia. The Seljuks' conquest of the Middle East was largely complete by 1055, in which year their leader, Tughril Beg, was proclaimed sultan by the Abbasid caliph in Baghdad. From about 1077 until the mid-twelfth century the sultans known as the Great Seljuks ruled over an empire that encompassed Persia, Mesopotamia, Syria, and Asia Minor. The most famous of these were Tughril Beg, Alp Arslan, Malik Shah, and Sinjar. After the death of Sinjar, branches of the Seljuk family established the independent states of Kerman, Iraq, Syria, and Rum, the last in Asia Minor. In Rum the Seljuks ruled from 1077 to 1300. Their capital, Konya, was adorned with many fine mosques and palaces, richly decorated with paintings, stone carvings, and stucco reliefs.

The Seljuks were succeeded by their officers or *atabegs*, who established a number of local Seljuk dynasties in Persia, Mesopotamia, and Syria. These rulers became great patrons of the arts and crafts, and at their courts in Merv, Herat, Rayy, Isfahan, Mosul, and Dyar-Bakr (Amida) art flourished as never before in the Islamic world. The artists and craftsmen not only invented and perfected many new techniques in ceramics, metalwork, sculpture, and textiles, but greatly enriched the decorative elements.

The arabesque, a true Islamic ornament, was now fully developed and used freely, covering both small and large surfaces. The beginnings of the arabesque go back to the Abbasid period, but its elements can be found even earlier, in Sasanian art.[1] The fully developed arabesque is usually composed of two systems of spiral scrolls or bands that cross, interlace, and send off branches that end in half-palmettes and full palmettes. Frequently the scrolls are joined together, forming various kinds of geometrical compartments (figure 24). Another characteristic feature is the merging of the half-palmettes with the scrolls, from which other half-palmettes often issue. In its fully mature form the arabesque did not appear before the tenth century. Seljuk artists of the twelfth and thirteenth centuries developed the arabesque into an elaborate pattern, as can be seen in their fine stucco or stone decorations, particularly of mosque *mihrabs*, or prayer niches, in Persia and Iraq. The Seljuk arabesque also appeared in textiles. In the decoration of rugs, however, the arabesque became important only after the Seljuk period, notably in Turkish and Persian rugs of the fifteenth, sixteenth, and seventeenth centuries.

The Seljuk artists also favored geometrical interlacings forming various types of compartments, star-shaped or polygonal, which are often filled with arabesques. Such interlacings appear in the illuminations of Seljuk Korans of the eleventh and twelfth centuries, and in the decoration of Seljuk buildings. In Konya the Sirçali madraseh (1242/43), the Laranda mosque (1258), and the Sultan Han (1228/29) are richly decorated with geometrical interlacings.[2] In

FIGURE 24   Jar with lustered decoration, Seljuk,
XII–XIII century. The Metropolitan Museum of Art,
Henry G. Leberthon Collection, Gift of Mr. and Mrs.
A. Wallace Chauncey, 57.61.1

buildings of the second half of the thirteenth century,
such as madrasehs in Sivas (1271/72) and a mausoleum in Amasia (1278/79), the geometrical patterns,
covering large areas, show the addition of elaborate
arabesques and a rich decoration of palmettes.[3]

Another outstanding achievement of Seljuk artists
was the development of beautiful calligraphy—
particularly the angular type known as Kufic—seen
in Korans, metalwork, and architectural applications.
The verticals of the Kufic letters often end in half-
palmettes, or they are knotted in various ways, ranging from a simple heart-shaped knot to a quite
complicated knot, derived from the Chinese "knot
of destiny." Such knots appear in Persian rugs of the
Timurid period (page 36) and Anatolian rugs of the
fifteenth century (page 181).

Of great importance for the history of oriental rugs
is the survival of a number of thirteenth-century
Seljuk rug fragments. The first lot of eight was discovered in 1905 in the Ala ad-din mosque in Konya.[4]
The mosque was built in 1220, and it is quite possible

that the rugs were made for it. In 1929 another group
of rugs was discovered by Rudolf Riefstahl in the
Eshrefoğlu mosque, built in 1296, at Beyshehir, south-
west of Konya.[5] Three of these, now in the Mevlana
Museum, Konya, can be regarded as Seljuk. Subsequently, in 1935 and 1936, Carl Johan Lamm found
seven fragments of Seljuk rugs in Egypt, in the ruins
of Fustat.[6]

All of these rugs are made entirely of wool and are
tied with the Ghiordes knot. They are rather coarse
in texture, some having less than fifty knots to the
square inch. The decoration is mainly geometrical,
with the motifs small in relation to the size of the
field. Seven of the rugs have Kufic borders, a type of
decoration known earlier in Arabic tapestries of the
eighth or ninth century (page 11). Because many of
the patterns and motifs of these Seljuk rugs became
standard in later Turkish and Caucasian rugs they
warrant consideration in some detail.

Three of the rugs have fields with lozenge diapers.
One large, almost complete rug from the Ala ad-din
mosque, measuring 17 feet by 9 feet 4 inches, has a
small-scale lozenge diaper in light red upon a dark

FIGURE 25   Fragment of a Seljuk rug. Museum of
Turkish and Islamic Art, Istanbul (from Erdmann,
Oriental Carpets)

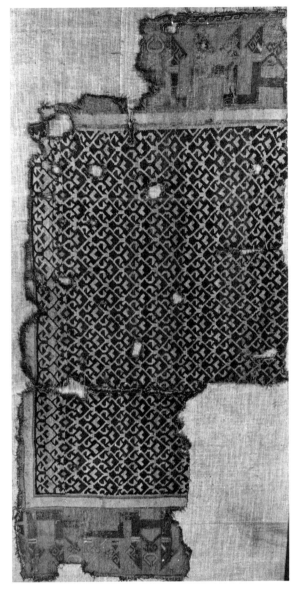

red ground (figure 25). Each lozenge contains a stylized lotus bud with two hooks, with spiral hooks in the corners of the lozenge. In strong contrast to the field, the wide dark blue border is filled with Kufic in a bold style. The wedgelike tops of the letters, which are in light blue with red cross bands and white outlines, are adorned with several hook motifs of a type to be found in some of the other Seljuk rugs as well. The guard bands have a row of blue stars within squares.

A second Ala ad-din rug has a lozenge diaper on a dark blue ground, the lozenges containing hooks and a heart-shaped motif (figure 26). The Kufic border, in dark red on light red, resembles that of the preceding example.

The third rug with lozenge diaper comes from the mosque at Beyshehir. Riefstahl dates it to the end of the thirteenth century, Kurt Erdmann to 1300. On its light blue ground, dark blue bands form lozenges filled with stars, their centers vermilion (figure 27). The bands are adorned with a series of angular hooks in a reciprocal pattern. Such hooks were derived from the Chinese meander, and were also known, as will be shown in chapter 4, in Mongol rugs of Central Asia that may be dated to the end of the twelfth or the early thirteenth century.

Several of the Ala ad-din rugs have patterns of geometrical figures arranged in staggered rows. One of the largest has an allover pattern of octagons in red on a yellowish ground (figure 28). Each octagon

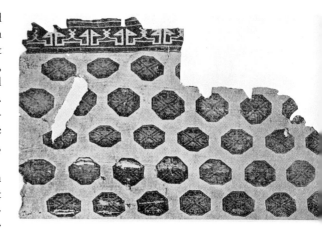

contains four symmetrically arranged heart-shaped
spirals. Single heart-shaped spirals may be found in
Chinese art and also in some of the Mongol rugs just
mentioned. The four-heart motif of the Seljuk rug,
combined into a rosette, survived in Turkish and
Caucasian rugs made as late as the nineteenth century.
The red border of the Ala ad-din rug shows a slender-
er Kufic than that of the preceding pieces, with the
letters, rendered in yellow and connected in pairs,
having wedgelike tops.

Another of these fragmentary rugs with its pattern
in staggered rows has, on a dark blue field, a repeat
pattern of geometrical rosettes consisting of rhomboids framed by light blue spirals (figure 29). In the
centre of each rosette is an angular S-motif in red.
These spiral rosettes, probably of Central Asian
origin, survived in Turkish and Caucasian rugs for
centuries. Many nineteenth-century Shirvan rugs of
the Caucasus show such motifs in the border, combined with Kufic writing.

Of importance in the study of fifteenth-century
geometrical rugs of Anatolia is one of the larger
Ala ad-din pieces measuring 10 feet 6 inches by 7 feet
10 inches. Its dark blue field has an allover pattern, in
staggered rows, of eight-pointed light blue stars
containing smaller red stars (figure 30). The blue
stars are connected vertically and horizontally by
angular interlaced double bands. These send out
trefoils and double hook motifs resembling Kufic
letters. As a whole, the pattern suggests the small-
patterned "Holbein" rugs of Anatolia, made in the
fifteenth and sixteenth centuries (page 179). The wide
red brown border of this rug has a repeat pattern in
light red, consisting of squares outlined in brown
containing blue stars. To the four sides of the squares
are attached wedgelike hooks. The guard bands have
a repeat pattern of hook devices. A similar field pattern appears in one of the Beyshehir rugs but in different colors, namely light brown on a red ground.[7] The
patterns of these two rugs have direct affinities with
the tall Kufic inscriptions to be seen in the mosaics
of the Ala ad-din mosque itself, and other buildings
in Konya including the Karatay madraseh built in
1252. The border of the last-mentioned rug has a
series of stars in light blue and red on a reddish
ground, alternating with a wedgelike motif derived
from Kufic. The red guard bands contain a three-
pointed gablelike motif. Star motifs of the type seen

FIGURES 28, 29, 30 Fragments of Seljuk rugs.
Museum of Turkish and Islamic Art, Istanbul

in these rugs are characteristic of Konya decorations, both in stone and ceramic tiles. Interlaced stars, forming an allover pattern, decorate the mihrab of the Laranda mosque, the Sirçali mosque and madraseh, and other buildings of Konya.

Two of the Seljuk rugs, one from Beyshehir, the other from Konya, are of particular interest in that they have patterns that seem to derive from floral designs of contemporary Chinese textiles. The Beyshehir rug, large in size—about 16½ feet long—has, on a dark blue ground, geometrically stylized floral scrolls in light blue, arranged in staggered rows (figure 31). The scrolls have attached hooks and stems with stylized lotus palmettes. The design was inspired by Chinese silks, which were known in the Islamic East during the Seljuk period. The rug has a wide border with angular interlacings bearing stylized trefoils in black on a mauve ground. Such trefoils were popular in Chinese textiles of the Han dynasty (206 B.C.–A.D. 220) and the T'ang dynasty (618–907). They are also to be found in the appliquéd felt saddlecloths of the Mongols of the twelfth and thirteenth centuries (page 22).

The second rug with floral pattern, from the Ala ad-din mosque,[8] has, on its dark purple field, fifteen staggered rows of stylized lotus palmettes in light red with a series of hooks on angular stems. In the center of each palmette is a swastika motif. The border of the rug has a pattern of interlaced bands in turquoise blue forming star motifs with attached trefoils on a brown ground. While this border is typically Seljuk, the field design bears some resemblance to a contemporary Chinese silk in the Metropolitan (46.156.20) that has a pattern of lotus blossoms on stems.

Judging from the impressive size of some of these pieces as well as their quite elaborate designs, the Seljuk rug industry was in a state of full development in the thirteenth century. It must have begun much earlier, since the Seljuks brought the art of rugmaking from their homeland in Central Asia, where the earliest-known pile rug was found (figure 8), and where their ancestors, the Turkish Uigurs, were

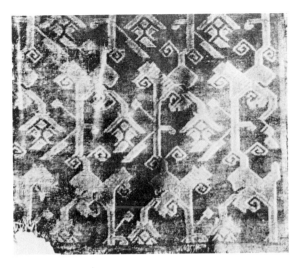

FIGURE 31 Fragment of a Seljuk rug. Formerly in the Konya Museum (from Erdmann, *Oriental Carpets*)

apparently familiar with rug knotting (page 13). Although Konya was probably the main center of Seljuk rug weaving, Sivas and Kayseri, cities that Marco Polo visited in 1271, probably also produced rugs. According to Marco Polo, "the finest and handsomest carpets in the world" were those that were made in the Seljuk empire. The fame of these rugs is confirmed by Islamic authorities as well. Ibn Said, a writer from Granada (died 1274), is quoted by the historian-geographer Abu al-Fida as saying, "In Aksaray [Nigde] are made . . . carpets which are exported to all countries." The famous traveler, Ibn Batuta, who visted Anatolia in the fourteenth century soon after the close of the Seljuk period, praised the rugs he found there and noted that they were being exported to Egypt, Syria, Iraq, Persia, and even to India and China.

Seljuk rugs were also esteemed in Europe at the end of the thirteenth century, particularly in Italy. One of the frescoes in the Arena Chapel at Padua, painted by Giotto in 1304, shows, according to Ernst Kühnel, a Seljuk rug with a pattern of star motifs connected by interlacing bands.

Notes to Chapter Three

1 Maurice S. Dimand, "Studies in Islamic Ornament," *Ars Islamica*, IV (1937), pp. 293–337.

2 Friedrich Sarre, *Denkmäler Persischer Baukunst*, pt. I, *Konia* (Berlin, n.d.), pls. I, II, XI, XII.

3 Rudolf M. Riefstahl, *Art Bulletin*, XIII, figs. 19–21, 23, 24.

4 Oktay Aslanapa, *Turkish Arts* (Istanbul, n.d.), pls. II–VIII A, following p. 31.

5 Riefstahl, *Art Bulletin*, XIII, figs. 1–4.

6 Carl Johan Lamm, *Svenska Orientsällskapets Årsbok* (1937), pp. 67–86.

7 Aslanapa, pl. VIII B, following p. 31.

8 Ibid., pl. V, following p. 31.

Four:

REPRESENTATIONS OF MONGOL RUGS IN CHINESE PAINTINGS

At least three Chinese paintings of the thirteenth century (Sung dynasty) are of particular importance to students of oriental rugs because they depict Mongol rugs, in use as floor or ground coverings, that can be dated to the early thirteenth century or possibly even the end of the twelfth. One is in Taiwan, another is in a private collection in New York, and the third, in which the design of the rugs is indistinct, is in the Museum of Fine Arts, Boston.[1] All of these paintings illustrate the same ancient story: Lady Wen-chi's return to China. Wen-chi, the daughter of a scholar of the second century, while traveling to Kansu in western China, was captured by Hiung-Nu raiders and taken to Mongolia. Here, after spending twelve years as the wife of a Mongol chief, she was ransomed by a Chinese embassy.

The rugs seen in detail in the first two of these paintings provide clues to the origin of certain geometrical patterns that were to travel westward into the Islamic realm and appear in Turkish rugs of Anatolia in the fourteenth and fifteenth centuries. The painting in Taiwan, a hanging scroll, is attributed to Chen Chü-chung, who specialized in Mongol horsemen and camp scenes, and is generally dated to about 1205. It depicts the parting of Wen-chi from her husband and children. In the scroll painting in New York, the work of an unknown artist, additional scenes are illustrated, including the arrival of the Chinese envoys and the departure of Wen-chi for China.

Although the colors of the Taiwan painting are somewhat faded, one can distinguish quite clearly the patterns of the rugs, as well as those of saddlecloths and saddlebags. In Turko-Mongolian fashion, Wen-chi and her husband are seated upon a rug (figure 32) with fringed ends. Its predominant color is red, with white and turquoise blue occurring in the field. The red field has a central square compartment containing a lozenge decorated with a geometrical pattern of Chinese symbols made up of triangles and crosses. The lozenge has a separate border with a zigzag pattern. In the spandrels of the square are triangles framing heart-shaped motifs or perhaps trefoils. At either end of the rug are six bands of scrolls with palmettes, three within the field, three separating the field from the border. The outer border of the rug has a series of discs or pearls, and an inner border surrounding the field contains double brackets forming a reciprocal pattern of crosses. The texture of the piece, as depicted by the painter, is that of a pile rug; this is further suggested by the presence of the fringed ends.

In this Mongolian rug we see a forerunner of Anatolian rugs depicted in Italian paintings of the fourteenth and fifteenth centuries. For example, lozenges within squares appear in a rug in a fourteenth-century painting of the Giotto school in Assisi,[2] and in a rug in a fifteenth-century painting of the Madonna and Child by Ghirlandaio.[3] In the second Anatolian rug the pattern is much more elaborate, but the principle is the same, even to the triangular corner-pieces.

FIGURES 32, 33, 34 Details from a scroll painting
attributed to Chen Chü-chung, early XIII century.
Collection of the National Palace Museum, Taipei,
Taiwan

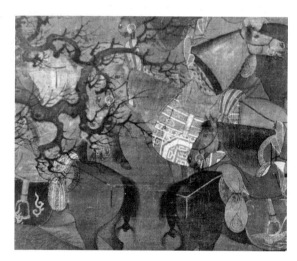

The rug upon which the Chinese envoy is seated
(figure 33) has a quite different design, consisting of
narrow lengthwise bands; some of these are filled
with a lozenge pattern in white on red, others with a
geometrical scroll with half-palmettes in white on
yellow brown, still others with an angularly rendered
scroll. The angular character of the scroll, together
with the absence of fringe at the ends, indicates that
this is a flat-woven, possibly a tapestry-woven rug.

Both types of rugs described above are also represented in the saddlecloths and saddlebags (figure 34).
The saddlecloth rolled up on the horse on the left
closely resembles the rug on which the Chinese envoy
sits. Another saddlecloth, apparently on a pile rug,
shows, within a square, an octagon decorated with
an angular design of Chinese characters, the spandrels of the squares containing trefoils. The bordering bands contain various motifs: a meander, brackets, a wavy palmette scroll, and trefoils with heart-
shaped scrolls. One of the saddlebags (not illustrated)
has several square compartments with octagons and
lozenges bordered by meanders and swastika motifs.
Some of the horses have saddlebags that appear to
be made of felt with appliqué decorations including
a golden goose, trefoils, Chinese scrolls, fire wheels,
and a *ch'i-lin*, a lionlike mythological beast. Felt
appliqué, a very old technique in Central Asia, already
known to the Scythians,[4] distinguishes the Mongol
saddlecloths from the Chinese, which were usually of
silk and without decoration.

FIGURES 35, 36, 37   Details from a scroll
painting, anonymous, XIII century. Collection of
C. C. Wang, New York

The painting in New York shows scenes taking
place in China as well as Mongolia. In a number of
scenes Chinese and Mongols are represented together. The two are readily distinguished by their
garb and their manner of life. The Mongols were
tent-dwelling nomads; the settled Chinese lived in
well-built houses. The Mongols wear kaftans, trou-
sers, boots, and either furred or conical cloth caps;
the Chinese wear colorful silk garments of flowing
cut. Depicted in this second painting are six rugs, a
pile saddlebag, and several saddlecloths similar to
those in the first painting. In addition, Chinese silk
cushions with floral designs in gold and light blue on
red grounds, as well as cotton or straw mats, are seen
in the round tents or *yurts*. The rugs are predominantly red brown, with red, white, light tan, light
blue, and dark blue occurring in the patterns. The
patterns of the rugs, as in the first painting, are fore-
runners of many fourteenth- and fifteenth-century
Anatolian rugs.

One of the rugs, visible within a tent (figure 35)
has a large octagon containing a cross-shaped medallion on a red ground. In the spandrels of the field are
triangular compartments with scalloped outlines. The
border of the rug is divided into rectangles containing circular motifs in white on dark blue. The guard
band has a T-pattern derived from the Chinese
meander.

The second rug, upon which Wen-chi and her
husband are shown seated, has, in a central octagon,
a cross-shaped medallion containing a disc with trefoils at each quarter (figure 36). Beyond the octagon,
at the ends of the field, are triangular panels with
spirals or cloud motifs. The border is divided into
rectangular compartments with T-motifs in white,
light blue, dark blue, and red.

The third rug, upon which Wen-chi sits, has a
pattern that is a variation of the two preceding. It
shows a central square containing a cross-shaped
medallion with a stylized blossom, possibly a peony
(figure 37). In each corner of the square are open
heart-shaped motifs. The square is bordered by a

band containing a series of Chinese cloud motifs. Enclosing this is a border containing a row of discs or pearls. At either end of the rug a wide band is divided into squares, each containing a cross in light or dark blue. Cross motifs of this type were frequently used in Central Asian garments and other fabrics. An Anatolian rug represented in an Italian painting of the first half of the fifteenth century in the Church of Santa Maria Novella in Florence shows a pattern of similar crosses separated by rows of pearls.[5]

The fourth rug is depicted in front of a tent, with Wen-chi's husband seated upon it. Its red brown field has, within a central square, an octagon containing a cross-shaped medallion (figure 38). In the spandrels of the square are open heart-shaped spirals. At either end of the field is a panel of three rectangles containing crosses and rosettes. The inner border is divided into square compartments containing crosses, circles, and other geometrical figures; the outer border has a series of T-motifs in light blue, dark blue, and red.

The fifth rug, seen within a pavilion, is partly obscured by a silk cushion (figure 39). Most probably it would have shown, like the others, a square and a cross-shaped medallion. At the ends of the field are rectangular panels with geometrical designs and discs. The border is divided into rectangular compartments containing crosses, the sections separated by pearl bands. At the four corners appear Chinese C-scrolls, known from early Chinese animal decorations of bronzes and other objects.

The sixth rug, upon which Wen-chi again appears, is depicted without a fringe, which, together with the repetitious nature of the design, suggests that it is a tapestry rug. It has a considerably different pattern (figure 40) from those of the preceding rugs, divided widthwise into bands containing the Chinese meander pattern in white, tan, light blue, and dark blue on a red brown ground. The meander was a popular motif in Chinese art as early as the Shang dynasty (second millennium B.C.), and it occurs in textiles of the Han dynasty (206 B.C.–A.D. 220). It was used, too, in Chinese bronzes of all periods, on which it covers large or small surfaces and is often combined with animal decoration. The meander was also popular in the ancient Near East; it occurs in a kilim of the fifth century B.C. found at Pazyryk,[6] and in textiles from Central Asia of the eighth century A.D. The Chinese meander differs from the Egyptian and Greek meanders in being composed of individual hooks or S- or C-forms rather than of a continuous line. It is probable that the angular hooks that appear

FIGURES 38, 39, 40   Details from a scroll painting, anonymous, XIII century. Collection of C. C. Wang, New York

in Anatolian rugs of the fourteenth century,[7] as well as other early oriental rugs, had their origin in the Chinese meander.

All of these thirteenth-century Mongol rugs may be regarded as predecessors of the Turkish geometrical rugs of the fourteenth and fifteenth centuries. In the Seljuk rugs of the thirteenth century, as we have seen, the allover design was on a small scale. The Turkish weavers of fourteenth-century Anatolia, in addition to continuing the Seljuk designs, adopted the Mongolian style of lozenges or octagons within squares. At first they used them in pairs. Later, according to the size of the rug, they used them in groups of four or more (page 177), as seen in Italian paintings of the fourteenth and fifteenth centuries.

While both the scroll paintings discussed here are the work of Chinese artists, it is clear that the rugs they depict are Mongol, not Chinese. The rugs appear only in the scenes taking place in Mongolia—none are depicted in the Chinese scenes. Supporting the view that the paintings depict Mongol rugs, Otto Kümmel states that in 1262 a special workshop was established in Karakorum to manufacture rugs for the Chinese imperial court at Peking.[8] Made the capital of the Mongols by Genghis Khan (1206–1227), Karakorum was visited by a number of European travelers: Plano Carpini in 1234, Rubuquis in 1253, and Marco Polo in 1275, the last of whom gives a detailed description of the place. Karakorum remained important even after Kublai Khan (1260–1294) moved his capital to Kai-pin-fu, near Peking.

In China the manufacturing of rugs never attained the importance it had in the wool-growing regions of Central Asia and the Near East. According to some scholars, no existing Chinese pile rugs can be dated before the Ch'ien-lung period (1736–1795), even though attempts have been made on stylistic grounds to date some of them as early as the Ming dynasty—that is, before 1645. The Mongol production of pile rugs and saddlecloths, on the other hand, was well developed by the early thirteenth century, as these paintings show, and it continued until recent times.

Notes to Chapter Four

1 Kojiro Tomita, *Portfolio of Chinese Paintings in the Museum (Han to Sung Periods)*, Museum of Fine Arts, Boston (Cambridge, 1938), pls. 61–65.

2 Kurt Erdmann, *Oriental Carpets*, fig. 18.

3 P. Michele Campana, *Il tappeto orientale*, pl. 16.

4 S. I. Rudenko, *Kul'tura naseleniia Gornogo Altaia v skifskoe vremia*, pls. LXXVII, CII, CIII, CXI, CXIV; Tamara Talbot Rice, *The Scythians* (New York, 1957), figs. 54–56, 61–65, pl. 30.

5 Campana, pl. 10.

6 Rudenko, pl. XCVIII, nos. 1–2.

7 Erdmann, fig. 17.

8 Otto Kümmel, *Die Kunst Chinas, Japans und Koreas* (Wildpark-Potsdam, 1929), p. 81.

CASPIAN SEA

TURKESTAN

• Tabriz

AZERBAIJAN

• Maragha

Sultaniya •

KURDISTAN

Meshed •

• Teheran

KHURASAN

• Senna

• Hamadan

• Herat

• Kum

• Sultanabad

• Kashan

LURISTAN

• Jushagan

• Isfahan

KHUZISTAN

ARABIA

• Kerman

• Shiraz

KERMAN

PERSIAN

FARS

GULF

GULF OF OMAN

Five:

RUGS
OF
PERSIA

Mongol Period
(Fourteenth Century)

Of great importance in the development of Persian art was the invasion of the Near East by the Mongols of Central Asia. Led by Chingiz Khan (1206–1227), the Mongols overran one Muslim country after another, looting and destroying. Then, not long before his death, Chingiz divided his vast empire, which stretched from China to southern Russia, among his sons. In Persia, in 1256, one of his grandsons, Hulagu, founded the Il-khan dynasty (the name meaning provincial chief), which ruled until 1353. In 1258 Hulagu captured Baghdad, partly destroying it. After establishing their government the Il-khans began the reconstruction of Persia and Mesopotamia. Baghdad, rebuilt, became the Il-khans' capital and winter residence. Visiting Baghdad early in the Il-khan period, Marco Polo found it "the noblest and greatest city of the region" and reported that its weavers were producing "many different kinds of silk stuffs and gold brocades" as well as "beautiful tissues richly wrought with figures of beasts and birds."

As converts to Islam the Il-khans assimilated the superior Persian culture and became enthusiastic patrons of Persian arts and crafts. They also opened the doors of Persia to foreign influence. To their courts at Maragha, Sultaniya, and Tabriz (the last their summer residence) came artists and craftsmen from all parts of the empire to work for the glory of their new masters. The Il-khans' admiration for Chinese culture and art had in turn a great influence on the development of Islamic art. From the Far East came Buddhist priests and artists, introducing many ele-

ments of Chinese art. The Il-khans also opened Persia to Western influence by establishing diplomatic relations with the Byzantine empire and with the Church of Rome.

The Mongol period saw the beginning of a school of Persian painting and illumination that influenced the design of Persian rugs of later times. This artistic development was greatly stimulated by Rashid ad-Din (died 1318), the vizier of the emperors Ghazan and Uljaitu. Outside Tabriz Rashid ad-Din had a new quarter built, named Rab-i-Rashidi (or Rashidiyya), which was devoted to the arts and sciences. Here craft shops, paper manufactories, caravanserais, and a library were erected, the last eventually containing sixty thousand volumes in several languages, including Chinese. To this new center came artists and craftsmen from various countries. Rashid ad-Din was particularly interested in the arts of the book, and many literary works were copied, illustrated, and illuminated in Rab-i-Rashidi, among them the vizier's own *Jami at-Tawarikh* (*Universal History*). A copy of this work in two parts, one in the library of Edinburgh University dated 1307 (707 H.), the other in the library of the Royal Asiatic Society, London, dated 1314 (714 H.), gives evidence of the strong Chinese influence in Persian painting. The figures are elongated, almost ascetic. The linear style, with color playing a subordinate role, recalls the brushwork of Chinese paintings of the Sung dynasty (960–1279) and the Yüan dynasty (1280–1368).

In their assimilation of Persian culture the Il-khans

FIGURE 41   The Funeral of Isfandyar, from a *Shah Namah*, first half of XIII century. Smithsonian Institution, Freer Gallery of Art, Washington, D.C.

encouraged their court painters to illustrate the *Shah Namah (Book of Kings)*, the epic poem of Firdausi (ca. 935–1025). One of the earliest surviving Mongol copies of this work is a large manuscript known today as the Demotte *Shah Namah*, after the dealer who once owned it. The manuscript was illustrated by several artists working at Tabriz for the Il-khan ruler Abu Said (1316–1335), the work probably beginning about 1320. The miniatures from this manuscript,[1] numbering about fifty-five, must be ranked among the masterpieces of Persian painting. They show an interesting mixture of Chinese and Persian styles. The landscapes, painted in subdued colors, are Chinese in style, while the figures, costumes, and architecture, rendered in brilliant colors, are Persian. Three of the paintings depict rugs of the Mongol period. Since the paintings were the work of court artists at Tabriz, we may assume that these are representations of court rugs, probably woven in northwest Persia.

Two of the rugs have geometrical patterns, the third has an animal design.

The red field of one of the geometrical rugs is decorated with an allover pattern of small squares, each of which contains a pair of interlaced angular ovals in white (figure 41). The border, separated from the field by three bands of geometrical motifs, is ornamented with Kufic in white on a red ground. The interlaced ovals seen in the squares of this fourteenth-century rug survived in rugs made by the nomads and peasants of the Caucasus as late as the nineteenth century.

The second of the geometrical rugs, seen in a painting in the Museum of Fine Arts, Boston,[2] shows in the field the corner of a square compartment framed by interlaced bands, popular in Mongol illuminations. The border of this rug is decorated with interlaced arabesques.

The rug in the third painting is decorated with

animals stylized in geometrical fashion and placed within double octagons decorated with geometrical S-motifs, or meanders (figure 42). The border consists of five bands, each with a different ornament: a zigzag motif, a cross pattern, a narrow T-pattern, Kufic writing, and an arrow motif. The animal design of the field is not unlike that of certain Anatolian rugs that are known in the original (figure 144) or from their representation in Italian and Flemish paintings of the fourteenth and fifteenth centuries (figures 143, 145). This animal style was probably general in the Near East in the fourteenth century.

The development of the Persian rug patterns of the fourteenth century was influenced to a great extent by Mongol illuminations. The illuminators working for the Mongol rulers created many masterpieces of abstract design. Several Mongol Korans have illuminated pages with geometrical designs of great variety. One written in Hamadan in 1313 (713 H.) for the ruler Uljaitu has many decorative pages with geometrical patterns. The fields are divided into compartments containing arabesques, rosettes, or occasional floral motifs. Some of these motifs are rendered in gold on blue, a favorite color combination of Persian illuminators of all periods. The geometrical design is of two types. In one, crossing bands

FIGURE 43   Illumination from a Mongol Koran, written in Hamadan, 1313. National Library and Archives, Cairo.

FIGURE 42   Dahhak Consults the Physicians, from a *Shah Namah*, first half of XIII century. Smithsonian Institution, Freer Gallery of Art, Washington, D.C.

form various polygonal compartments, chiefly octagons, and these are filled with interlaced arabesques and other motifs (figure 43). In the other, many circles cross one another, creating numerous small compartments of various shapes, and these are filled with units of arabesque scrolls (figure 44). In some cases the scrolls are combined with endless knots, which, as noted earlier (page 16), were introduced into Islamic art by the Seljuks. The endless knot was to become an important motif in rug decoration in the time of the Mongols' successors, the Timurids.

As a result of the Mongol invasion there appeared in Persian art naturalistic landscapes with lotus, peony, and other blossoms used either alone or combined with various birds and animals, some of Chinese origin. Naturalistic Chinese ornament eventually penetrated all branches of Islamic art. In Mongol ceramic art, for example, the process may be followed step by step from the end of the thirteenth century through the fourteenth in underglaze painted

FIGURE 44   Illumination from a Mongol Koran, written in Hamadan, 1313. National Library and Archives, Cairo

that form endless knots. Although known earlier in the illuminations of Uljaitu's Koran of 1313, this is the earliest known representation of such interlaced knottings in a rug.

Timurid Period (Fifteenth Century)

Beginning in 1380, Persia and other regions were overrun by a new conqueror from Transoxiana: Timur (or Tamerlane), who was related to the family of Chingiz Khan. In 1386 Timur took Tabriz from the Jalairids, in 1387 he took Shiraz in southwestern Persia, and in 1393 he conquered Baghdad. To Samarkand, his capital, Timur transported Muslim artists and craftsmen, and the city became one of the great centers of Islamic culture and art. That splendid rugs were known in Samarkand in the time of Timur is evident from the narrative of Ruy Gonzales de Clavijo, the head of a Spanish mission that visited the city in 1404, not long before Timur's death. The Spaniard found the "Sultan of Babylon," as he called Timur, seated in a garden of his palace, "cross-legged on silk-embroidered carpets, amongst round pillows." After mentioning details of Timur's dress—a robe of silk, a high white hat adorned with pearls and precious stones—Gonzales tells us that "in the center of the garden was a beautiful house adorned with carpets," while nearby stood a pavilion "furnished with a crimson carpet beautifully ornamented and embroidered with gold threads." The doors of this pavilion were of carpeting, Gonzales continues, and the ground of a tent "was covered with rich silken carpets."

and lustered tiles, many of which are dated.[3] In the illuminations of Persian Korans and other manuscripts, on the other hand, the naturalistic floral ornament combined with Chinese animals and birds does not appear until the beginning of the fifteenth century, under the Timurids.

Toward the end of the fourteenth century, at the court of the Mongol Jalairid ruler Sultan Ahmad (1382–1410), fine manuscripts were produced. One of the most important of these is a *diwan*, or book of poems, by Khwaju Kirmani, copied in Baghdad in 1396 by the celebrated calligrapher Mir Ali of Tabriz.[4] One of the paintings is signed by Junaid Nakkash al-Sultani, who was in the service of Sultan Ahmad. This miniature shows two rugs (figure 45), one with an allover pattern of star shapes and octagons in blue and red on a cream yellow ground, the other with its field divided into square compartments that are variously yellow, green, red, and purple. The borders of both rugs have Kufic inscriptions. A rug depicted in another miniature of this manuscript has a repeat pattern of octagonal stars connected by interlacings

Under the Timurids, the descendants and successors of Timur, the eastern cities of Samarkand, Bukhara, and Herat grew in importance. Herat, in the province of Khurasan, became the Timurid capital and a center of Muslim science, literature, and art. Timur's favorite son, Shah Rukh (1404–1447), was a great patron of the arts of the book, employing many artists in his library. Shah Rukh's son, Baisunker Mirza, established in Herat a library and academy devoted to the arts of the book, and here forty calligraphers, illuminators, painters, and binders, most of them from Tabriz, were employed.[5] The head of the academy was the calligrapher Jafar at-Tabrizi. A branch of the Timurid school was established in

FIGURE 46 Brush drawing from a Timurid album,
xv century. Topkapu Seray Museum, Istanbul

Shiraz, which was the residence of Prince Ibrahim
Sultan, another of Shah Rukh's sons.

The Chinese influence, so strong in the Mongol
period, continued in the Timurid miniature paintings
and illuminations. As may be seen in several albums
in the Topkapu Seray Museum, Istanbul, including
the one of Sultan Mehmet II (1451–1481), the Timurid artists often copied Chinese paintings and brush
drawings.[6] Ghiyat ad-Din, a famous Timurid painter,
traveled to China in 1419 with a Persian embassy,
and there became familiar with Chinese painting.
Ming porcelain, imported from China, is frequently
depicted in Timurid miniatures, and costumes worn
by figures in the paintings show panels embroidered
in gold with Chinese landscapes and animals.

The artists of Herat and Shiraz produced some of
the most sumptuous illuminations ever seen, and
some of these influenced the designs of later Persian
rugs. Early Timurid illuminations are found in two
manuscripts written for Iskandar Sultan in 1410/11,
an *Anthology* belonging to the Gulbenkian Foundation, Lisbon, and an *Anthology* in the British Museum.[7] Many pages of these and other manuscripts
are decorated in the new Timurid style, with lotus
blossoms and leaves, peonies, pomegranate palmettes, and fungus scrolls (figure 46). In some of
these illuminations the floral motifs are combined
with geometrical interlacings and arabesques, and in
some others, dragons, phoenixes, and deer appear
(figure 47). Naturalistic plant ornament, derived from
China, is frequently combined with Chinese birds and
mythological animals. This type of ornament became
a standard ingredient of sixteenth-century Persian
rugs. Some of the elements of this design will be
discussed further in connection with the sixteenth-
century Herat rugs (page 53). The fully developed
Timurid illuminations consist of intricate geometrical patterns with interlaced arabesques and delicate
floral scrolls. They have an astounding richness of
detail and brilliance of color, as seen in a magnificent
Shah Namah dated 1429/30 (833 H.), made for Baisunker Mirza, now in the Gulistan Museum,
Teheran.[8]

The decorative schemes in the Timurid illuminations were to influence the design of sixteenth-
century Safavid rugs, for example, a double title page

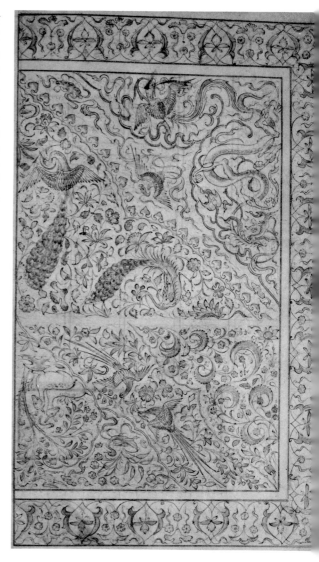

FIGURE 47 Illumination from a Timurid *Anthology*,
1410/11. Gulbenkian Foundation, Lisbon

FIGURE 48   Double title page from Kazwini's *Ajaib al-Makhluqat*, xv century. The Metropolitan Museum of Art, Fletcher Fund, 34.109

from a manuscript of Kazwini's *Ajaib al-Makhluqat* (*Marvels of Creation*) (figure 48). This has a central medallion with pendants above and below, the medallion on the left-hand page surrounded by fabulous Chinese creatures—ch'i-lins, and a dragon in combat with a phoenix—the medallion on the right-hand page surrounded by two houris, the female angels of the Muslim paradise, an elephant being attacked by a giant bird, and a unicorn. In the borders of these pages is a decoration consisting of animal-head grotesques interlaced with a delicate floral scroll. Such scrollwork with animal heads appeared earlier in the thirteenth-century Seljuk metalwork produced in the province of Khurasan. We will encounter it again in animal rugs of the sixteenth century attributed to the looms of Herat (page 53).

Other decorative schemes to be found in Persian rugs of the sixteenth century, particularly elaborate medallions, were also first developed by the Timurid illuminators. The multipointed star medallion often used in Safavid medallion rugs (figure 63), appears in the decorative pages of the Gulbenkian *Anthology* of 1410/11 (figure 49), where it is filled with floral scrolls.

As important as the Timurid illuminations in the evolution of Persian rug designs were the often elaborately decorated leather bindings of Timurid manuscripts.[9] Most of the surviving examples, showing great technical skill, were produced in the Herat academy for Shah Rukh and his successors. Some of the finest of these bindings are in the Topkapu Seray Museum and the Museum of Turkish and Islamic Art, Istanbul. The exteriors of a number, usually stamped, show landscapes in which apes, ch'i-lins, phoenixes, and dragons appear, often in combat. Decoration was also lavished on the interior faces, usually in cut leather on a colored background, usually blue. The interiors of bindings dated 1437/38 (841 H.) and 1445 (849 H.), both in the Topkapu Seray Museum, show phoenixes against a ground of floral scrolls. A similar design occurs on the interior of a binding of a copy of Nizami's *Khamsa* (*Quintet*), dated 1449 (853 H.) (figure 50). A lacquer-painted cover in gold on black belonging to a manuscript in the Museum of Turkish and Islamic Art, Istanbul, dated 1482/83 (887 H.) has a central medallion and a

FIGURE 49   Illumination from a Timurid *Anthology* (detail), 1410/11. Gulbenkian Foundation, Lisbon

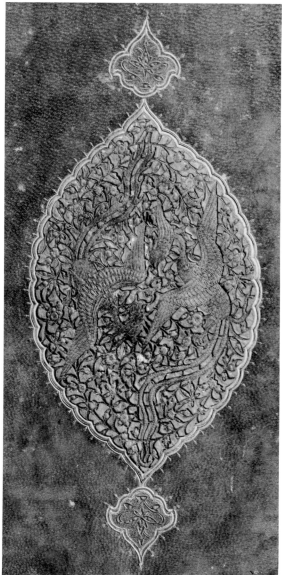

FIGURE 50   Interior of binding from Nizami's *Khamsa* (detail), 1449. The Metropolitan Museum of Art, Gift of Alexander Smith Cochran, 13.228.3

field with an allover design of curling blossoms and leaves (figure 51). This recalls the floral ornament of the famous Ardabil rug of 1539 (figure 68). The multipointed star medallion that appears in the Timurid *Anthology* of 1410/11 was also used by bookbinders, since it appears on a binding in the Museum of Turkish and Islamic Art dated 1436/37 (840 H.).

Toward the end of the fifteenth century, at the close of the Timurid period, a new motif, the cloud band, was added to the floral and arabesque decorations of the illuminations and book covers (figure 52). This undulating, wormlike ornament appeared often in Timurid landscape paintings. Together with another cloud motif, a lobed form appearing in varying shapes, the cloud band became a character-

istic feature of many Persian rugs of the sixteenth and seventeenth centuries.

Numerous representations of rugs in the miniature paintings produced in Herat for Shah Rukh and for Baisunker Mirza suggest that the manufacture of rugs must have been highly developed at this period. These Timurid rugs show a great variety of patterns.

FIGURE 51   Lacquer-painted binding from a Timurid manuscript, 1482/83. Museum of Turkish and Islamic Art, Istanbul

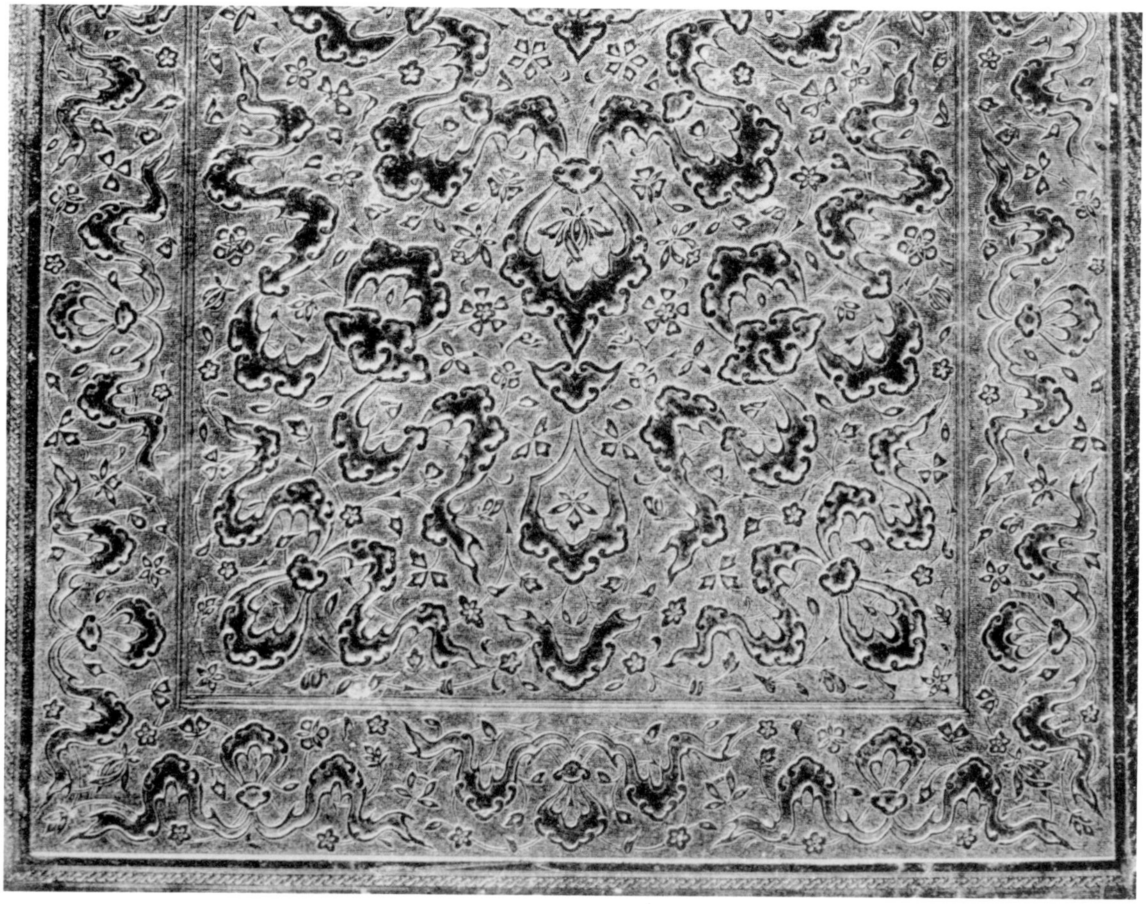

FIGURE 52 Exterior of binding from a Timurid manuscript (detail), 1459. Museum of Turkish and Islamic Art, Istanbul

FIGURE 53 Miniature from Sadi's *Gulistan* (detail), 1426/27. Chester Beatty Library, Dublin

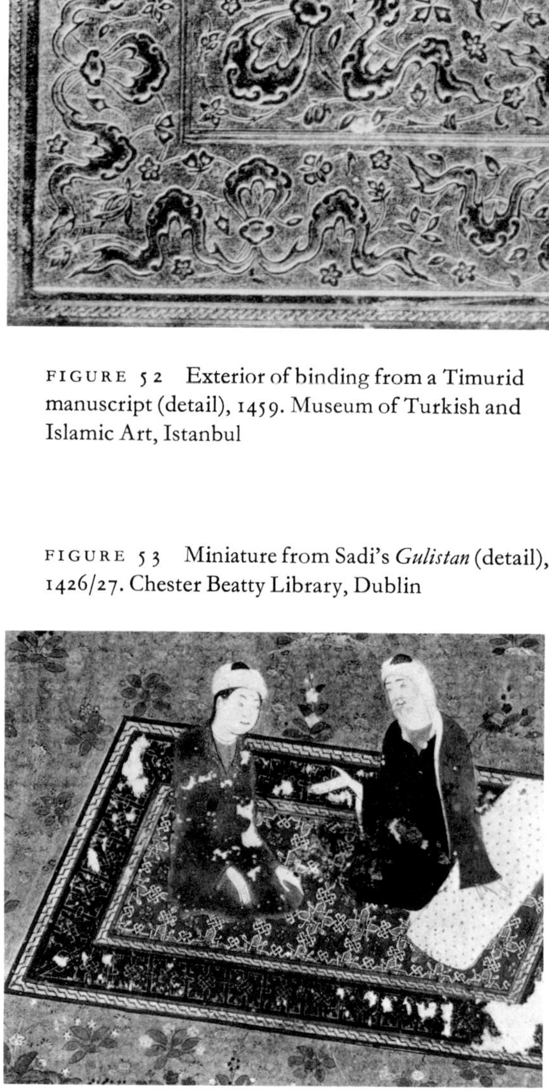

Several classes have been differentiated based on squares, stars and crosses, octagons, hexagons, and circles.[10] The geometrical designs are enriched with interlacings, endless knots, or stylized plant forms. In addition some show changes of color in their compartments, a feature already noted in a Mongol rug of the end of the fourteenth century (figure 45). A miniature in a manuscript of Sadi's *Gulistan* (*Rose Garden*) dated 1426/27 (830 H.) shows Sadi and his teacher seated upon a typical Timurid rug (figure 53). The pattern consists of cross motifs and stars, connected with knotted interlacings. Several Timurid court rugs are represented in the *Shah Namah* of 1429/30 made for Baisunker Mirza. One of its miniatures shows a geometrical rug (figure 54) with a vermilion ground upon which appear hexagons in green and blue containing stars and knotted motifs. The hexagons are separated by wreaths of leaves. Another rug in the same manuscript has a repeat pattern of octagons (figure 55), alternately red and green, formed by knotted bands and filled with leafy devices. The borders of most of the Timurid rugs, like the three illustrated, are decorated with interlaced

and floral patterns, some with central medallions or with circular rather than angular compartments, formed by intersecting circles or wavy lines and rendered in contrasting colors. In addition to the traditional geometrical designs, two new types of design appear in a double-page miniature by Bihzad (figure 56). One of the rugs has an allover pattern of arabesques interlaced with floral scrolls bearing various

FIGURE 54   Miniature from a *Shah Namah* (detail), 1429/30. Gulistan Palace Museum, Teheran

FIGURE 56   Left side of a double-page miniature by Bihzad. Gulistan Palace Museum, Teheran

and knotted Kufic. This decoration appears in many Turkish and Caucasian rugs of later periods (figures 151, 234–236). The Timurid rugs, which were probably made in the court manufactories of Herat, are closely related in design to the geometrical rugs of Anatolia, particularly to the so-called "Holbeins" (page 176).

Judging from the representations of rugs in miniatures painted toward the end of the fifteenth century, chiefly by the celebrated Bihzad and his pupil Kasim Ali, a great change in rug design took place at that time. The traditional geometrical rugs still appear but they are outnumbered by rugs with arabesques

FIGURE 55   Miniature from a *Shah Namah* (detail), 1429/30. Gulistan Palace Museum, Teheran

FIGURE 57   Miniature from Sadi's *Bustan*, by Bihzad, 1487. National Library and Archives, Cairo

kinds of flowers in white, yellow, orange, and red on a dark blue ground. The second rug has spiral floral scrolls on a red ground. The basic designs may be regarded as prototypes of many Persian rugs of the sixteenth century. In a miniature by Bihzad in a manuscript of Sadi's *Bustan* (*Fruit Garden*) dated 1487 (892 H.), two more rugs of a new type occur (figure 57). One is a compartment or cartouche rug in red, yellow, and blue with a red border, the other a tent rug with rounded compartments containing not only arabesques and floral scrolls but flying birds and animals of Chinese derivation, placed against a background of plants. In a miniature attributed to Bihzad in a *Zafar Namah* (*Book of Timur's Victories*) of about 1485, there occurs the earliest representation known of a true medallion rug (figure 58). The design is chiefly floral, with interlaced arabesques in the border. In the light of these paintings, it must have been the rug designers of Herat who were responsible for the striking changes to be seen in the Safavid rugs of the sixteenth and seventeenth centuries. In 1510 Bihzad and some of his pupils moved to Tabriz, the new capital and residence of the Safavid rulers. Doubtless they brought with them from Herat the new type of rug design.

Turkoman Rugs of Northwest Persia (End of Fifteenth Century)

Early in the fifteenth century the Kara-Kuyunli, or Turkomans of the Black Sheep (so called because of the insignia on their banners), gained possession of Tabriz, adding this city to a domain that included eastern Asia Minor. The Turkoman ruler Jahan Shah (1437–1467) was the builder of the famous Blue Mosque in Tabriz, so named because of the brilliant cobalt blue ground of its magnificent faïence mosaics.[11] These mosaics show arabesques interlaced with floral scrolls bearing small leaves, rosettes, and peony blossoms, placed within cross-shaped lobed medallions and cartouches, in white, yellow, turquoise green, purple, and black. Safavid rugs of the

FIGURE 58   Miniature from a *Zafar Namah* (detail), attributed to Bihzad, about 1485. Walters Art Gallery, Baltimore, on loan from J. W. Garrett Library, Johns Hopkins University

FIGURE 59 Medallion rug, Tabriz, end of xv century. Catalogue no. 1

sixteenth century have many parallels with this faïence decoration.

In 1469 the Black Sheep Turkomans were succeeded by the Ak-Kuyunli, or Turkomans of the White Sheep. In the time of the White Sheep ruler Uzun Hasan (1466–1478), as we know from Western accounts, splendid rugs for court use were made in Tabriz. Josafa Barbaro, a Venetian ambassador who visited Tabriz in 1471, reported that many rugs he saw in the king's palace far surpassed those woven at Cairo, or at Brusa in Asia Minor. Describing his audience with Uzun Hasan, Barbaro relates that he was received in a domed chamber of which "all the floor was covered with excellent good carpets, being about fourteen paces over," and he adds that the king "caused certain silk carpets to be brought forth, which were marvelous fair." An unidentified Italian merchant whose account was published along with Barbaro's relates that the floor of the great hall of Uzun Hasan's palace was covered with a magnificent rug "worked in the Persian manner with beautiful patterns, which is round"—the phrase referring, no doubt, to the roundness of the rug's floral scrolls.

It is quite probable that some existing rugs which are usually assigned to the early Safavid period may have been made earlier in Tabriz, under the Turkomans. To this period may be assigned a medallion rug that shows its late fifteenth-century origin in the comparative simplicity of its arabesque and floral decorations (figure 59). Chinese cloud bands, a characteristic feature of most sixteenth-century Persian rugs, do not appear in this piece—a further indication of its early date. The border, with its simple arabesque scrolls, recalls those to be seen in some of the rugs in the Timurid miniatures of the end of the fifteenth century. Another medallion rug that may be of Turkoman manufacture, having a related floral and arabesque design, is now in the Museum of Fine Arts, Boston.[12]

Safavid Period
(Sixteenth to Early Eighteenth Century)

In 1502 the White Sheep Turkomans were overthrown and a new dynasty, that of the Safavids, came to power. Its first ruler, Shah Ismail, a descendant of Shaikh Safi-ad-Din of Ardabil (after whom the dynasty was named), established his capital at Tabriz. Under Shah Ismail (1502–1524) and his son and successor, Shah Tahmasp (1524–1576), Tabriz became one of the great art centers of Persia. Some of the leading painters and illuminators worked here, among them Bihzad, Mirak, Mirza Ali, Sultan Muhammad, and Mir Sayyid Ali.[13] Moving to Tabriz in 1510, Bihzad was in 1522 appointed director of the royal library and studio of the arts of the book. The style of this group of artists influenced all the other arts and crafts of Persia, including rug weaving.

The Safavid rulers established many looms for the weaving of textiles and rugs, not only in Tabriz but in Kashan, Herat, and other places. The rugs produced in these centers were increasingly considered to be works of art as well as objects of daily use. Save for certain pieces that were woven in pairs, no two of the surviving examples are alike, although many are closely related. All have the basic form of oriental rugs—field and border—but the border is more elaborate and important than it was in earlier rugs. Accompanied inside and outside by narrow guard bands, the border accentuates the design of the field by means of contrast in pattern and color. Because most of the large rugs were conceived as floor covers, the favored principles of composition are symmetry and rhythmic repetition, permitting the observer to see the pattern "right side up" from either end. The exceptions are the pictorial rugs, in which animal or figure subjects or both are arranged in one direction only.

The basic motifs continued to be those developed in the late Timurid period, namely the arabesque and the floral scroll. Usually several systems of scrolls, bearing various kinds of palmettes and blossoms and sending off spiraling stems, interlace with the arabesques. The palmettes and blossoms are distributed symmetrically over the field.

In their adoption of Chinese floral motifs, the Safavid designers were not satisfied with mere imitation. They created a new floral ornament of lotuses and peonies, represented either as blossoms or palmettes. They also invented new varieties of palmettes. The palmette leaves, treated individually, have either lobed or serrate outlines, and they are shown either close together or freely unfolding. Often a palmette encloses a leaf or blossom; sometimes a large palmette encloses two smaller ones. Floral scrolls are often combined with arabesques, which intersect them at various points. The Safavid designers also made the Chinese cloud band an essential part of their decorations. Their great achievement was the ingenious combination of these various and endlessly variable elements and decorative devices into

FIGURES 60, 61 Miniatures from Nizami's *Khamsa* (details), Herat, 1524/25. The Metropolitan Museum of Art, Gift of Alexander Smith Cochran, 13.228.3

beautiful patterns—which in turn were often only the background for representations of birds, animals, and human figures. To the Persians of the Safavid

FIGURE 62   Medallion rug, Tabriz, early XVI
century. Catalogue no. 2

period such designs suggested gardens. The verses
that appear in a number of Safavid rugs (figures 64,
70, 76) confirm this, those of the rug of figure 76
reading in part, "This is no carpet, but a wild white
rose . . . a garden full of tulips and roses."

Because our knowledge of the localities in which
the Safavid rugs were woven is still more or less
hypothetical, most of them are classified according to
their design. Stylistic and historical evidence permits
assigning certain types to Tabriz, Herat, Kashan,
Isfahan, Kerman, or other centers. Several dated
rugs, discussed further on, help in establishing a
stylistic chronology. Some types are represented in
early Safavid manuscripts. In miniatures of a manuscript of Nizami's *Khamsa* (*Quintet*) dated 1524/25
(931 H.), there occur a medallion rug with cloud
bands and a compartment rug (figure 60) as well as
rugs with allover patterns of floral scrolls interlaced
with arabesques (figure 61). All three types resemble
rugs that exist today in museums and private collections. Other representations of rugs occur in miniatures of the Houghton *Shah Namah*, made for Shah
Tahmasp during the second quarter of the sixteenth
century, some of whose pages are in the Metropolitan.

MEDALLION AND
COMPARTMENT RUGS

As early as the fourteenth century Persian designers
were breaking up their endlessly repeating geometrical patterns with diapers, medallions, or compartments. The process continued in the Timurid period,
as we have seen, with the introduction of central
medallions, often with complicated outlines. With
the beginning of the sixteenth century the medallion
and compartment designs were further developed.
The typical medallion rug, usually large in size, has
a field dominated by a large central medallion, sometimes fairly simple in form, more often complex, with
shape ranging from circular through oval to star.
In many cases cartouches are attached to the medallion on the long axis of the rug, and to these cartouches are often attached escutcheon-shaped panels.
Two rugs (figure 62, catalogue no. 4) have an eight-
pointed star medallion and a field decorated with a
repeat pattern consisting of arabesques and floral
scrolls interlacing with one another. At intervals the
arabesque scrolls form geometrical devices, and the
delicate floral scrolls form spiral convolutions that

are overlaid with a multitude of palmettes, rosettes, and blossoms. The interlaced arabesque bands in the border were a popular Safavid pattern, seen in a number of sixteenth- and seventeenth-century rugs. An unusually large rug has a sixteen-pointed medallion and a similar field decoration to which large and small cloud bands are added (figure 63). The border has a series of cartouches, another popular Safavid pattern. Early medallion rugs related to the foregoing are in the Victoria and Albert Museum, the collection of the Gulbenkian Foundation, and the collection of Joseph V. McMullan; another was once in the Staatliche Museen, Berlin.[14]

All these early medallion rugs may be assigned to northwest Persia, particularly to Tabriz, the Safavids' main artistic center. The style of the ornament, especially of the floral decoration, indicates that they were made in the time of Shah Ismail (1502–1524). Stylistic evidence for this dating appears in a medallion hunting rug in Milan (figure 64) whose inscription gives us not only the year of its manufacture, 1522/23 (929 H.), but the name of its maker, Ghiyath al-din Jami. This rug shows an interesting mixture of Persian and Chinese motifs. The sixteen-pointed red medallion, sections of which are repeated in the field, contains forty Chinese cranes in flight and cloud bands against a background of floral scrolls. The dark blue field is decorated with hunting scenes that recall those of contemporary miniature paintings. The costumes and turbans of the huntsmen closely resemble those found in miniatures by Shaikh Zada in the *Khamsa* of Nizami (figure 60), a diwan of Mir Ali Shir Nawai in the Bibliothèque Nationale, Paris, dated 1526/27, and a miniature in a diwan by Hafiz in a private collection.[15] In both the rug and the miniatures the figures wear Safavid turbans with a *kula*, or pointed cap, the turban cloth less tightly wound than in manuscripts written for Shah Tahmasp.

A medallion rug with animal decoration, probably contemporary with the rugs discussed above, formerly in the Mackay collection, is now in the J. Paul Getty Collection in the Los Angeles County Museum (figure 65). It is known as the Coronation Rug in recognition of its use in Westminster Abbey during the coronation of Edward VII. The medallion, like that of the Milan hunting rug, shows forty flying cranes as

FIGURE 65 Medallion animal rug, Tabriz, early XVI century. Los Angeles County Museum of Art, Gift of J. Paul Getty

FIGURE 66 Animal rug, probably Tabriz, second half of XVI century. Catalogue no. 5

well as two pairs of reclining gazelles. In the field is a symmetrically arranged landscape of cypresses, blossoming trees, and shrubs, rendered in polychrome on a white ground, upon which are placed groups of animals, some in combat, others grazing. Some of these are mythical animals of Chinese origin, others are taken from nature. In the corner sections of the field houris appear.

In addition to producing large medallion rugs, the sixteenth-century looms of Tabriz produced small medallion rugs, for example, one decorated with groups of animals, pomegranate trees, and floral motifs (figure 66). Several other small medallion rugs are known, including two in the Musée des Tissus, Lyon, and one formerly in the Pannwitz collection.[16] All of these can be dated to the second half of the sixteenth century.

The division of the field into compartments, as seen in the rugs represented in the Timurid miniatures, continued to be popular in the Safavid period. A masterpiece of the Tabriz looms has a field decorated with a repeat pattern of cartouches and lobed medallions, forming several groups (figure 67, page 134). It combines an elegance of design and a richness of color that are encountered in only the finest of Persian rugs. Each compartment forms an ornamental unit. The large eight-lobed medallions, containing a Chinese dragon and a phoenix in combat, are surrounded by eight cartouches that are decorated alternately with arabesques and flying geese. The smaller eight-lobed medallions centered between each four of the larger ones are decorated with Chinese ch'i-lins. The cartouches and medallions of the border are filled with floral scrolls and cloud bands, with the medallions repeating the combat of the dragon and phoenix. Stylistically related to both the Coronation Rug and the Milan hunting rug, this rug can likewise be assigned to the period of Shah Ismail.

Related compartment rugs are in the Musée des Tissus, Lyon, the Düsseldorf Art Museum (a fragment), and the Austrian Museum of Applied Art, Vienna.[17] The Vienna rug has a large central sixteen-pointed medallion together with multiple cartouches containing floral decoration. This decoration and the rug's border of interlaced arabesque bands recall the early medallion rugs. The Vienna rug (and its companion piece, in a private collection in New York) may therefore be assigned to the period of Shah Ismail.

The Chinese animals seen in the rug of figure 67, and in others to be discussed further on, had a different meaning for the Persians than for the Chinese.

To the Chinese the phoenix or *feng-huang* symbolized the empress, while the dragon, thought to bring rain to crops, was the emblem of the emperor. The phoenix and dragon appearing together were a symbol of good omen. The lion symbolized valor and energy, the crane immortality. The Persians, adopting these creatures, invested some of them with their ancient Zoroastrian concept of the struggle between good and evil. In Persian art the phoenix appears on the side of good, and the dragon and lion represent evil.

In the time of the Safavid ruler Shah Tahmasp (1524–1576) the weavers attained perfection both in design and technique, and produced some of the finest Persian rugs now in existence. This perfection is to be seen in a famous pair of rugs that came from the shrine of Shaikh Safi in Ardabil. The more complete rug is in the Victoria and Albert Museum; its somewhat fragmentary companion piece[18] is in the J. Paul Getty Collection in the Los Angeles County Museum. According to their inscription, which appears in a panel at one end of the field, the rugs were woven in 1539/40 (946 H.), either by or at the order of Maksud of Kashan, as an offering to the shrine. The deep blue field is dominated by an elaborate sixteen-pointed yellow medallion surrounded by small oval medallions, from two of which hang mosque lamps (figure 68). The rest of the field is completely covered by a dense and intricate pattern of floral scrolls with blossoms and palmettes. Many of the palmettes are composed of freely delineated leaves that curl and fold in various directions. Among the types of palmettes and composite forms are some with a seminaturalistic treatment of the leaves, often combined into new devices. Such leaves were in the repertory of the Timurid artists of Herat in the last quarter of the fifteenth century, as we know from their illuminations and bookbindings (figure 51). It is clear, therefore, that the designer of the Ardabil rugs was familiar with Herat work. As compared with other Safavid rugs, the Ardabil rugs show a greater emphasis on detail in the floral motifs. The technical advance is to be seen in the handling of its curved and complicated outlines. The earlier rugs, those of the period of Shah Ismail, showed a certain restraint in the rendering of such outlines; in the Ardabil rugs the weavers overcame this difficulty entirely. Some authorities have been inclined to attribute this pair of rugs to Kashan, largely on the basis of their inscription. However, it is evident from both their decoration and their characteristically restrained color scheme that they must have come from a Tabriz workshop.

FIGURE 68   Ardabil rug (detail), Tabriz, 1539/40. Crown Copyright the Victoria and Albert Museum

Another masterpiece of the Shah Tahmasp period is the Anhalt medallion rug (figure 69, page 136). According to tradition it was part of the treasure abandoned by the Turks in 1683 when they failed in their second attempt to take Vienna. It then became the property of the dukes of Anhalt and remained in their palace in Dessau, forgotten, until the middle of the nineteenth century. Published by Friedrich Sarre, it was first shown publicly in 1931 in a London exhibition of Persian art. The elaborate decoration of this rug, which can be dated to the second half of the sixteenth century, consists of several systems of floral and arabesque scrolls, with cloud bands scattered over the entire field. The abundance of detail is reminiscent of contemporary book illuminations. Twelve stylized peacocks, rendered in brilliant, enamellike colors, are an important feature in the field. Notable too are the half-palmettes of the border, their "inlaid" design recalling contemporary Persian faïence mosaics.

Other masterpieces of the Shah Tahmasp periods are in various museums and private collections. Outstanding among them are a multiple medallion rug decorated with animals, in the Victoria and Albert Museum, and a rug with central medallion decorated with flowering trees and animals, in the Poldi Pezzoli Museum, Milan.[19] The latter rug was made, according to its inscription, for "the Darius of the world"—probably Shah Tahmasp. A feature in both these rugs is the use of Chinese vases, rather than cartouches, in the field. To this group belongs a medallion rug partly brocaded with metal threads, whose design includes pairs of peacocks and Chinese bowls (figure 70). The border cartouches contain an ode that speaks of the rug as "the carpet of spring."

Not all of the sixteenth-century medallion and compartment rugs were made in Tabriz or in other centers of northwest Persia. It is known that silk rugs were woven in Kashan (page 59) in central Persia during the time of Shah Tahmasp, and it may be assumed that wool rugs were also produced there. A cartouche rug in the Austrian Museum of Applied Art, and a medallion rug in the Schwarzenberg collection, Vienna,[20] both of which show a vivid color scheme related to that of the silk rugs and silk brocades of Kashan, may well have been made there.

To Herat, in the eastern province of Khurasan, may be attributed floral rugs with peculiar stylistic features, with or without animal decoration, that differ in many ways from the rugs attributed to northwest Persia. Probably of Herat manufacture is a pair of small medallion rugs whose fields are decorated

with floral scrolls bearing several types of palmettes, among them fan-shaped palmettes and composite leaf formations with serrate outlines (figure 71, page 138). As will be explained further on (page 67), the fan-shaped palmette and serrate leaf are typical of the floral rugs made in Herat. Upon the rich floral background of this pair of rugs, animals appear in symmetrical arrangement, singly, pursuing one another, or in combat. Of particular interest is the central medallion with figure subjects representing a garden party. Some of the seated figures, probably nobles, wear richly brocaded costumes; other figures play musical instruments. Behind them servants hold lambs that are to be slaughtered for a feast. The figures are grouped around a pool in which four ducks swim. The floral and animal decorations are characteristic of rugs of the sixteenth century that are attributed to Khurasan, and in particular to Herat. The men's turbans, characteristic of eastern Persia, are seen in sixteenth-century miniature paintings of the Bukhara school.[21]

The manufacture of medallion rugs continued in the time of Shah Tahmasp's successor, Shah Abbas (1587–1628). Fine medallion rugs of the Shah Abbas period are in the Instituto de Valencia de Don Juan, Madrid, and private collections, including one formerly in the collection of Countess de Béhague,[22] and another in the collection of Prince Roman Sanguszko. The deep blue field of the latter rug (figure 72) is decorated with animals, either alone or attacking one another, while in the central red medallion, the cartouches, and the pendants there are houris and musicians. In the yellow corner sections of the field appear hunting scenes of the type to be found in sixteenth-century Persian miniatures and silk weaves. The red border is decorated with medallions containing pairs of peacocks, houris, and tigers attacking gazelles. The medallions are separated by dragons in combat with phoenixes. This rug is distinguished by rich polychromy and its decorative treatment of the figures and animals. Judging by its color scheme and design, it and some related rugs were probably made in Azerbaijan, of which province Tabriz was the capital. The making of medallion rugs continued throughout the seventeenth and eighteenth centuries, and a number of these later rugs, which are often wrongly dated to the sixteenth century, are in existence.

A particular group of early seventeenth-century rugs, often called "Portuguese," has been attributed by some scholars to the Portuguese colony of Goa in India, and by others to southern Persia. The rugs

FIGURE 70 Medallion animal rug, probably Tabriz, middle of XVI century. Catalogue no. 8

FIGURE 72 Medallion animal rug (detail), end of XVI century. Collection of Prince Roman Sanguszko, Paris

have several large concentric stepped-lozenge medallions, covering most of the field. In the corners of the field are figures of Portuguese or Dutch mariners in seagoing vessels, surrounded by fish and sea monsters. There are two classes of these rugs, one with an elaborate design and vivid polychromy, represented by a fine example in the Austrian Museum of Applied Art, a rug once in the Staatliche Museen, Berlin, now destroyed, and another in the collection of Lord Sackville.[23] The other class has a simplified design (figure 73). Other rugs of this second group are in the Winterthur Museum, Delaware, and the collection of the Gulbenkian Foundation.[24] The design of both groups points to Persia rather than India as their place of origin. Representations of Europeans, mostly Dutchmen, are also known in wall paintings of the Shah Abbas period in the Chihil Sutun palace, Isfahan, and in faïence tiles that once adorned the garden pavilions of Isfahan.[25] Some contemporary Persian silk brocades show a repeat pattern of European men in boats (figure 74). The "Portuguese" rugs were copied in the seventeenth century by the peasant weavers of the Caucasus (page 268).

FIGURE 73 Floral rug with figure subjects ("Portuguese"), southern Persia, early XVII century. Catalogue no. 10

FIGURE 74 Fragment of a silk brocade, about 1600. The Metropolitan Museum of Art, Rogers Fund, 42.185

Persian   53

FIGURE 75 Animal rug, Tabriz, middle of XVI
century. Catalogue no. 11

ANIMAL RUGS

In addition to using animals in medallion and compartment rugs, the Safavid designers produced rugs in which animals combined with floral design constitute the chief decoration. A famous rug of this type (together with its companion piece, now in the collection of Mrs. John D. Rockefeller, Jr.) came from the shrine of Shaikh Safi at Ardabil. A masterpiece of balance and rhythm, the rug has five groups of animals disposed symmetrically from side to side on a deep red field (figure 75). Each group consists of a lion and a tiger attacking a spotted stag, accompanied by single animals. The animal decoration is ingeniously combined with floral scrolls issuing from the imaginary center and bearing peony palmettes and blossoms. The dark blue border is decorated with arabesques interlaced with floral scrolls and overlaid with cloud bands. The restrained color scheme, the dignified composition, and the perfection in delineation of the ornament are all characteristic of many rugs produced at Tabriz during the early Shah Tahmasp period, between 1524 and 1550.

Animal rugs were also made in eastern Persia. Attributed to the looms of Herat is a pair of rugs known as the Emperor's Carpets because, according to tradition, they were presented to Leopold I of Austria by Peter the Great of Russia in 1698. Both rugs were once in the Austrian Museum of Applied Art; one of the pair is now in the Metropolitan. Verses in the inner guard bands compare the rugs with a meadow, the sky, flowers, and gems, ending with a laudation of the shah—undoubtedly Shah Tahmasp, for whom they must have been made. The ruby red fields are covered with a dense floral and animal pattern, arranged symmetrically, side to side and end to end (figure 76, page 140). Intersecting systems of spiraling floral scrolls send off stems with blossoms, simple lotus or peony palmettes, pomegranate palmettes, large fan-shaped palmettes, and various composite leaf palmettes with serrate outlines. Upon this background appear various animals, alone or in combat. Some are derived from nature, others are Chinese dragons and ch'i-lins. The pomegranate palmettes, fan-shaped palmettes, and large composite leaf palmettes are rendered in brilliant colors. The floral motifs of these rugs are typical of the group of rugs made in the province of Khurasan, mainly in the city of Herat, which was one of the great artistic centers of Persia. Many of the floral motifs in these rugs and related ones derive from Chinese models, and were developed in Herat by the Timurid illuminators, as mentioned earlier (page 32). A fifteenth-century brush drawing (figure 77) has the elaborate fan-shaped palmettes, pomegranate palmettes, and composite leaves that appear in the Emperor's Carpets and other Herat rugs of the sixteenth century. It also has animal heads connected with its scrolls and leaves, and additions to some of its palmettes, including the bust of a man. In the borders of the Emperor's Carpets slender floral stems intersect arabesque scrolls and cloud bands, the latter overlaid with naturalistic heads of horses, deer, ibex, and jackals. Such scrollwork goes back to the Seljuk period (page 15) and it also occurs in fifteenth-century Timurid illuminations and bookbindings (figure 48). Like the fan-shaped palmettes, pomegranate palmettes, and the composite, serrate leaves, the

FIGURE 77 Brush drawing, XV century. The Metropolitan Museum of Art, Rogers Fund, 41.46

scrolls with animal heads are an indication of manufacture in Khurasan, more particularly Herat.

There are significant stylistic differences between the rugs of the Tabriz workshops and the Emperor's Carpets. In the Tabriz rugs there is a definite restraint in design and color, and the floral design is subordinate to the animal design. In the Emperor's Carpets there is a tendency to conceal the animal design. It is often intimately connected with the floral stems and blossoms. In several instances lion heads or entire animals are placed directly upon the large composite leaves and palmettes, a feature, as noted above, known to Herat artists of the fifteenth century.

In color scheme the Emperor's Carpets are livelier and richer than the Ardabil animal rug. In every respect their style is more elaborate, and might be described as baroque. As we will see further on, this style is characteristic of the whole group of Herat floral rugs with or without animal decoration.

The manufacture of animal rugs continued in the seventeenth century and later. In the time of Shah Abbas (1587–1628) both wool animal rugs and silk animal rugs were made in Isfahan and Kashan. In the eighteenth century, with the decline of the Safavid dynasty and the end of royal patronage, Kurdish weavers began to copy various kinds of Safavid rugs, including those with animal decoration and hunting scenes. Notable Kurdish rugs of this type are now in private collections. One, a rug with groups of strongly stylized animals, is in the collection of Arthur M. Brilant, New York, and a similar rug was once in Istanbul.[26] A late eighteenth-century Kurdish rug with crude stylized human figures, horses, and a variety of small animals is in the collection of Joseph V. McMullan.[27]

SILK RUGS

The most luxurious products of the Persian court manufactories were silk rugs. These were made, according to literary sources, as early as the fifteenth century. In the sixteenth century these fine rugs, of both large and small size, were often enriched with a brocading of metal threads. They were made both for the Safavid courts and as gifts for foreign rulers, and their production was fully developed in the time of Shah Tahmasp (1524–1576). When the Turkish sultan Selim II ascended his throne in 1566, among the gifts presented to him by the Persian ambassador to Adrianople were twenty large rugs and many smaller ones of silk and gold, decorated with birds, animals, and flowers.

Of the Safavid production of large silk rugs only four have survived: hunting rugs in Vienna, in the Museum of Fine Arts, Boston, and in the royal house of Sweden, Stockholm,[28] and an animal rug, the property of the Polish government.[29] The most famous of the group is the rug in Vienna, generally regarded as one of the greatest Persian rugs ever woven (figure 78). Its central eight-pointed green medallion contains groups of dragons in combat with phoenixes. In the salmon pink field, rendered in brilliant colors, are horsemen with spears, swords, and bows and arrows, hunting lions, leopards, wolves, bears, antelopes, wild asses, jackals, and hares. The hunting scenes are placed in a landscape indicated by flowering shrubs. The decoration of this rug is in many ways similar to that of the wool medallion rug of 1522/23 (figure 64). The symmetry of the Vienna rug is less severe than in the Milan rug, however, since it is observed only at the ends of the field. The hunters, wearing Safavid costumes and the tightly wound turbans with kulas typical of the Shah Tahmasp period, gallop over the field in all directions. The red border has groups of seated houris against a background of birds, cloud bands, and flowers. The pictorial character of the field resembles that of hunting scenes in contemporary miniatures, particularly those by Sultan Muhammad, Shah Tahmasp's chief court painter. The rug must have been made for the shah, and it is quite possible that Sultan Muhammad designed the cartoon. Likewise, Sultan Muhammad may have been responsible for the cartoon of a wool medallion rug (fragmentary) formerly in the Hatvany collection, Budapest, the dark blue medallion of which contains a royal garden party rendered in true miniature style.[30] The second of the large silk rugs has hunting scenes similar to those of the Vienna rug, but in less vivid colors; a princely garden party is represented in the border.[31] Like the Vienna rug, this rug, which is now in the Museum of Fine Arts, Boston, may be assigned to the period of Shah Tahmasp, to about 1535.

Of the small sixteenth-century silk rugs approximately fourteen have survived. In general their fields have either an animal decoration only or a central medallion with animal and floral motifs. Four exquisite rugs of this group are in the Metropolitan. One has six rows of animals on a red field, presented either singly or in combat, placed in a landscape of trees and flowering plants (figure 79, page 142). The composition is entirely pictorial, and the animals show a close observation of nature. The green border has a pattern of palmettes between pairs of pheasants. A

FIGURE 78 Silk hunting rug (detail), Kashan, about 1535. Osterreichisches Museum für angewandte Kunst, Vienna

similar rug is in the Detroit Institute of Arts and a nearly identical border occurs in a very fine silk medallion-animal rug belonging to the Gulbenkian Foundation.[32]

The small silk rugs with medallions show various arrangements. One has a quatrefoil medallion containing arabesques and floral scrolls, the field decorated with floral scrolls and peony palmettes (figure 80).

FIGURE 80 Silk medallion rug, Kashan, second half of XVI century. Catalogue no. 14

FIGURE 81   Silk medallion rug, Kashan, second half of xvi century. Catalogue no. 15

FIGURE 82 Silk medallion rug, Kashan, second half of xvi century. Catalogue no. 16

In another the quatrefoil medallion is enriched by an arabesque band overlaid with floral scrolls (figure 81). A similar rug is in the Bavarian National Museum, Munich.[33] The third of the medallion rugs in the Metropolitan has an eight-pointed star medallion surrounded by floral scrolls bearing palmettes and leaves (figure 82). The most elaborate of the medallion rugs, similar to the rug of figure 80, is in the Musée des Gobelins, Paris.[34] Characteristic features of these rugs are their brilliant colors and their technical perfection. Their knotting is so fine, in some cases numbering up to eight hundred knots per square inch, that their texture is like that of sixteenth-century Kashan silk velvets. In both color and design the rugs recall Kashan velvets and brocades, and we may assume, therefore, that the rugs came from Kashan looms.

The weaving of fine silk rugs continued in the time of Shah Abbas (1587–1628), who made Isfahan his capital and here established *karkhanas*, state manufactories, for the production of silk rugs and brocades. The silk rugs of this period and later can be divided into two groups: one without metal threads, the other with additional brocaded threads of silver or silver gilt. Most of the silk rugs of the Shah Abbas period are of the latter class, and have color schemes in which pastel shades predominate. These rugs were once thought to be of Polish origin, and they are still often referred to, for convenience' sake, as "Polish" or "Polonaise."[35] The attribution had its beginning when some of the rugs, then belonging to Prince Czartoryski of Poland, were exhibited in Paris at the Universal Exposition of 1878. Several of the rugs bore the Czartoryski coat of arms; others bore the coats of arms of other European families. One of the Czartoryski rugs (figure 84) has a coat of arms that was once regarded as Polish, but according to Polish and other authorities, is not. The Polish attribution of the silk rugs was discarded long ago, and it is now generally accepted that all of them came from the looms of Kashan and Isfahan. As a matter of record, silk rugs were made in Poland during the eighteenth century, but they show great differences from the Persian rugs in design, colors, and techniques.

In the time of Shah Abbas the production of silk rugs was at its height, but their manufacture continued in the time of Shah Safi (1629–1642), Shah Abbas II (1642–1674), and even later. Interesting references to seventeenth-century silk rugs appear in Polish and other European sources. Paul Simon, a Polish Carmelite father who visited Kashan in 1608, described it as a rich city where Shah Abbas had built himself a splendid palace. Woven in Kashan, he tells us, were rugs of silk and gold, brocades, velvets, and "tissues of the Arras kind," by which he meant tapestry-woven rugs. From other Polish sources we know that silk rugs were made in Kashan to the special order of foreign rulers. In the spring of 1602 King Sigismund Vasa of Poland sent an Armenian merchant, Muratowicz, to Persia to order rugs and supervise their weaving. In Kashan the king's agent ordered rugs of silk and gold, tapestry-woven rugs, a tent, and other fabrics. As for the *karkhanas* of Isfahan, a Polish Jesuit named Krusinski who visited that city early in the eighteenth century, but whose reports cover the early seventeenth century, tells us that its state looms were producing not only what was necessary for the court but silk rugs, brocades, and textiles that were dispatched with government salesmen to both Europe and India, thus enriching the shah. A later traveler, Sir John Chardin, who visited Persia in 1666 and 1672, relates that the weavers of the Isfahan manufactories were obliged to work for the shah only on command, leaving them time to weave for other persons. And from John Fryer, a visitor to Isfahan in 1676, we learn that special bazaars handled the selling of such "choice commodities" as Persian rugs, "both woollen and silk, intermixed with Gold and Silver very costly, which are the peculiar manufacture of this country."

Representations of "Polish" silk rugs in paintings are rare. A scene by Terborch (figure 83) shows such a rug in use as a table cover. The trefoils in its outer guard band are to be seen in several actual "Polish" rugs, including that of figure 89.

The first known appearance in Europe of these rugs was in 1603. In that year a Persian embassy brought lavish gifts from Shah Abbas to the doge of Venice, Mariano Grimani, an event commemorated in a fresco by Gabriele Caliari in the Palazzo Ducale.[36] Among the shah's offerings were a coat of gold brocade, a velvet with a representation of the Madonna and Child, and a brocaded silk rug. In 1622 another Persian embassy brought gifts to Venice including four silk rugs, which, together with the brocaded rug presented in 1603, are preserved in the treasury of Saint Mark's Cathedral. The rug presented in 1603 has a blue central medallion surrounded by a band,[37] a design recalling that of a sixteenth-century silk rug

FIGURE 83   A Lady Playing the Theorbo, by
Gerard Terborch (1617–1681). The Metropolitan
Museum of Art, Bequest of Benjamin Altman,
14.40.617

(figure 81). Another has, on a gold ground, a design
of scrolling bands ending in serrate lanceolate leaves,
together with lotus and leaf palmettes.[38] In the shrine
of Imam Ali at al-Najaf, Iraq, in a collection of magnificent rugs and textiles, is a related silk brocaded rug
larger in size than the Venice rug.[39] Another rug in the
shrine has an allover pattern of large arabesque bands
and floral stems on a crimson ground; a similar rug
(fragmentary), formerly in the collection of Lord
Aberconway, is now in the Victoria and Albert
Museum.[40] In the shrine, in addition to these two
silk rugs with metal thread, are several wool rugs
with metal thread, two of which are inscribed: "Donated by the dog of this shrine, Abbas." It is known
that Shah Abbas often called himself the "dog" of
Ali. The rugs of this group are some of the finest
products of the Shah Abbas period, and because the
design of the wool rugs as well as the silk rugs is related to that of the Venice rugs, we may assume that
they were made at the same time—that is, before
1622—and probably in the manufactories of Isfahan.
    In 1639 a Persian embassy sent by Shaikh Safi to
Duke Frederic of Holstein Gottorp presented him

with gifts that included brocades, velvets, and five
magnificent silk rugs with gold threads, one of them
knotted, the others embroidered. The rugs are preserved in Rosenborg Castle, Copenhagen. Recent
research has established that another knotted rug
in the castle, at one time thought to be part of this
gift, was in fact a gift of the Dutch East India Company to Queen Sofie Amalie of Denmark in 1666.
This rug is known as the Coronation Carpet because
of its use at the coronation of King Frederic of Denmark in 1700. Its gold ground is decorated with four
lengthwise rows of floral scrolls with leaves, large
rosettes, palmettes, and cloud bands in polychrome.[41]
    Approximately three hundred of the so-called
"Polish" rugs are recorded. Although they have a
great variety of pattern, their decoration is mainly
floral, consisting of scrolling stems with large palmettes, blossoms, and lanceolate leaves—all of these
elements familiar from seventeenth-century Persian
wool rugs, chiefly of the Herat variety (page 67). The
floral scrolls are often interlaced with arabesques and
cloud bands. Very few seventeenth-century silk rugs
exist with animal decoration, which continues the
sixteenth-century style of Kashan (figure 79, page 142).
One such rug, in the Residenz Museum, Munich,[42]
can be dated to the middle of the seventeenth century.
    According to their designs, the "Polish" rugs fall
into several groups. The earliest seem to be those
with well-defined systems of intersecting delicate
arabesques and floral scrolls. To this group, which
can be dated to the early Shah Abbas period, belong a
rug in the Lichtenstein collection, a rug in the Czartoryski collection in the National Museum, Cracow, and
a rug in the collection of Miss Marjorie Kevorkian.[43]
The Kevorkian rug recalls some of the splendid silk
velvets of the Shah Abbas period. It is probable that
these three rugs and similar ones were made in
Isfahan in the manufactories established by Shah
Abbas.
    Others of these rugs have one or more medallions,
some medallions defined by arabesque bands (figures
84, 85). In some rugs the fields are divided into
regular compartments outlined by bands or arabesques
with the compartments rendered in several colors.
In one pair, four-lobed lozengelike compartments
formed by arabesque bands enclose symmetrical floral
designs (figure 86). Another pair has an allover pattern of cartouchelike compartments (figure 87, page
144), reminiscent of a floral compartment rug in wool
(figure 105) that is probably of the same period.
    In another group, assignable to about the middle
and second half of the seventeenth century, there is

FIGURE 84   Silk floral rug ("Polish"), Kashan, first
quarter of XVII century. Catalogue no. 17

FIGURE 85   Silk multiple medallion rug ("Polish"),
Kashan, first quarter of XVII century. Catalogue no. 18

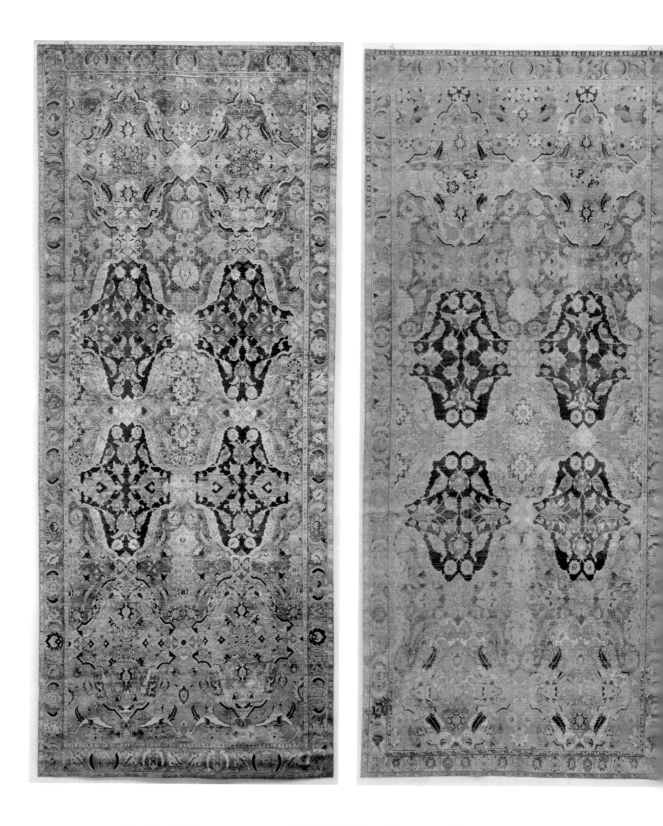

FIGURE 86 Pair of silk compartment rugs ("Polish"), Isfahan, first quarter of XVII century. Catalogue nos. 19a, b

no clear division of the field except that certain areas outlined by scrolls or arabesques are rendered in contrasting colors. In some cases the variety of colors is so great that the pattern structure is obscured (figure 88).

In still another group the fields have repeat patterns consisting of large palmettes connected by short stems, as seen in a rug decorated with thirteen transverse rows of arabesque palmettes connected by half-palmettes in various colors (figure 89). Another example with a palmette design is in the Austrian Museum of Applied Art.[44]

As mentioned earlier, some of the seventeenth-century silk rugs are without metal brocading. An early Shah Abbas piece of this type is the rug in the Kevorkian collection, already mentioned. To the second half of the seventeenth century may be assigned a floral rug also of silk only (figure 90), whose deep red field has a pattern of arabesques and floral scrolls. The green border has wavy scrolls with large palmettes and lanceolate leaves. As we shall see further on, both the palmettes and leaves are a characteristic feature of seventeenth-century wool rugs of the Herat variety. This silk rug and related ones were probably made in the manufactories of Isfahan.

Silk rugs manufactured in the second half of the seventeenth century are preserved in the mausoleum of Shah Abbas II at Kum. One has a floral pattern with pairs of vases and floral sprays; the others have repeat patterns of trees.[45] One is inscribed "the

FIGURE 88   Silk floral rug ("Polish"), probably Isfahan, middle of XVI century. Catalogue no. 21

FIGURE 89   Silk arabesque rug ("Polish"), probably Isfahan, first quarter of XVII century. Catalogue no. 22

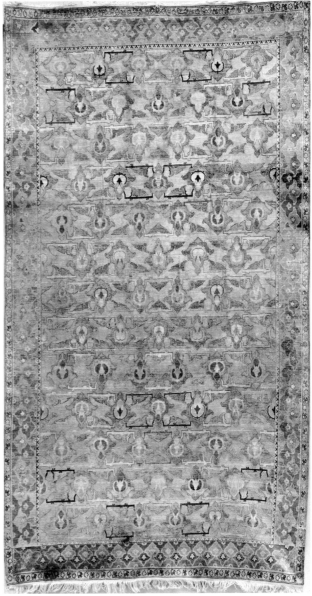

FIGURE 90   Silk floral rug, probably Isfahan, second half of XVII century. Catalogue no. 23

work of the master Nimat Allah of Jushagan, in the year 1082"—that is, 1671. On the basis of this inscription all of the mausoleum's rugs have been assigned by Arthur Upham Pope to the looms of Jushagan, near Isfahan.

The knotting of some of the seventeenth-century silk rugs is in general coarser than that of the earlier ones, most of the rugs having from about 170 to 264 knots to the square inch. Rugs with finer knotting have as many as 378 knots to the square inch (figure 87).

TAPESTRY-WOVEN AND EMBROIDERED RUGS

In the time of Shah Abbas (1587–1628) the looms of Kashan and Isfahan produced not only knotted silk rugs but tapestry-woven pieces as well. Most of these, like the knotted silk rugs, are enriched with metal threads. Because some of the rugs bear Polish coats of arms they, too, have been called "Polish" or "Polonaise."

The representation of animals, birds, and human figures—rare in the knotted silk rugs—is quite frequent in the tapestry-woven rugs. A magnificent tapestry medallion rug with hunting scenes is in the Residenz Museum, Munich.[46] Houris appear in the central medallion; horsemen in Safavid costumes of the sixteenth century appear in the gold field. There can be little doubt that the designer of this rug copied sixteenth-century hunting rugs like that of figure 78. Stylistic differences, such as a more realistic rendering of the floral motifs, show that the tapestry rug must be of later date, namely, the first quarter of the seventeenth century. It is probable that this rug and two others in the Residenz Museum that are decorated with Polish coats of arms[47] were part of the dowry of the Polish princess Ann Katherina Konstanza at her marriage to the Elector Palatine Philip Wilhelm in 1642. These rugs may have been part of the group ordered in Kashan in 1601–1602 by the Armenian merchant Muratowicz (page 59).

Three fine tapestry-woven medallion rugs in the Metropolitan belong to about the same period. Two have floral decoration (figures 91, 92). The third has

FIGURE 91   Silk medallion rug ("Polish"), Kashan, first quarter of XVII century. Catalogue no. 24

FIGURE 92   Silk medallion rug ("Polish"), Kashan, first quarter of XVII century. Catalogue no. 25

FIGURE 93   Silk medallion rug ("Polish"), Kashan, first quarter of XVII century. Catalogue no. 26

a decoration of flying cranes and animals in combat (figure 93), doubtless inspired by the designs of contemporary knotted rugs.

The tapestry rugs were used in the shah's palaces, as we know from European sources, chiefly a French merchant named Tavernier who visited Isfahan in 1664. To this group probably belongs a rug in the Staatliche Museen, Berlin, with animal decoration.[48] The word *padishah*, emperor, appears in four cartouches in its field, indicating that the rug may have been made in a court manufactory for the shah himself, rather than for export.

duced rugs with an allover floral pattern, often combined with arabesques and cloud bands. One type, known in the trade as Isfahan, may be assigned to the province of Khurasan, and particularly to Herat, like the related animal rugs, exemplified by the Emperor's Carpets (page 53). These floral rugs, which vary considerably in size, were imported to Europe in great quantity, especially to Portugal, Spain, and Holland. They are depicted in many seventeenth-century paintings, including works by Velázquez, Rubens, Van Dyck, Vermeer, Terborch, de Hooch, Bol, and Metsu (figure 94). Many of

FIGURE 94   A Visit to the Nursery, by Gabriel Metsu (1630–1667). The Metropolitan Museum of Art, Gift of J. Pierpont Morgan, 17.190.20

Most of the tapestry-woven rugs have brilliant colors, and these were probably woven in Kashan. A few, woven in subdued colors, with blues and greens predominating, were probably made in the manufactories of Isfahan. One such rug is in the Louvre, another in the Textile Museum, Washington.[49]

Four of the rugs presented to Duke Frederic of Holstein Gottorp and now in Rosenborg Castle, Copenhagen, were, as mentioned earlier, embroidered in silk and metal thread. In their designs and brilliant colors these embroidered rugs[50] follow the knotted and tapestry-woven varieties of Kashan and Isfahan.

FLORAL RUGS OF THE HERAT TYPE

From the middle of the sixteenth century until the beginning of the eighteenth Persian looms pro-

these so-called "Isfahans" are today preserved in Spanish and Portuguese churches and museums. Approximately forty are in the Museu Nacional de Arte Antiga, Lisbon. In the United States the rugs were very popular in the late nineteenth and early twentieth centuries. Notable examples are in the Frick Collection, New York, and the Clark Collection in the Corcoran Gallery of Art, Washington.[51]

The appearance of the "Isfahans" in paintings enables us to establish their chronology. The typical rugs of the second half of the sixteenth century have either a floral design alone or a floral design combined with animal decoration, as in the Emperor's Carpets. Probably the earliest of the Herat floral group is a rug with the characteristic large fan-shaped palmettes, composite palmettes, and serrate leaves, to which birds,

including birds of paradise, have been added (figure 95). Although the color schemes differ, the Emperor's Carpets having ruby red fields and green borders, this rug a dark blue field and a white border, the intricate pattern of floral stems is the same. From the imaginary center of the field the scrolls issue in four directions, corresponding to the four quarters of the field. Each scroll forms three circular spirals, and these intersect secondary scrolls, also having three spirals. The rug's various palmettes and composite leaves with serrate outlines originated, as we have

FIGURE 95   Floral rug, Herat, second half of XVI century. Catalogue no. 27

FIGURE 96   Floral rug, Herat, second half of XVI century. Catalogue no. 28

already seen, in fifteenth-century Herat illuminations and brush drawings (figure 77).

Several other fine rugs of the end of the sixteenth and beginning of the seventeenth century are in the Victoria and Albert Museum, the Austrian Museum of Applied Art, and the Frick Collection, New York.[52] The border of the rug in the Frick Collection has arabesque bands alternating with palmettes. A related border occurs in a small "Isfahan" in the Metropolitan (figure 96) and in a similar rug depicted in a painting by Bol, dated 1649.[53] The example in the Austrian Museum of Applied Art has another popular type of sixteenth-century border consisting of cartouches.

At the close of the sixteenth century or early in the seventeenth, in the time of Shah Abbas, the palmettes gradually increased in size and lanceolate leaves were added. A large rug of this type (figure 97) still retains many features of the earlier sixteenth-century rugs discussed above (figure 76). In the seventeenth century, as seen in paintings, notably Van Dyck's Children of Charles I of England and Rubens' Orientale,[54] as well as a portrait by Philippe de Champagne dated 1649 (figure 98), the floral pattern becomes bolder and the lanceolate leaves sometimes encircle palmettes in the field and border (figure 99), a feature continued in Herat rugs as late as the nineteenth century. The large lanceolate leaves, introduced in the time of Shah Abbas, were used much earlier in the Ottoman art of Turkey, particularly in textiles and ceramics (page 197). In view of the political and military contacts between the Persians and Turks during the sixteenth century we may assume that there were artistic cross-influences.

In the Herat floral rugs of the second half of the seventeenth century the number of spirals in each quarter of the field decreases from three to two. In some of the rugs dating from the end of the century only one spiral appears in each quarter and the design is often careless (figure 100).

As already noted, Herat rugs were highly regarded in Europe. Adam Olearius, who visited Persia in 1637 as head of an embassy from Duke Frederic of Holstein Gottorp, reported that the handsomest rugs of Persia were those being made in Herat. During the first half of the seventeenth century, as we know from old records and from the surviving rugs themselves, the Herat rugs were exported to India. Many of these rugs are now in the Jaipur Museum.

FIGURE 97 Floral rug, Herat, second half of XVI century. Catalogue no. 29

FIGURE 99   Floral rug, Herat, first half
of XVII century. Catalogue no. 30

FIGURE 98   Omer Talon (detail), by
Philippe de Champagne, 1649. National
Gallery of Art, Washington D.C., Samuel
H. Kress Collection, 1950

FIGURE 100   Floral rug, Herat, end of XVII century.
Catalogue no. 33

The Herat patterns became very popular in other parts of Persia, and during the seventeenth and eighteenth centuries they were copied in Isfahan, Azerbaijan, Kurdistan, and even in the Caucasus. Such rugs are often wrongly regarded as Herat rugs. A fine northwest Persian version of a Herat type, a medallion rug of the early seventeenth century, is in the collection of Louis E. Seley. The color schemes of the northwest Persian rugs often differ from those of the true Herat rugs. An example of a northwest version, seen in a painting by Vermeer (figure 101), has a red field and dark blue border.

Versions of Herat rugs made in Isfahan in the time of Shah Abbas have, in most cases, deep colors—dark red in the field, dark blue in the border—and a brocading of metal threads. A fine example in wool without brocading (figure 102) is now in the Metropolitan. At first glance this rug might be regarded as of Herat manufacture, since the pattern of the dark blue border shows typical Herat motifs such as large fan-shaped palmettes, leaf palmettes with pomegranates, and rosettes. The inner guard band, however, has a pattern of trefoils, characteristic of a number of silk rugs often attributed to Isfahan. The design of the field, too, is quite different from that of any of the Herat rugs. Scrolling arabesque bands, four in dark blue and four in light blue, intersect each other and end in several places in double lanceolate leaves that have a strong naturalistic appearance. At one end and at each side, near the center, small lanceolate leaves are attached to large leaves, forming a pointed arch. Delicate floral scrolls run parallel to the dark blue bands. The field pattern is in many ways related to that of a number of rugs attributed to Isfahan—some of the so-called "Polish" silk rugs, and an arabesque silk carpet in the shrine of Imam Ali, at al-Najaf presented, together with other rugs, by Shah Abbas, and the arabesque silk rug in Saint Mark's Cathedral, Venice, the latter two already mentioned (pages 59, 60). The composition of scrolling arabesque bands, repeated in several units, appears in the al-Najaf and Saint Mark's rugs. Important in assigning the Metropolitan's rug to Isfahan is a brocaded silk rug, formerly in the Kevorkian collection,[55]

FIGURE 101   Woman with a Water Jug (detail), by Jan Vermeer (1632–1675). The Metropolitan Museum of Art, Marquand Collection, Gift of Henry G. Marquand, 89.15.21

72

ORIENTAL RUGS

FIGURE 102 Floral and arabesque rug, Isfahan, early
XVII century. Catalogue no. 36

whose field contains two quatrefoil medallions, each
formed by four pairs of large and several small curling lanceolate leaves attached to four bands that issue
from a central rosette. Again, as in so many silk rugs,
the outer guard band has a reciprocal pattern of
trefoils: this can be regarded as almost a trademark of
the Isfahan rug school. Other Isfahan rugs of wool
are a rug in Colonial Williamsburg, a rug formerly
in the Cassirer collection, Berlin, and a rug in the
shrine of Imam Riza in Meshed, the last, according
to tradition, a gift of Shah Abbas to the shrine.[56] All
three of these rugs, unlike the Metropolitan's rug,
have brocading in metal threads.

VASE RUGS AND RELATED FLORAL RUGS

A distinct group of Safavid rugs takes its name
from the vases introduced into their designs. The
central symmetry known in many Persian rugs is here
replaced by a vertical composition that is "right side
up" in one direction only. In some of the rugs there
is also a partial side-to-side symmetry, although the
colors of the corresponding areas differ. A technical
feature of the vase rugs, as well as a group of floral
rugs related in design, is that they have double
warps, lying on two levels.

The designs of these rugs, characteristically bold,
have no parallels in contemporary Persian illuminations. Three main types of vase rugs may be differentiated. One has a lozenge diaper of lanceolate
leaves. The lozenges, in various colors, enclose
composite palmettes, stylized lyre-shaped lilies (these
are common to all the vase rugs), and Chinese vases
containing bouquets of flowers. Perhaps the earliest
rug of this type, in the Museum of Turkish and
Islamic Art, Istanbul,[57] may be assigned to the
beginning of the Shah Abbas period, that is, to the
end of the sixteenth century.

In the second type a lozenge diaper is formed by
slender leafy stems enclosing a pattern of large composite palmettes, floral sprays, and vases. There are
numerous varieties of palmettes, each having a central motif framed by petals in contrasting colors.
There is also a secondary lozenge diaper that inter-
sects the main one. The decorative effect is enhanced
by the variety of ground colors in the lozenges, such
as white, light blue, dark blue, and orange. A rug of
this type is in the Baltimore Museum of Art (figure
103). Other examples were formerly in the collection

FIGURE 103 Vase
rug, end of XVI century.
Baltimore Museum of
Art

of Miss E. T. Brown, Glasgow, and the Staatliche Museen, Berlin (destroyed in World War II).[58] Like the first group, this group may be assigned to the end of the sixteenth century.

The third type of vase rug, the one best represented by surviving examples, has a design of increased complexity (figure 104). At first glance it may seem that the large palmettes are placed arbitrarily over the field. However, analysis of the design reveals a definite pattern based on three systems of wavy scrolls forming a lozenge diaper. The large palmettes, rosettes, and vases are placed at the junctions of the stems or on the diagonal stems. The large palmettes are surrounded by floral sprays, smaller palmettes, and leaves. Usually two or three motifs are superimposed, some containing floral sprays, others the characteristic lyre-shaped lilies. The ground color is usually red (as it is in the rug of figure 104) or blue; occasionally it is white, as in a vase rug in the Austrian Museum of Applied Art.[59] An example with a green field in the same museum, showing variations from the usual design, with vases arranged in rows, is of a later date, probably the end of the seventeenth century.[60] Other rugs of the third type are in the Victoria and Albert Museum; another was once in the collection of Lady Baillie; still another was in the Staatliche Museen, Berlin, until it was destroyed in World War II.[61]

Opinions differ as to the dating of the vase rugs. The earliest ones Ernst Kühnel assigned to the middle of the sixteenth century, Kurt Erdmann to the end of the sixteenth century. From the stylistic point of view the latter dating—to the early period of Shah Abbas—seems more plausible. It is strengthened by parallels between the design of these rugs and the painted stucco decorations of two buildings in Isfahan, both of the time of Shah Abbas, the Ali Kapu and the Chihil Sutun.[62] Like the rugs, these stucco decorations show not only vases but the abundance of detail in their floral design that is characteristic of the period.

There is also a difference of opinion concerning the place of manufacture. Kühnel, Erdmann, F. R. Martin, and A. F. Kendrick have favored Kerman, in southern Persia, pointing to the fact that many rug weavers originated in this city from the eighteenth century onward. Pope, on the other hand, suggests that the vase rugs as well as many of the "Polish" silk rugs were produced at Jushagan, near Isfahan. His theory is based on the silk rug with a pair of vases

FIGURE 104 Vase rug, probably Isfahan, end of XVI century. Catalogue no. 37

FIGURE 105   Floral compartment rug, probably Isfahan, early XVII century. Catalogue no. 39

FIGURE 106   Vase compartment rug, probably
Isfahan, first half of XVII century. Colonial
Williamsburg, Virginia

and floral sprays, mentioned on page 63, in the
mausoleum of Shah Abbas II at Kum. Pope dates
this rug to the same year as the mausoleum's inscribed rug, namely 1671. Some support is given his
view by a group of floral rugs of the eighteenth and
nineteenth centuries, related in design both to the
vase rugs and the Herat rugs, and justly regarded as
of Jushagan origin. But still another possibility
exists. The vase rugs and the group of related seventeenth-century floral rugs to be discussed below may
have been produced in the court manufactories of
Isfahan, perhaps by the Armenian weavers who came
from Julfa in the Caucasus and are known to have
been settled by Shah Abbas in a suburb of Isfahan
that was also called Julfa. A fragment of a Caucasian
dragon rug found in the Armenian church of the
Isfahan suburb is now in the Textile Museum,
Washington. The relationship of the lozenge diapers
of the dragon and other Kuba rugs (figures 227, 228)
and the vase rugs can be explained if one assumes
that Armenian weavers were working in the manufactories of Isfahan.

Related to the vase rugs in both design and technique are several floral compartment rugs. Belonging
to this group is a unique rug with an allover pattern
of cartouches and sections of cartouches in various
colors (figure 105). Each compartment contains
various kinds of palmettes, many of them composite.
Some of the palmettes formed by curling leaves suggest vases. Notable too is the way in which the stems
cover the field without regard for the compartments.
As mentioned earlier, this rug is related in design to a
pair of "Polish" silk rugs of the Shah Abbas period
(figure 87, page 144).

To the middle of the seventeenth century belongs
a floral compartment rug in the Victoria and Albert
Museum, with a series of large lobed and pointed
compartments of various colors on a red field.[63] Its
palmettes and floral stems are disposed over the entire field. Among the palmettes are composite types
and lilylike forms known from the vase rugs. A vase
appears once complete in this rug, twice incomplete.
A related rug in the collection of Colonial Williamsburg has, on a red field, an allover pattern of compartments and cartouches in white, pink, cream yellow, light blue, and dark blue (figure 106). Its palmettes are not unlike those of the vase rugs, and small
vases with floral sprays appear in two of its compartments. The dating of these rugs to the middle of the
seventeenth century is confirmed by a fragmentary
multiple medallion rug with floral design in the Sara-
jevo Museum that is dated 1656 (1067 H.).[64]

OTHER TYPES OF FLORAL RUGS

Related to the foregoing types are a number of
floral rugs of the seventeenth century that show a
mixture of the Herat patterns and those of the vase
rugs. One of the finest examples of this group has
a repeat pattern of large lanceolate leaves encircling
palmettes in pairs, with floral sprays and branches
of pomegranates filling the intervening spaces (figure
107). The seminaturalistic style of these floral sprays
differs from the Herat floral patterns and the Kurdish
imitations. Other rugs of this group are a splendid
multiple medallion rug in the collection of Robert
Lehman, a rug in the collection of the Gulbenkian
Foundation, and a rug formerly in the collection of
Miss E. T. Brown, Glasgow.[65] These rugs differ from
the vase and related floral rugs in having a great
richness of color, and it is not improbable that they
are products of Kerman looms. Persian sources
mention Kerman as a center for the manufacture of
fine rugs in the Shah Abbas period. Such floral rugs
were imported to India and used as models by the
Mughal rug weavers of the time of Jahangir and Shah
Jahan. A Mughal manuscript, the *Akbar Namah*
(*History of Akbar*), names Kerman as a source of fine
rugs. The making of rugs continued in Kerman in the
eighteenth and nineteenth centuries, and the floral
designs of these later pieces are quite similar to those
of many seventeenth-century floral rugs.

The looms of Isfahan in the time of Shah Abbas,
as mentioned earlier, produced a luxurious type of
wool floral rug enriched with metal threads. To this
group belong several fragments of large rugs and
multiple-niche prayer rugs in the shrine of Imam Ali
at al-Najaf. One of these fragments has a gold-brocad-
ed field decorated with scrolling arabesques interlaced
with floral scrolls in white, salmon red, red, light blue,
dark blue, green, and black.[66] Also to the looms of
Isfahan may be attributed a fine rug with brocading
in gold and silver in the shrine of Imam Riza in
Meshed, of the same period. Its rich floral pattern
recalls some of the Herat rugs but is closer to
those of the two silk rugs in the al-Najaf shrine.

All types of floral rugs, particularly those of Herat,
were copied from the end of the seventeenth century
through the eighteenth by weavers of Kurdistan
and Azerbaijan. Several interesting examples of these
rugs are in museums and private collections. An
outstanding one, in the Skokloster Castle, Sweden,
has in its field and border very large lanceolate leaves
framing large palmettes in brilliant colors.[67] This
rug, which is perhaps of Jushagan manufacture, can
be dated to the end of the seventeenth century. An

FIGURE 107   Floral rug, probably Kerman, early
XVII century. W. A. Clark Collection, The Corcoran
Gallery of Art, Washington, D.C.

Azerbaijan copy of a Herat rug, dated 1720 (1133 H.),
is in a private collection.[68] Other types of floral rugs
have fields covered with various kinds of palmettes
arranged in rows (figure 108). A Kurdish rug with a
similar pattern is in the Austrian Museum of Applied
Art and another rug, dated 1807 (1222 H.) was
formerly in the Lamm collection.[69]

TREE RUGS AND GARDEN RUGS

Gardens, forming an essential part of palace and
house, played an important part in the daily life of
Persia.[70] As far back as the Sasanian period Persia's
rulers created elaborate gardens and parks, filling
them with blossoming plants, orchards, and foliage

FIGURE 108   Floral rug, Kurdistan, early XIX century.
Catalogue no. 52

trees. Persian writers of all periods mention gardens
frequently, naming their poems after them, and
Persian painters delighted in depicting them, either
alone or more often as a background for figure subjects. Among the most favored flowers were roses,
iris, tulips, carnations, and jasmine. Popular ornamental trees were cypress, plane, and poplar or
chenar. Favorite orchard trees were orange, lemon,
pomegranate, apple, cherry, peach, apricot, and plum.
In the larger gardens animals and birds were kept,
particularly nightingales. Especially beautiful were
the gardens constructed in the time of Shah Abbas in
Isfahan, Shiraz, and along the coast of the Caspian,
particularly in the province of Mazanderan. Sir John
Chardin, visiting Shiraz in 1674, wrote that the most
beautiful of sights were "the public gardens, twenty
in number, which contain the largest trees of their
kind in the world . . . cypresses, plane trees . . . and
pines." Sir Thomas Herbert, who visited Isfahan in
the time of Shah Abbas, was greatly impressed by the
gardens he saw, particularly the one at the palace of
Chihil Sutun. During the eighteenth and nineteenth
centuries many more fine gardens were established
in Shiraz, some of which are still in existence.

There are two types of garden rugs, one in which
landscapes with trees are depicted, another in which
formal gardens are represented. One of the earliest
Safavid landscape and tree rugs has, arranged on a
red field, a composition of cypresses, flowering
trees, and shrubs bearing palmettes, all arranged
vertically and symmetrically on either side of the long
axis (figure 109). Some of the intervening spaces are
filled with large and small palmettes, attached either
to the branches of the flowering trees, or to small
stems. The angular stylization of the trees and plants
and the restraint of the color scheme both suggest an
early date. It is probable that the rug was woven in
a court manufactory of Tabriz in the time of Shah
Ismail (1502–1524). In style it is related to several of
the early medallion and cartouche rugs of Tabriz
(figures 62, 63).

Landscape and tree rugs, made in various sizes,
were popular in Persia throughout the Safavid period
and even later. In a small landscape rug of the second
half of the sixteenth century we see a small pond with

FIGURE 109   Tree and garden rug, Tabriz, early
XVI century. Philadelphia Museum of Art, photograph
by A. J. Wyatt, staff photographer

FIGURE 110   Tree rug, probably northwestern
Persia, second half of XVI century. Catalogue no. 40

FIGURE 111   Tree rug, probably Isfahan, early
XVII century. Catalogue no. 41

FIGURE 113   Tree rug, Kurdistan, end of XVII
century. Catalogue no. 42

FIGURE 112   Tree rug, middle of XVII century. The
Metropolitan Museum of Art, Gift of Joseph V.
McMullan. 1970.302.2

fish in the center of a red field surrounded by flowering trees with birds and palmettes (figure 110). The
rendering of the trees, which is more naturalistic
than in the rug of figure 109, recalls some of the rugs
of Tabriz and Kashan of the middle and second half
of the sixteenth century.

Several examples of the Shah Abbas period are
related stylistically as well as technically to the vase
rugs. In one, the red field is patterned with rows of
flowering shrubs and plants growing out of patches
of ground (figure 111). Among its flowers are roses,
carnations, and iris. The border of this rug is very
close to that of a fragmentary vase rug in the Metro-

politan (catalogue no. 38). Other tree rugs have patterns in which plants are enclosed within a trellislike framework, as may be seen in a rug formerly in the collection of the Countess de Béhague, and a fragment in the Musée des Arts Décoratifs.[71] In another rug in the Metropolitan the flowering shrubs are arranged around a small eight-pointed star medallion (figure 112).

In northwest Persia, in the Kurdish district bordering on the Caucasus, tree as well as garden rugs were made during the seventeenth and eighteenth centuries. Representative of this group is a rug with stylized floral design showing a repeat pattern of medallions, and shieldlike compartments (figure 113). Fruit trees grow diagonally from some of the medallions. A similar rug was formerly in the Lamm

FIGURE 114
Garden rug (detail),
probably Isfahan,
early XVIII century.
Department of
Archaeology and
Museums, Central
Museum, Rajasthan,
Jaipur

84

collection; another is in the McIlhenny Collection in the Philadelphia Museum of Art.[72] For some time such rugs were regarded by some experts as Caucasian. In the eighteenth century, the stylization became even more pronounced, with the trees and foliage rendered angularly.

The classic Persian garden was known as *chahar bag* or "four gardens," since it consisted of four parts divided by crossing water canals. At the intersection of the canals there was ordinarily a pool lined with blue tiles and a domed pavilion in which the garden's owner entertained his guests. The usual garden rugs depict such arrangements from two points of view at once: from above, giving the architectural plan, and from the side, showing the trees and pavilion. In size these rugs vary considerably. The most splendid surviving example, measuring more than twenty-eight feet by twelve, was discovered in 1937 in a sealed room in the palace of the Maharaja of Jaipur, at Amber, India,[73] and is now in the Central Museum in Jaipur. Its field (figure 114) is divided by the main canals into four garden plots, each of which is divided by secondary canals into smaller plots. The canals are full of fish, ducks, and monsters. The large central pavilion has an elaborate dome. The ground color of the main avenues is red; the colors of the plots are dark blue, azure, gray green, golden yellow, copper red, rose, and brown. The many kinds of trees, birds, and animals are drawn realistically, although in vivid colors reminiscent of the vase rugs. The date of this rug can be approximated from record labels found on its lining. The earliest one, dated August 29, 1632, states that it is of foreign make. It must have been made, therefore, in the time of Shah Abbas, and it probably represents one of the actual gardens of Shah Abbas in Isfahan or Shiraz. This magnificent rug, the earliest of the group, was probably woven in Isfahan, and may be regarded as a prototype of all Persian garden rugs of the formal architectural type. Similar in style and colors are a small rug, formerly in the Figdor collection, now in the Austrian Museum of Applied Art, and a fragmentary rug with an elaborate garden in the Burrell Collection, Glasgow Art Gallery and Museum.[74] The dating of the Austrian Museum's rug by Sarre and Trenkwald to the first half of the sixteenth century can no longer be considered correct: its relation to the Jaipur rug

FIGURE 116 Garden rug, Kurdistan, about 1800. Catalogue no. 45

indicates that it should also be assigned to the Shah Abbas period.

The making of garden rugs continued in the eighteenth and nineteenth centuries in the province of Kurdistan. The naturalistic style of the Shah Abbas period was replaced by a conventional one in which trees and water are stylized in geometrical fashion, the water being indicated by parallel zigzag lines. This geometrical style occurs in three small rugs whose stylized shrubs and plants may remind the Western viewer of Christmas-tree ornaments. One of these rugs is in the Metropolitan (figure 115, page 146), another was formerly in the Staatliche Museen, Berlin, and the third is the collection of Joseph V. McMullan.[75] A large rug of this type in the Metropolitan (figure 116) has a more elaborate garden, its style and deep color scheme characteristic of rugs made in Kurdistan. Another rug is in the Fogg Art Museum, Harvard University, and a similar pair was formerly in the Kevorkian collection.[76] Also of Kurdish origin are eighteenth-century garden rugs that differ from the foregoing chiefly in their brighter colors. A large example of this type of rug is in the McLaren collection, England.[77] Several large and small fragments of such rugs are in existence (figure 117), and it is possible that some of these may be portions of the same rug.

ARABESQUE RUGS

In this group arabesques are the most conspicuous feature of the decoration and cover the whole field in the form of scrolls or broad bands. The secondary pattern consists of floral motifs. Such rugs were made in all parts of Persia from the late sixteenth to the nineteenth century. Of several early pieces only fragments remain. One is in the Austrian Museum of Applied Art, and two were formerly in the Staatliche Museen, Berlin.[78] In this colorful group, related through its floral patterns to the vase rugs, two systems of interlacing arabesque scrolls in contrasting colors cover the field, with flowering shrubs filling the intervening spaces. In a later variation, vases are introduced, as may be seen in a rug of the Bernheimer collection, Munich.[79] The arabesque borders are identical with those of certain of the vase rugs, and both types must have had a common origin.

In another type of arabesque rug the scrolls are replaced by bands, usually dark blue, that are overlaid with floral stems. The bands form half-palmettes or combine into full palmettes, and the rest of the

FIGURE 117   Garden rug (fragment), Kurdistan, XVIII century. Catalogue no. 46

field has palmettes of various sizes and leaf motifs known from the floral rugs of the Shah Abbas period. One of the finest of these rugs is in the Corcoran Gallery of Art, Washington (figure 118); another fine one is in the Museum for Art and Industry, Hamburg.[80] Similar rugs are depicted in miniature paintings of the sixteenth century, among them works by the court painter Mir Sayyid Ali. The use of arabesque bands is also to be seen in faïence mosaic decorations of the late sixteenth and early seventeenth centuries in Ardabil and Isfahan, notably

century example has a pattern of interlaced arabesques in red and ivory on a dark blue ground (figure 120). The spaces formed by the latticework are filled with a great variety of flowering shrubs and plants, including roses, carnations, iris, and narcissi. A cartouche at the top of the field contains this inscription: "Ordered by his excellency Ali-Riza Khan, made in Garus, 1794 [1209 H.]." The style and colors are typical of rugs made in Kurdistan, where the district of Garus had important looms. The designer, copying an earlier arabesque rug, preserved a great

FIGURE 118   Arabesque rug (detail), Isfahan, XVI century. W. A. Clark Collection, The Corcoran Gallery of Art, Washington, D.C.

FIGURE 119   Arabesque rug, probably Kurdistan, middle of XVII century. Catalogue no. 47

FIGURE 120   Arabesque rug, Garus, Kurdistan, 1794. The Metropolitan Museum of Art, Gift of Joseph V. McMullan, 1970.302.6

those of the Mashid-i-Jami and the Lutfullah mosque, both in Isfahan. It is probable that the rug of figure 118 and others of this type were made in the royal manufactories of Isfahan at the beginning of the seventeenth century in the time of Shah Abbas.

A rug with a pattern of interlaced arabesque bands in white and blue and a dense floral pattern in vivid colors (figure 119) recalls the floral rugs of the vase variety; stylized animals are introduced in the floral design. Judging from its design and color scheme, this rug can be assigned to the mid-seventeenth century and regarded as a product of Azerbaijan.

The production of arabesque rugs continued in various parts of Persia through the seventeenth and eighteenth centuries. An interesting late eighteenth-

deal of the original spirit and composition, although the arabesque palmettes are more angular than those of the earlier period.

PRAYER RUGS

Essential to the Muslim's acts of worship was his prayer rug. The custom of using mats or small rugs for prayers at home or while one was traveling goes back to the beginning of the Islamic era. In the early period, as already noted (page 13), some of these mats were of reeds. Most of the pile prayer rugs have a *mihrab* or prayer niche, indicating the *qiblah* or direction toward Mecca. Also typical, in view of the prohibitions expressed in the *Hadith* (*Traditions of the Prophet*)—not in the Koran, as is sometimes thought

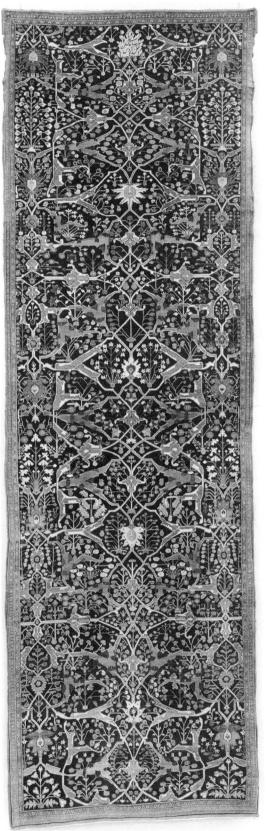

—is the absence from the decoration of representations of living creatures. The earliest known representation of a Persian prayer rug appears in a Timurid miniature of 1436.[81]

The prayer rugs of the Safavid period follow the decoration of Safavid rugs in general. A fine example dating to the early Shah Tahmasp period, or second quarter of the sixteenth century, has a mihrab filled with a typical Safavid pattern of floral scrolls and cloud bands (figure 121). The spandrels of the niche are divided into irregular compartments filled with Koranic inscriptions. The border has two patterns, the lower part having a design of floral scrolls and arabesques, the upper, Koranic inscriptions. Judging from the design and the restricted color scheme, the rug must have been made in Tabriz.

A later sixteenth-century prayer rug has a mihrab filled with seminaturalistic trees and shrubs (figure 122). In the apex of the niche, instead of the characteristic mosque lamp, there is a vase with blossoms. In this rug the Koran inscriptions are confined to the border. The style indicates that the rug was woven elsewhere than in Tabriz, probably in Kashan.

In addition to those intended for individual worshipers, larger rugs for family prayers were made, with two mihrabs placed one above the other or several mihrabs placed side by side. Two multiple-niche rugs, important historically as well as artistically, are in the shrine of Imam Ali at al-Najaf. Both are of wool with brocading in gold and silver. One has three mihrabs; the other, incomplete, has six and part of a seventh.[82] Both rugs are richly decorated with floral scrolls, interlaced arabesques, and cloud bands, and their colors are deep and brilliant. The inscription on the first rug, "Donated by the dog of this shrine, Abbas," was mentioned earlier. Both of these prayer rugs were probably made in Isfahan before 1622—the date established by the related silk rugs in Venice (pages 59, 60).

Of a later period—the second half of the seventeenth century—is a double prayer rug with its mihrabs one above the other (figure 123). The floral pattern and lanceolate leaves that decorate its spandrels and the upper niche resemble those of the Herat rugs of the seventeenth century.

The making of prayer rugs continued in the eighteenth century. Of great beauty are the colorful rugs made in the province of Fars, probably in Shiraz; these show a dense floral pattern, the so-called mille-fleurs, of various flowers growing out of vases. These fine rugs, including one now in the Metropolitan (figure 124), one in the collection of Joseph V.

McMullan, and another now in the Art Institute of Chicago,[83] were probably made in the time of Shah Karim Kahn (1750–1779) of the Zand dynasty.

Nineteenth and Twentieth Centuries

Although the Metropolitan possesses only a few Persian rugs of the nineteenth century, a brief survey of the main types is offered here, to round out the history of Persian rugmaking.[84] Modern Persian rugs are usually divided into groups corresponding to various regions. The main groups are Azerbaijan, Kurdistan, Kerman and Fars, Irak-Ajemi, and Khurasan. Classification is sometimes difficult because many centers borrowed patterns of other centers; nevertheless certain districts and localities produced rugs with characteristic patterns.

In the north of Persia were made the Azerbaijan and Kurdistan groups. The best known of the Azerbaijan rugs were made in Tabriz, the capital of the province and an important rug-trading center. The rugs made by the nomads of Azerbaijan are known as Heriz, Bakshis, Gorovan, Sirab or Serapi, and Karadagh. The floral design with central medallion is usually strongly stylized. The colors are copper red, buff, white, and blue. The Karadagh (Black Mountain) rugs were made by nomads to the north of Tabriz. They show a blend of Persian and Caucasian motifs, with the field usually filled by a repeat floral pattern.

South of Azerbaijan lies the mountainous country of Kurdistan, with its central province of Ardalan, inhabited by the nomadic Kurds. Here, in the district of Garus, and particularly in the towns of Garus and Bijar, Kurdish weavers copied floral rugs with large palmettes, usually on a dark blue ground (figure 125). Other rugs made by the Kurds have patterns ranging from large medallions to repeats of large and small floral motifs. The Bijars, as these rugs are called, are technically superior to many nineteenth-century Persian rugs. Several dated examples exist.

The town of Senna (or Sehna, Senné, and other spellings) in the province of Ardalan produced fine rugs with delicate patterns and as many as four hundred knots to the square inch. Their fields usually have small allover patterns of pear- or cone-shaped palmettes made up of small flowers. Their colors range from rose and ivory, used as backgrounds, to

FIGURE 121   Prayer rug, Tabriz, first half of XVI century. Catalogue no. 48

FIGURE 122 Prayer rug, probably Kashan,
second half of XVI century. Catalogue no. 49

FIGURE 123 Prayer rug, probably Isfahan,
second half of XVII century. Catalogue no. 50

FIGURE 125   Floral rug, Kurdistan, early XIX
century. Catalogue no. 53

dark, rich reds, blues, and greens in the patterns.
Justly famous are the nineteenth-century Senna kilims (figure 126), with their delicate allover floral
patterns in rich polychromy related to those of knotted rugs. Technically, their weaving surpasses that
of Turkish and Caucasian kilims. Other well-known
Kurdish rugs are the Suj Bulaks, made south of Lake
Urmia, showing a pattern of small flowering shrubs
and a lozenge medallion in dark red on blue. French
floral patterns are also often introduced in these
nineteenth-century rugs. Their wool is soft and shiny.

East of Hamadan, where certain types of rugs with
camel's hair were made in the nineteenth century,
are the regions of Irak-Ajemi (or Aragh) and Isfahan.
Here were produced rugs known as Feraghans,
Sultanabads, Saruks, Serabends, Kashans, and Jush-
agans. The typical Feraghans, sometimes confused
with Herat rugs, have a small-scale allover pattern,
usually rose colored on a blue field, with a green
border. Other Feraghans have the *guli hinnai* (henna
flower) pattern arranged in rows on a red ground.
An especially fine rug from Feraghan, often regarded
as a collector's piece, is the *zelle-sultan* (shadow of the
sultan), with an allover design of vases combined
with nightingales on a cream ground.

The Serabends (or Sarawans) are fine rugs with an
allover design of small pear- or cone-shaped blossoms or palmettes arranged in rows, facing alternately right and left. The grounds are reddish brown,
dark blue, or cream white, with the pattern in contrasting colors.

Between Hamadan and Sultanabad lies the village
of Saruk. Here a well-known type of rug was made.
The pattern is usually traditional, consisting of
medallions with floral scrolls bearing various large
palmettes and blossoms, sometimes combined with
cypress and willow trees, realistically rendered. The
colors are rich, usually deep blue and red, green, and
ivory on a cream white or red ground. Other rugs of
the Irak-Ajemi group, varying in quality of design
and knotting, are the Mahals and Muskabads.

Kashan, situated between Teheran and Isfahan,
was famous in the sixteenth and seventeenth centuries for its silk rugs and brocades. In the nineteenth
century its weavers continued to make silk rugs and
wool rugs with medallions and a floral pattern based
on a traditional Kashan design. The rendering of the
floral motifs inclines toward the realistic, with a great
deal of detail. The color schemes are vivid, with
many nuances used.

Jushagan or Jushagan Kali (Rug Town), situated
between Kashan and Isfahan, was a known rug manu-

facturing center in the Shah Abbas period. The Shah Abbas design of large palmettes and floral motifs was preserved in the nineteenth-century rugs of Jushagan, one type having large palmettes separated by rosettes and small flowers. Vase motifs appear in some of these rugs. The color schemes have a rich rose and blue combined with greens, yellows, and ivory white.

To the Kerman and Fars group of southern Persia belong rugs made in Kerman and the district of Shiraz by the Kashgai and Afshari nomads. Kerman was famous as a rug-weaving center throughout the seventeenth and eighteenth centuries, and in the eighteenth century weavers of Kerman were employed in Isfahan by the Afsharid ruler Nadir Shah (1736–1747). The names of Kerman weavers appear in a number of eighteenth- and nineteenth-century rugs, one of which is dated 1835. Characteristic features of the rugs are realistic roses combined with vases, cypresses, and palmette medallions with floral centers. Other flowers in these rugs, often arranged in bouquets and rendered naturalistically, are lilies, tulips, and peach blossoms. A variety of Kerman rug known in the trade as Laver (a misspelling of the village named Rawar) is finely knotted and has medallions and a floral design. The color schemes of the Lavers are usually less brilliant than those of the Kashan and Isfahan rugs, and their backgrounds are often cream white.

Most of the Shiraz rugs were made by the Kashgai nomads. Their patterns consist of medallions, usually multiple, filled with and surrounded by cone-shaped palmettes and small flowers, including roses, mostly geometrically stylized. Some of the palmettes, almond- or pear-shaped, are formed of small roses. Geometrically stylized birds and human figures appear here and there in the fields. The usual colors of these rugs and of many other Shiraz types are dark shades of blue and red brown with patches of white.

The weavers of Khurasan, continuing an old tradition, manufactured rugs in the nineteenth century in such centers as Herat, Meshed, Birjand, Dorosh, and Gahyn. The color scheme of these rugs is based on the rich reds of the old Herat rugs. The patterns of many of the nineteenth-century Herats recall the Feraghans, with their minute floral patterns with

FIGURE 126 Kilim, Senna, Kurdistan, XIX century. The Metropolitan Museum of Art, Gift of Joseph V. McMullan, 1970.302.8

lanceolate leaves framing rosettes in white, red, green, and blue on a dark blue ground. Other nineteenth-century Herat rugs have a leaf pattern on a blue or red ground, usually with a dominant blue effect, with white, green, yellow, and sometimes purple as subordinate colors. The Meshed rugs have a minute floral pattern with or without a medallion, in dark, rich colors on a dark blue ground, with borders of multiple stripes. The rugs of Birjand, Dorosh, and Gahyn are the closest in appearance to the antique Herats.

Notes to Chapter Five

1 Arthur Upham Pope (ed.), *A Survey of Persian Art*, V, pls. 835–42; Laurence Binyon, J. V. S. Wilkinson, and Basil Gray, *Persian Miniature Painting* (London, 1933), pls. xxv–xxvii.

2 Pope, *Survey*, V, pl. 838.

3 Ibid., pls. 704, 721–27.

4 F. R. Martin, *The Miniature Painting and Painters of Persia, India, and Turkey from the 8th to the 18th Century*, II (London, 1912), pls. 45–50.

5 Ivan Stchoukine, *Les Peintures des manuscrits timûrides* (Paris, 1954); Pope, *Survey*, V, pls. 858–82.

6 Arménag Bey Sakisian, *La Miniature persane du XIIᵉ au XVIIᵉ siècle* (Paris, 1929), pls. xlii–xlv; Ernst Kühnel, *Miniaturmalerei im islamischen Orient* (Berlin, 1922), figs. 28, 32.

7 Pope, *Survey*, V, pls. 942 B, 943 B, 945 A–C.

8 Ibid., pls. 869–74.

9 Mehmet Aga-Oglu, *Persian Bookbindings of the Fifteenth Century* (Ann Arbor, Mich., 1935).

10 Amy Briggs, *Ars Islamica*, VII, pp. 20–54; and XI–XII, pp. 146–58.

11 Pope, *Survey*, IV, pls. 452–56.

12 Chicago, The Art Institute, *An Exhibition of Antique Oriental Rugs* (1947), no. 24.

13 Binyon, Wilkinson, and Gray, pp. 105–50.

14 Pope, *Survey*, VI, pls. 1112, 1122; Joseph V. Mc-Mullan, *Islamic Carpets*, no. 12; Kurt Erdmann, *Oriental Carpets*, fig. 59.

15 Sakisian, pl. lxvii; Binyon, Wilkinson, and Gray, pl. lxxxiv b.

16 Pope, *Survey*, VI, pls. 1150, 1151; Friedrich Sarre and Hermann Trenkwald, *Old Oriental Carpets*, II, pls. 35, 36.

17 F. R. Martin, *A History of Oriental Carpets before 1800*, figs. 96, 106; Pope, *Survey*, VI, pl. 1125.

18 Arthur Upham Pope, *Catalogue of a Loan Exhibition of Early Oriental Carpets*, no. 6.

19 Pope, *Survey*, VI, pls. 1130, 1154.

20 Sarre-Trenkwald, II, pls. 17, 21.

21 Binyon, Wilkinson, and Gray, pls. lxxvii–lxxxi.

22 Pope, *Survey*, VI, pls. 1207, 1210.

23 Sarre-Trenkwald, I, pl. 33; Erdmann, fig. 93; Pope, *Survey*, VI, pl. 1216.

24 Martin, *History of Oriental Carpets*, pl. vi; Lisbon, Museu Nacional de Arte Antiga, *Oriental Islamic Art:* *Collection of the Calouste Gulbenkian Foundation* (1963), no. 79.

25 Maurice S. Dimand, *A Handbook of Muhammadan Art*, fig. 138.

26 Maurice S. Dimand, *Peasant and Nomad Rugs of Asia*, no. 12; Erdmann, fig. 121.

27 McMullan, no. 46.

28 Pope, *Survey*, VI, pls. 1193, 1194.

29 Ibid., pls. 1195, 1196.

30 Ibid., pl. 1141.

31 Sarre-Trenkwald, II, pls. 24–26.

32 Chicago, 1947, no. 21; Pope, *Survey*, VI, pl. 1200.

33 Pope, *Survey*, VI, pl. 1202.

34 Ibid., pl. 1201.

35 Maurice S. Dimand, *Loan Exhibition of Persian Rugs of the So-called Polish Type*.

36 Ibid., frontispiece.

37 Pope, *Survey*, VI, pl. 1245.

38 Ibid., pl. 1244.

39 Mehmet Aga-Oglu, *Safawid Rugs and Textiles*, pl. ii.

40 Ibid., pl. i; Pope, *Survey*, VI, pl. 1252.

41 Martin, *History of Oriental Carpets*, pls. vii, viii.

42 Pope, *Survey*, VI, pl. 1251.

43 Ibid., pls. 1242, 1243, 1261.

44 Sarre-Trenkwald, I, pl. 30.

45 Pope, *Survey*, VI, pls. 1257–1260.

46 Sarre-Trenkwald, II, pls. 47–49.

47 Pope, *Survey*, VI, pl. 1268 B.

48 Sarre-Trenkwald, II, pl. 45.

49 Pope, *Survey*, VI, pls. 1262, 1269 B.

50 Martin, *History of Oriental Carpets*, pls. xi–xiv.

51 *The Frick Collection*, vol. XI, *Renaissance Furniture, Oriental Carpets, English Silver* (New York, 1956), pls. xii–xvii; Washington, D.C., "Carpets for the Great Shah: The Near-Eastern Carpets from the W. A. Clark Collection," *Corcoran Gallery of Art Bulletin*, II (October, 1948), ills. i, iv–vii, ix.

52 Erdmann, fig. 79; Sarre-Trenkwald, I, pl. 16; *The Frick Collection*, XI, pl. xii.

53 Wilhelm von Bode and Ernst Kühnel, *Antique Rugs from the Near East*, fig. 83.

54 Arthur Urbane Dilley, *Oriental Rugs and Carpets*, pl. XVI.

55 Maurice S. Dimand, *The Kevorkian Foundation: Collection of Rare and Magnificent Oriental Carpets*, cover.

56 Maurice S. Dimand, "The Seventeenth-Century Isfahan School of Rug Weaving," in *Islamic Art in The Metropolitan Museum of Art*, fig. 8; Pope, *Survey*, VI, pls. 1178, 1185.

57 Erdmann, fig. 71.

58 Pope, *Survey*, VI, pl. 1221; Sarre-Trenkwald, II, pl. 6.

59 Sarre-Trenkwald, I, pl. 23.

60 Ibid., pl. 24.

61 Pope, *Survey*, VI, pls. 1218, 1227, 1225, 1229.

62 Ibid., V, pls. 552, 553 A.

63 Ibid., VI, pl. 1237.

64 Ibid., pl. 1238.

65 Ibid., pls. 1179 A, 1235, 1236.

66 Aga-Oglu, *Safawid Rugs and Textiles*, pl. VI.

67 Martin, *History of Oriental Carpets*, pl. XXII.

68 Pope, *Survey*, VI, pl. 1190.

69 Sarre-Trenkwald, I, pl. 21; Martin, *History of Oriental Carpets*, pl. XXIII.

70 Donald N. Wilber, *Persian Gardens and Garden Pavilions* (Rutland, Vt., 1962).

71 Pope, *Survey*, VI, pl. 1233; Erdmann, fig. 75.

72 Bode-Kühnel, fig. 44; Erdmann, fig. 122.

73 Maurice S. Dimand, *Ars Islamica*, VII, pp. 93–96.

74 Sarre-Trenkwald, II, pl. 12; Bode-Kühnel, fig. 104.

75 Erdmann, fig. 125; McMullan, no. 28.

76 McMullan, no. 29; Dimand, *The Kevorkian Foundation*, pl. VII.

77 Pope, *Survey*, VI, pl. 1270.

78 Sarre-Trenkwald, I, pl. 31; ibid., II, pl. 9; Bode-Kühnel, fig. 80.

79 Hamburg, Museum für Kunst und Gewerbe, *Orientalische Teppiche aus vier Jahrhunderten* (Hamburg, 1950), fig. 29.

80 Pope, *Survey*, VI, pl. 1215.

81 Bode-Kühnel, fig. 115.

82 Aga-Oglu, *Safawid Rugs and Textiles*, pls. III, IV.

83 McMullan, nos. 31, 32.

84 For further information about modern Persian rugs, see Dilley; and Werner Grote-Hasenbalg, *Der Orientteppich*, vols. I–III.

CATALOGUE

1

FIGURE 59

Medallion rug, Tabriz, end of xv century, period of Turkomans of the White Sheep

19′ 2″ × 7′ 10″

WARP: Cotton

WEFT: Cotton; 2 shoots after each row of knots

KNOTTING: Wool. Senna knot, about 156 knots per square inch

COLORS: 11. *Ground*: terracotta red (field), light blue, blue (medallion), red (central star), light green (border, inner guard band), reciprocal white and red (outer guard band). *Pattern*: white, orange, pink, terracotta red, red, light blue, blue, dark blue, red brown, brown.

DECORATION: *Field*: In the center, a sixteen-pointed angular medallion containing an eight-pointed star, in the center of which is an octagon; both star and medallion are filled with floral scrolls bearing blossoms, palmettes, and buds. The rest of the field has an allover pattern of interlaced arabesques and floral scrolls forming circular convolutions; the arabesques bear full and half-palmettes. *Border*: An arabesque scroll and a floral scroll interlaced; at intervals two half-palmettes form devices containing palmettes. *Inner guard band*: An arabesque scroll interlaced with a floral scroll bearing blossoms and leaves. *Outer guard band*: Reciprocal trefoils. *Inner edging*: A rectangle alternating with three discs.

PUBLISHED: Breck-Morris, no. 1; Dilley, pl. VI; Dimand, *Handbook*, fig. 187.

Gift of James F. Ballard, the James F. Ballard Collection

22. 100. 75

2

FIGURE 62

Medallion rug, Tabriz, early xvi century, period of Shah Ismail

23′ 2″ × 8′ 10″

WARP: Cotton

WEFT: Cotton; 3 shoots after each row of knots

KNOTTING: Wool. Senna knot, about 156 knots per square inch

COLORS: 11. *Ground*: red (field, central star, outer guard band), dark blue (medallion), blue green (escutcheon-shaped panels, border), tan (cartouches), light green (corner medallions), cream white (compartments between medallion points, inner guard band). *Pattern*: cream white, tan, orange, pink, red, blue, blue green, light green, brown, black brown.

DECORATION: *Field*: In the center, an eight-pointed lobed medallion containing an eight-pointed star with a central octagon; the star and medallion are filled with floral stems sending off leaves, buds, and palmettes of various sizes. Between the points of the medallion, lobed compartments contain floral scrolls with palmettes, buds, and leaves. At either end of the medallion in the long axis is attached a cartouche and an escutcheon-shaped panel, both decorated with floral scrolls. In each corner of the field, a quarter of an angular medallion filled with floral scrolls. The ground of the field has slender floral stems bearing palmettes and leaves, intersecting with a double system of arabesques; these form spirals ending in half-palmettes. At regular intervals, the scrolls form lozenges that terminate in full palmettes. *Border*: Interlaced arabesque bands overlaid with floral scrolls; the bands send out large palmettes containing smaller palmettes. *Inner guard band*: An arabesque scroll interlaced with a floral scroll bearing blossoms and leaves. *Outer guard band*: A scroll with blossoms and leaves. *Inner edging*: A rectangle alternating with three discs.

PUBLISHED: Dimand, *Handbook*, fig. 188.

Bequest of Benjamin Altman

14. 40. 718

3

FIGURE 63

Medallion rug, Tabriz, early xvi century, period of Shah Ismail

40′ 7″ × 15′ 2½″

WARP: Cotton

WEFT: Cotton; 3 shoots after each row of knots

KNOTTING: Wool. Senna knot, about 200 knots per square inch

COLORS: 14. *Ground*: red (field, small lobed medallion, outer guard band), dark blue green (medallion, border), blue (escutcheon-shaped panels), white (cartouches, inner guard band), light tan (border of medallion). *Pattern*: white, light tan, yellow, light orange, orange, pink, red, light blue, blue, dark blue, dark blue green, light green, green, black.

DECORATION: *Field*: In the center, a sixteen-pointed lobed medallion containing floral scrolls, palmettes, blossoms, and a small lobed medallion filled with rosette and floral stems. The large medallion has a border containing floral stems. At either end of the medallion in the long axis is a cartouche and an escutcheon-shaped panel, both containing floral stems and palmettes. The rest of the field is filled with two systems of floral scrolls and spiraling stems, sending off blossoms, palmettes, and leaf devices. Large cloud bands and small cloud motifs are placed symmetrically on the ground pattern. *Border*: Cartouches divided into compartments and filled with floral stems bearing palmettes, blossoms, or arabesque devices. In the alternate cartouches, a small lobed medallion containing a floral device. The ground of the border is filled with floral scrolls bearing palmettes, buds, and leaves. *Inner guard band*: A wavy floral scroll bearing palmettes, buds, and leaves. *Outer guard band*: A floral scroll interlacing with an arabesque scroll bearing palmettes. *Inner edging*: A scroll with blossoms and leaves.

NOTE: The companion piece (fragmentary) to this rug is in the Art Institute of Chicago.

PUBLISHED: Mumford, pl. XXVI; Pope, *Survey*, VI, pl. 1113.

EX COLL. Charles T. Yerkes

Gift of George Blumenthal

41. 100. 113

4   RIGHT

Medallion rug, Tabriz, early XVI century, period of Shah Ismail

28′ 2″ × 10′ 8″

WARP: Cotton

WEFT: Cotton; 3 shoots after each row of knots

KNOTTING: Wool. Senna knot, about 132 knots per square inch

COLORS: 13. *Ground*: salmon red (field), dark blue (large medallion, escutcheon-shaped panels), light blue (angular medallion), cream yellow (lobed medallion, compartments between large medallion ends), white (cartouches, inner guard band), light green (corner medallions), blue green (border), reciprocal white and light brown (outer guard band). *Pattern*: white, cream yellow, red, blue, dark blue, blue green, light green, green, light brown, black.

DECORATION: *Field*: In the center, an eight-pointed lobed medallion filled with floral scrolls bearing palmettes of various sizes, buds, and leaves. Between the points are compartments containing the same floral pattern. The center of the medallion contains an octagon surrounded by an angular and a lobed medallion, all containing palmettes and buds on stems. At either end of the large medallion in the long axis, a cartouche and an escutcheon-shaped panel, each decorated with floral scrolls bearing palmettes, buds, and leaves. In each corner of the field, a portion of a medallion filled with floral scrolls and cloud bands. The rest of the field has an allover pattern of floral scrolls intersecting with a double system of arabesques that form spirals and end in half-palmettes. The floral scrolls send off blossom and leaf palmettes, rosettes, buds, and leaves. *Border*: Interlaced arabesque bands overlaid with floral scrolls; the bands send out large palmettes containing smaller

ones. *Inner guard band*: A wavy floral scroll with palmettes, buds and leaves. *Outer guard band*: Reciprocal leafy motifs. *Inner edging*: A scroll with lilylike blossoms.

PUBLISHED: Bode, fig. 12; McMullan, no. 11.

EX COLL.: Stefano Bardini, Charles T. Yerkes, J. Seligmann

Gift of Joseph V. McMullan

64.311

5   FIGURE 66

Animal rug, probably Tabriz, second half of XVI century

7′ 7″ × 5′ 8″

WARP: Cotton

WEFT: Cotton; 2 shoots after each row of knots

KNOTTING: Wool. Senna knot, about 225 knots per square inch

COLORS: 12. *Ground*: red (field, small lobed panel), dark blue (inner medallion), yellow (outer medallion, border), blue green (cornerpieces), light blue (inner guard band), black (outer guard band). *Pattern*: white, tan, yellow, orange, red, light blue, dark blue, blue green, light green, green, brown, black.

DECORATION: *Field*: In the center, a lobed medallion containing birds superimposed on a floral scroll bearing blossoms and palmettes. Within this, a second medallion containing floral scrolls, arabesques with half-palmettes flanking palmettes, and a small lobed panel filled with a palmette device. In each corner of the field, a squarish area containing a pomegranate tree, a flowering tree, and two birds. The rest of the field is filled with floral scrolls bearing blossoms and palmettes, and animals, including leopards, ibexes, tigers, deer, and lions attacking oxen. *Border*: A broad arabesque band sending out palmettes within leaf-shaped panels; the design and ground are overlaid with floral scrolls bearing palmettes and rosettes. *Inner guard band*: A geometrical motif. *Outer guard band*: A wavy floral scroll with rosettes.

PUBLISHED: Hawley, pl. 15; Mumford, pl. VI; Pope, *Survey*, VI, pl. 1149; Valentiner, no. 30.

EX COLL. Charles T. Yerkes

Frederick C. Hewitt Fund

10.61.1

6   FIGURE 67, PAGE 134

Cartouche rug, Tabriz, early XVI century, period of Shah Ismail

16′ 4″ × 11′ 2″

WARP: Silk

WEFT: Silk; 3 shoots after each row of knots

KNOTTING: Wool. Senna knot, about 625 knots per square inch

COLORS: 12. *Ground*: white (field), tomato red (some cartouches in field, border), dark blue (some medallions in field), blue green (some cartouches in field), brown (some medallions in field, medallions in border), blue (border cartouches), yellow (guard bands). *Pattern*: white, yellow, salmon, pink, tomato red, light blue, blue, blue green, light green, green, brown.

DECORATION: *Field*: An allover lozenge pattern of cartouches and medallions of various shapes. The largest medallions, eight-lobed, contain a dragon and phoenix in combat. From these medallions radiate eight cartouches filled alternately with interlaced arabesques or flying geese, floral scrolls, and cloud bands. Smaller eight-lobed medallions placed between each four of the larger ones are filled with four lion ch'i-lins and floral scrolls. The larger spaces between the cartouches and medallions are filled with floral scrolls; the smaller, with cloud bands. *Border*: Cartouches alternating (one end of the rug excepted) with lobed medallions. The cartouches contain interlaced floral scrolls with superimposed cloud bands; the medallions repeat the combat of the dragon and phoenix. The ground of the border is patterned with floral scrolls and flying geese. *Inner guard band*: Interlaced floral scrolls with arabesques and cloud bands. *Outer guard band*: Floral scrolls.

PUBLISHED: Bode-Kühnel, fig. 90; Dimand, *Handbook*, fig. 189; Erdmann, *Oriental Carpets*, fig. 58; Hawley, pl. 13; Mumford, pl. XXV; Sarre-Trenkwald, II, pl. 14.

EX COLL.: Vincent Robinson, Baron Adolph Thiem, Charles T. Yerkes

Frederick C. Hewitt Fund

10.61.3

7   FIGURE 69, PAGE 136

Medallion rug, Tabriz, second half of XVI century, period of Shah Tahmasp

26′ 6″ × 13′ 7″

WARP: Cotton

WEFT: Silk; 3 shoots after each row of knots

KNOTTING: Wool. Senna knot, about 400 knots per square inch

COLORS: 10. *Ground*: golden yellow (field), red (medallion, escutcheons, border), black brown (central panel), light blue (cartouches, inner guard band), orange (outer guard band). *Pattern*: white, yellow, orange, red, light blue, dark blue, light blue green, light green, black brown.

DECORATION: *Field*: In the center, a lobed medallion containing a design of floral scrolls with palmettes intersecting arabesque scrolls with half-palmettes and cloud bands. Centered in the medallion is a circular panel containing floral scrolls and cloud bands. At each end of the medallion in the long axis is a cartouche and an escutcheon-shaped pendant. The cartouches contain floral scrolls with blossoms and palmettes. The pendants contain floral scrolls overlaid with an arabesque device. The ground of the field is filled with two systems of intersecting floral scrolls bearing leaves, blossoms, and peony palmettes. Upon this floral pattern are placed arabesque scrolls with large half-palmettes. Numerous cloud bands intersect the scrolls. Rendered in a mosaiclike polychrome design, four peacocks are placed in a row across each end of the field, and four more are placed around the medallion. *Border*: Floral scrolls bearing blossoms and palmettes, with superimposed spiral arabesques bearing half-palmettes; cloud bands intersect the arabesque scrolls. *Inner guard band*: A floral scroll bearing blossoms and palmettes with a scroll of arabesques and cloud bands superimposed. *Outer guard band*: Intersecting floral scrolls overlaid with cloud bands.

PUBLISHED: Bode-Kühnel, fig. 60; Dimand, *Handbook*, fig. 246; Erdmann, *Oriental Carpets*, fig. 66; Pope, *Survey*, VI, pls. 1137-1139.

EX COLL. Duke of Anhalt, Dessau. According to tradition, captured at the siege of Vienna, 1683.

Gift of Samuel H. Kress Foundation (through Rush H. Kress)

46. 128

8   FIGURE 70

Medallion animal rug with inscriptions, probably Tabriz, middle of XVI century, period of Shah Tahmasp

14′ × 6′ 1″

WARP: Silk

WEFT: Silk; 3 shoots after each row of knots

KNOTTING: Wool. Senna knot, about 550 knots per square inch

BROCADING: Silver strips wound around a silk core

COLORS: 11. *Ground*: red (field), black (medallion), green (quatrefoil rosette, panels, guard bands), light blue (corner medallion sections), white (border). *Pattern*: white, yellow, orange, pink, red, light blue, dark blue, green, light brown, black, silver.

DECORATION: *Field*: In the center, a somewhat flattened circular medallion filled with an inscription superimposed on floral stems. Centered in the medallion is a quatrefoil rosette filled with floral stems, blossoms, and cloud bands. The areas between the rosette leaves are filled with arabesques. In the center of the rosette, a square with a central circle containing floral stems and an elaborate quatrefoil. At either end of the medallion in the long axis, a panel emerging from a Chinese bowl patterned with floral scrolls. The panel contains floral stems and a pair of confronted peacocks, and it is crowned at the top by animal heads. In each corner of the field, a portion of a lobed medallion filled with

floral stems, cloud bands, lion ch'i-lins, and fish. The ground of the field is patterned with floral scrolls with palmettes of various sizes. Amid the scrolls, a variety of animals including tigers, hares, lions attacking stags, lynxes, wolflike animals, leopards in combat with ibexes, and lions. *Border*: Alternating cartouches and octofoils, the cartouches containing an inscription on a ground of floral scrolls, the octofoils containing a single bird or two birds in combat. The ground is patterned with floral stems and cloud bands. *Inner guard band*: An arabesque scroll with palmettes superimposed on a floral scroll. *Outer guard band*: Medallions of half-palmettes enclosing full palmettes; intermittent floral scrolls fill the spaces.

INSCRIPTIONS (in Persian; translations from Sarre-Trenkwald, II, pl. 33):

In the medallion:

O! in the heart of the tulip is a wound from the hand of grief for thee!
Alas for the narcissus and the rose of the carpet in the chamber of thy sanctuary!
Through longing to kiss thy feet, O trembling cypress,
The fresh rose has fallen beneath thy feet.

In the cartouches:

When the first down appeared around thy face,
From the streaming of our tears is the carpet of spring.
The charter of our good and evil fortune is a down,
Which grows on the rosy cheek of a youthful lover.
A down, fragrant as musk, has come up round thy cheek.
It has become as the garden of the cheek, O fresh rosy cheek.
O cypress, when thou wast bending towards the rose-garden,
Hidden in thy breath were cypress and poplar green.
Al Khizr in spring, in quest of the water of life
Has again appeared at this season, enveloped in green.
As though the earth, through the bitterness of parting, had sucked up the water
From it springs up grass in every verdant meadow.
Sufi, burn the blue robe, now that there is a temptation
From wine and flute to turn aside to the green river.

PUBLISHED: Bode-Kühnel, fig. 66; Pope, *Survey*, VI, pl. 1153; Sarre-Trenkwald, II, pls. 33, 34; Valentiner, no. 26.

Gift of George F. Baker

32. 16

9 a, b   FIGURE 71, PAGE 138

Pair of medallion animal rugs with figure subjects, probably Herat, second half of XVI century

(a) 8′ 4″ × 5′ 10″
(b) 8′ 3″ × 5′ 7½″

WARP: Silk

WEFT: Cotton; 3 shoots after each row of knots
KNOTTING: Wool. Senna knot, about 306 knots per square inch
COLORS: 11. *Ground*: red (field, central pool, outer guard band), yellow (medallion), dark green (border), white (inner guard band). *Pattern*: white, yellow, orange, pink, red, blue gray, light blue, dark blue, light green, dark green, black.
DECORATION: *Field*: In the center, a lobed medallion containing a central pool in which appear four ducks. In the medallion is the representation of a garden party; four pairs of figures, probably nobles, seated amidst stems and blossoming trees, attended by eight seated musicians playing instruments and four standing servants holding lambs. The noble figures wear rich garments and turbans in a style associated with Khurasan and Bukhara. Outside the medallion the field is decorated with floral scrolls bearing a variety of blossoms and palmettes, including the fan-shaped palmette associated with Herat. At either end of the medallion in the long axis is a pair of dragons, back to back, threatened by tigers. Other animals are grouped symmetrically over the field: stags pursued by leopards, lions attacking spotted deer, lynxes, pairs of ch'i-lins in combat, and ibexes placed between wolflike animals. *Border*: Spiraling scrolls bearing various palmettes and blossoms with birds in their midst. *Guard bands*: Intersecting floral scrolls bearing rosette blossoms and palmettes.
PUBLISHED: Dimand, *Handbook*, fig. 191; Hawley, pl. 16; Mumford, pl. VIII; Sarre-Trenkwald, II, pl. 37.
EX COLL.: (a) Capponi, Charles T. Yerkes (b) Stefano Bardini, Isaac D. Fletcher
(a) Mr. and Mrs. Isaac D. Fletcher Collection, Bequest of Isaac D. Fletcher
17. 120. 127
(b) Gift of Alexander Smith Cochran
08. 100

10 FIGURE 73

Floral rug with figure subjects (so-called "Portuguese"), southern Persia, early XVII century

13′ 6″ × 5′ 9″
WARP: Cotton
WEFT: Cotton; 2 shoots after each row of knots
KNOTTING: Wool. Senna knot, about 225 knots per square inch
COLORS: 13. *Ground*: white (field, outer guard band), rose red (central lozenge, border), light tan (second lozenge), light blue (third lozenge), dark blue (fourth lozenge), buff (fifth lozenge), blue green (inner guard band). *Pattern*: white, light tan, buff, orange, salmon, pink, rose red, light blue, dark blue, blue green, green, light brown, dark brown.

DECORATION: *Field*: A series of concentric lozenges with stepped outlines, the innermost one containing a central rosette surrounded by four ogee-shaped panels containing a leafy palmette on a floral stem. The ground of the center lozenge is patterned with large palmettes connected by floral stems. Each of the successive lozenges contains floral scrolls bearing leaves, buds, and various kinds of palmettes. The corner areas of the field are patterned with zigzag lines representing water; in each area appear a fish, a sea monster, a swimmer, and a sailing vessel containing two Portuguese figures. *Border*: Arabesque bands ending at intervals in ogee-forms enclosing a palmette. The bands are overlaid with floral scrolls; similar scrolls fill the background. *Guard bands*: A wavy scroll bearing buds and lilylike blossoms.
PUBLISHED: Pope, *Survey*, VI, pl. 1217.
EX COLL. Mrs. Chauncey J. Blair
Fletcher Fund
44. 63. 6

11 FIGURE 75

Animal rug, Tabriz, middle of XVI century, period of Shah Tahmasp

11′ 7½″ × 5′ 11″
WARP: Silk
WEFT: Silk; 3 shoots after each row of knots
KNOTTING: Wool. Senna knot, about 576 knots per square inch
BROCADING: Silver strips wound around a silk core
COLORS: 12. *Ground*: wine red (field, outer guard band), dark blue (border), white (inner guard band). *Pattern*: white, yellow, orange, rose, wine red, light blue, dark blue, light green, gray brown, brown, black, silver.
DECORATION: *Field*: An allover symmetrical pattern of animals on a background of floral scrolls. From the center of the field issue spiral stems bearing palmettes, blossoms, rosettes, and leaves. Upon this floral background are placed five groups of animals in combat, arranged symmetrically from side to side. Each group consists of a spotted stag attacked by a lion, and a tiger accompanied by four smaller animals—wolf, bear, lynx, and wild cat—placed in the direction of the spiral scrolls. *Border*: Two intersecting floral scrolls with palmettes placed at their intersection. Upon this background are placed arabesques with half-palmettes and cloud bands. *Inner guard band*: A scroll bearing rosettes interlaced with arabesques. *Outer guard band*: An intermittent wavy stem with small palmettes and leaves.
NOTE: This rug, with others, came from the shrine of Shaikh Safi at Ardabil. The companion piece is in the collection of Mrs. John D. Rockefeller, Jr., New York.
PUBLISHED: Bode-Kühnel, fig. 85; Dimand, *Handbook*, fig. 192; Hawley, pl. 14; Mumford, pl. XVIII; Pope, *Survey*, VI, pl. 1177; Sarre-Trenkwald, II, pl. 38;

Friedrich Sarre, *Denkmäler Persischer Baukunst*, pt. II, *Ardabil* (Berlin, n.d.), pp. 26–27.

EX COLL.: Vincent Robinson, Charles T. Yerkes

Frederick C. Hewitt Fund

10. 61 2

12   FIGURE 76, PAGE 140

Animal and floral rug, Herat, middle of XVI century, period of Shah Tahmasp

24′ 8″ × 10′ 10″

WARP: Silk

WEFT: Silk; 3 shoots after each row of knots

KNOTTING: Wool. Senna knot, about 350 knots per square inch

COLORS: 18. *Ground*: ruby red (field, outer guard band), green (border), light blue (inner guard band). *Pattern*: white, off-white, light tan, yellow, orange, pink, rose, ruby red, light blue, blue, dark blue, yellow green, gray green, light green, green, gray brown, brown, black.

DECORATION: *Field*: An allover design of floral scrolls and animals. The center is indicated by stems forming a lozenge configuration with four symmetrically arranged small palmettes. These are extended by four larger palmettes with two pheasants above each one. From the center issues a twofold system of intersecting spiraling floral scrolls bearing large composite palmettes, some with cloud bands attached, blossoms, buds, and leaves. The palmettes include the fan-shaped type, well known in the so-called Isfahan rugs attributed to Herat looms, the peony type composed of a series of leaves, and large palmettes enclosing animal heads, dragons, and dragonlike ch'i-lins. Animals, singly or in combat, are distributed regularly across the stems. In each quarter, starting from the center, appear a lion, a lion ch'i-lin attacking a deer ch'i-lin, a lion, a panther attacking an ibex, a single ibex, a tiger, a lion and buffalo in combat, a panther, a wolflike animal, a pheasant, a dragonlike ch'i-lin, a buck, and a pheasant. *Border*: A spiraling floral scroll bearing palmettes, blossoms, and leaves interlaced with a spiraling arabesque scroll overlaid with small cloud motifs. Against this, cloud bands decorated with animal heads. *Inner guard band*: Cartouches separated by rosettes; the cartouches contain Persian inscriptions on a background of floral scrolls. *Outer guard band*: A floral scroll with palmettes and cloud bands.

INSCRIPTIONS: The verses on one of the long sides end in a laudation of the shah, probably Shah Tahmasp (translation from Sarre-Trenkwald, I, pl. 6):

Of rosebuds the meadow shows a thousand green tents
The new-born blossom gives up the wine, which it has, to the wind.
The tender cloud scatters every ruby which it finds

To them who fondly imagine the meadow like the roof of heaven.
Raise thy head and see the trees, which at daybreak
Make their prayer for the ruler of the world and entreat
That he may ever enjoy fame and might.

NOTE: The companion piece is in the Austrian Museum of Applied Art, Vienna (Sarre-Trenkwald, I, pls. 6–8). According to Austrian records, both rugs were gifts of Peter the Great of Russia to Leopold I, Emperor of Austria.

PUBLISHED: Pope, *Survey*, VI, pl. 1174.

EX COLL. Mrs. Edith Rockefeller McCormick

Rogers Fund

43. 121. 1

13   FIGURE 79, PAGE 142

Silk animal rug, Kashan, second half of XVI century, period of Shah Tahmasp

7′ 10″ × 5′ 10½″

WARP: Silk

WEFT: Silk; 3 shoots after each row of knots

KNOTTING: Silk. Senna knot, about 576 knots per square inch

COLORS: 14. *Ground*: red (field, outer guard band), dark blue green (border), yellow (inner guard band). *Pattern*: white, tan, yellow, red, blue, dark blue, light gray green, yellow green, olive green, green, light blue green, dark blue green, brown, black.

DECORATION: *Field*: Six horizontal rows of animals placed in a landscape of shrubs and flowering trees. Starting with the top, first row: two running hares, a lion attacking a bull, a wolflike animal, another hare; second row: a leopard in combat with a bear, a dragonlike ch'i-lin, a tiger attacking a bull; third row: a lion ch'i-lin, a dragon attacking a wild ass, a leopard; fourth row: a lion attacking an ibex, a hare, a dragonlike ch'i-lin attacking a bull; fifth row: a wild dog, a lion ch'i-lin attacking a bull ch'i-lin, a calf, a lion attacking a bull; sixth row: a bird of paradise in a tree, a lion ch'i-lin, a leopard attacking a deer, a lion ch'i-lin, two birds in a tree. The shrubs, bearing blossoms and palmettes, are scattered irregularly over the field, most of them growing from patches of ground. They are rendered more naturalistically at the lower edge of the field. *Border*: Two intersecting floral scrolls with blossoms, buds, and dentated leaves. At the intersection of the stems appear alternately two varieties of palmettes; every other one is flanked by two pheasant-like birds back to back. *Inner guard band*: A wavy floral scroll bearing palmettes, buds and leaves. *Outer guard band*: A wavy floral scroll upon which are placed alternately blossoms and cloud bands. *Inner edging*: Reciprocal heart motifs.

PUBLISHED: Bode-Kühnel, fig. 108, Dimand, *Handbook*,

fig. 195; Erdmann, *Oriental Carpets*, fig. 68; Pope, *Survey*, VI, pl. 1199; Sarre-Trenkwald, II, pl. 39.
EX COLL.: Prince Princezza, Edouard Chappey
Bequest of Benjamin Altman
14.40.721

14   FIGURE 80

Silk medallion rug, Kashan, second half of XVI century, period of Shah Tahmasp

8′ 2″ × 5′ 7″

WARP: Silk

WEFT: Silk; 3 shoots after each row of knots

KNOTTING: Silk. Senna knot, about 624 knots per square inch

COLORS: 13. *Ground*: wine red (field, outer guard band), blue (central medallion), yellow (corner medallions), originally black (border), white (inner guard band). *Pattern*: white, yellow, light red, wine red, blue, dark blue, blue green, light green, green, light brown, black brown, gray.

DECORATION: *Field*: In the center, a lobed quatrefoil medallion with ogee points; each lobe of the medallion is filled with floral scrolls and a large palmette flanked by two half-palmettes that stem from a central lozenge. A small lobed panel containing a palmette is attached to each end of the medallion in the long axis. In each corner of the field is a quarter of a lobed medallion filled with floral scrolls intersected by arabesques. The ground of the field is filled with floral scrolls bearing palmettes, blossoms, and leaves interspersed with cloud motifs. *Border*: Two varieties of palmette enclosed in lobed heart-shaped motifs formed by arabesque bands overlaid with floral scrolls. *Inner guard band*: A wavy floral scroll bearing alternately rosettes and blossoms. *Outer guard band*: Quatrefoils alternating with oblong cartouches decorated with blossoms.

PUBLISHED: Dimand, *Handbook*, fig. 193; Sarre-Trenkwald, II, pl. 41; Valentiner, no.29.
Bequest of Benjamin Altman
14.40.715

15   FIGURE 81

Silk medallion rug, Kashan, second half of XVI century, period of Shah Tahmasp

8′ 5″ × 5′ 5″

WARP: Silk

WEFT: Silk; 3 shoots after each row of knots

KNOTTING: Silk. Senna knot, about 506 knots per square inch

COLORS: 9. *Ground*: wine red (field, outer guard band), blue green (medallion, border), blue (corner medallions), white (band), yellow (inner guard band). *Pattern*: white, light tan, yellow, wine red, light blue, blue, blue green, light green, black.

DECORATION: *Field*: In the center, a lobed quatrefoil medallion containing an eight-pointed star enclosing floral stems; each lobe of the medallion is filled with floral scrolls and a palmette flanked by half-palmettes. The medallion is surrounded by a broad band overlaid with a floral scroll bearing blossoms; placed upon the band are lobed panels of three sizes, those at the points in the long axis being leaf-shaped; the panels each contain a palmette. In each corner of the field is a quarter of a lobed medallion filled with arabesques intersecting with cloud bands. The ground of the field is filled with floral scrolls bearing leaves, blossoms, and palmettes. *Border*: Two interlaced scrolls with large palmettes surrounded by rosettes, cloud bands, and other cloud motifs. *Inner guard band*: A wavy floral scroll bearing alternately palmettes and blossoms. *Outer guard band*: A wavy floral scroll bearing two types of palmette in alternation, rosettes, and leaves.

PUBLISHED: Bode-Kühnel, fig. 62; Sarre-Trenkwald, II, pl. 42.
EX COLL. J. E. Taylor
Bequest of Benjamin Altman
14.40.724

16   FIGURE 82

Silk medallion rug, Kashan, second half of XVI century, period of Shah Tahmasp

8′ 3″ × 5′ 6″

WARP: Silk

WEFT: Silk; 3 shoots after each row of knots

KNOTTING: Silk. Senna knot, about 242 knots per square inch

COLORS: 9. *Ground*: red (field, central panel, outer guard band), dark blue (central medallion), light tan (corner medallions, inner guard band), green (border). *Pattern*: light tan, yellow, pink, red, light blue, dark blue, light green, light brown.

DECORATION: *Field*: In the center, an eight-pointed panel filled with palmettes; surrounding it in a symmetrical arrangement, filling an eight-pointed lobed medallion, are floral scrolls bearing rosettes and eight large palmettes. At either end of the medallion in the long axis, a small cartouche containing a leafy scroll, and an escutcheon-shaped pendant filled with an arabesque device. In each corner of the field, a quarter of a medallion filled with floral scrolls and palmettes, with portions of the center cartouche and pendant. The ground of the field is patterned with floral scrolls bearing leaves, rosettes, and several types of palmette, including a large leafy composite one. *Border*: Floral scrolls bearing two types of palmette in alternation, rosettes, and leaves. *Inner guard band*: A wavy floral scroll bearing alternately rosettes and palmettes. *Outer guard band*: Floral scrolls bearing two types of palmette in alternation, rosettes, and leaves.

PUBLISHED: Erdmann, *Pantheon*, XIX, color plate opp. p. 159.
EX COLL. John Taylor Johnston
Gift of Mrs. Douglas M. Moffat
58.46

17　　　　　　　　　　　　　　　　FIGURE 84

Silk floral rug (so-called "Polish") with coat of arms, probably Isfahan, first half of XVII century, period of Shah Abbas

15′ 10″ × 7′ 1″

WARP: Cotton
WEFT: Silk; 2 shoots after each row of knots
KNOTTING: Silk. Senna knot, about 210 knots per square inch
BROCADING: Silver and silver-gilt strips wound around a silk core
COLORS: 13. *Ground*: gold (field), silver (border), green (inner guard band), dark blue, gray green (outer guard band). *Pattern*: white, yellow, orange, pink, light blue, blue, dark blue, gray green, green, light brown, black, silver, gold.
DECORATION: *Field*: In the center, a lobed lozenge medallion formed by an arabesque band overlaid at intervals with cloud motifs. Centered in the medallion, and repeated in each corner of the field, is a European coat of arms: a shield blazoned with a cross and four birds, a camel head issuing from a coronet as the crest. According to the Polish Institute in New York, this is not a Polish coat of arms. The College of Arms in London believes it is a mixture of several European coats of arms, and that it was probably misunderstood by the rug's designer. The medallion and the field are patterned with two interlaced systems of arabesques; these intersect with floral scrolls bearing lanceolate leaves, blossoms, and composite palmettes. *Border*: Floral scrolls bearing blossoms and palmettes flanked by curving lanceolate leaves and arabesque scrolls. *Guard bands*: Interlaced floral scrolls bearing lilylike blossoms and rosettes.
PUBLISHED: Dimand, *Handbook*, fig. 248.
EX COLL. Prince Ladislas Czartoryski
Gift of John D. Rockefeller, Jr.
45.106

18　　　　　　　　　　　　　　　　FIGURE 85

Silk multiple medallion rug (so-called "Polish"), Kashan, first half of XVII century, period of Shah Abbas

13′ 2″ × 5′ 9½″

WARP: Silk
WEFT: Silk; 3 shoots after each row of knots

KNOTTING: Silk. Senna knot, about 225 knots per square inch
BROCADING: Silver and silver-gilt strips wound around a silk core
COLORS: 12. *Ground*: silver, gold (field), red (central medallion, border), dark blue (lobed panel, outer guard band), reciprocal light green and brown (inner guard band). *Pattern*: white, yellow, orange, pink, red, light blue, dark blue, light green, green, brown, silver, gold.
DECORATION: *Field*: In the long axis, a lobed panel containing arabesques with half-palmettes and a medallion with interlaced arabesques. Portions of similar medallions and panels are repeated at both ends, along the sides, and in the corners. The rest of the field is filled with large composite palmettes, small palmettes, blossoms, and lanceolate leaves. *Border*: Floral scrolls bearing palmettes, blossoms, and lanceolate leaves intersecting with arabesques decorated with cloud motifs; at intervals compartments are formed by the arabesques. *Inner guard band*: Reciprocal trefoils. *Outer guard band*: A wavy floral scroll.
PUBLISHED: Dimand, *Persian Rugs*, no. 5.
EX COLL. Prince Doria
Gift of John D. Rockefeller, Jr.
50.190.5

19 a, b　　　　　　　　　　　　　FIGURE 86

Pair of silk compartment rugs (so-called "Polish"), Isfahan, first half of XVII century, period of Shah Abbas

(a) 13′ 3″ × 5′ 6″
(b) 13′ × 5′ 9½″

WARP: Cotton
WEFT: Silk; 2 shoots after each row of knots
KNOTTING: Silk. Senna knot, about (a) 360, (b) 288 knots per square inch
BROCADING: Silver and silver-gilt strips wound around a silk core
COLORS: 13. *Ground*: silver, gold (compartments, border), salmon, dark blue (compartments), white (inner guard band), light brown (outer guard band). *Pattern*: white, yellow, orange, salmon, light blue, dark blue, light green, olive green, light brown, gray brown, black brown, silver, gold.
DECORATION: *Field*: An allover pattern of elongated, four-sided, lozengelike compartments formed by arabesque bands overlaid with leaves and cloud motifs. The compartments, separated from each other by lozenge devices with arabesques, are filled with symmetrically arranged stems with small and large palmettes, blossoms, rosettes, and lanceolate leaves. *Border*: A wavy floral scroll bearing palmettes flanked by pairs of lanceolate leaves. *Inner guard band*: A wavy floral scroll. *Outer guard band*: Interlaced floral scrolls bearing lilylike blossoms and rosettes.

PUBLISHED: Bode-Kühnel, fig. 112; Sarre-Trenkwald, II, pl. 43.
Gift of John D. Rockefeller, Jr.
(a) 50. 190. 3
(b) 50. 190. 4

20 a, b   FIGURE 87, PAGE 144

Pair of silk compartment rugs (so-called "Polish"), Isfahan, first half of XVII century, period of Shah Abbas

(a) 13′ 1″ × 5′ 7″
(b) 13′ 3″ × 5′ 6½″

WARP: Cotton
WEFT: Silk; 2 shoots after each row of knots
KNOTTING: Silk. Senna knot, about (a) 378, (b) 336 knots per square inch
BROCADING: Silver and silver-gilt strips wound around a silk core
COLORS: 12. *Ground*: silver, gold (compartments, border), yellow, orange gold, salmon red, green (compartments) brown (compartments, outer guard band), light blue (inner guard band). *Pattern*: white, yellow, orange gold, light salmon, salmon red, light blue, blue, green, brown, black, silver, gold.
DECORATION: *Field*: An allover pattern of cartouches divided into irregular compartments with cloud motifs placed at their junctures. Each compartment contains a palmette and floral scrolls or symmetrically arranged stems with blossoms, palmettes, and leaves. *Border*: A wavy floral scroll bearing palmettes flanked by pairs of lanceolate leaves. *Guard bands*: A wavy floral scroll.
PUBLISHED: Dimand, *Persian Rugs*, nos. 3, 4; Dimand, *Handbook*, fig. 249.
EX COLL. Marchioness of Graham
Gift of John D. Rockefeller, Jr.
(a) 50. 190. 1
(b) 50. 190. 2

21   FIGURE 88

Silk floral rug (so-called "Polish"), probably Isfahan, middle of XVII century

8′ 8″ × 4′ 10″
WARP: Silk
WEFT: Silk; 2 shoots after each row of knots
KNOTTING: Silk. Senna knot, about 256 knots per square inch
BROCADING: Silver and silver-gilt strips wound around a silk core
COLORS: 12. *Ground*: silver, gold, gray, light blue (portions of the field), orange (portions of the field, outer guard band). *Pattern*: yellow, orange, red, light blue, blue, blue green, olive green, brown, black, silver, gold.
DECORATION: *Field*: An allover design of floral scrolls

intersecting with arabesques, forming irregular compartments. The floral stems send off leaves, blossoms, and composite palmettes. Both the scrolls and arabesques are overlaid with cloud motifs. *Border*: A wavy floral scroll bearing blossoms and palmettes flanked by pairs of lanceolate leaves. *Inner guard band*: A wavy scroll. *Outer guard band*: A wavy floral scroll with blossoms.
PUBLISHED: Dimand, *Handbook*, fig. 198; Valentiner, no. 37.
Bequest of Benjamin Altman
14. 40. 716

22   FIGURE 89

Silk arabesque rug (so-called "Polish"), probably Isfahan, first half of XVII century, period of Shah Abbas

9′ 10″ × 4′ 10″
WARP: Cotton
WEFT: Silk; 3 shoots after each row of knots
KNOTTING: Silk. Senna knot, about 210 knots per square inch
BROCADING: Silver and silver-gilt strips wound around a silk core
COLORS: 11. *Ground*: light orange red (field), reciprocal green and metal (border), reciprocal blue and yellow (inner guard band), yellow (outer guard band). *Pattern*: white, yellow, light blue, blue, green, red, black, silver, gold.
DECORATION: *Field*: Thirteen transverse rows of arabesque palmettes, the palmettes connected by stems bearing half-palmettes. *Border*: Reciprocal trefoils. *Inner guard band*: Reciprocal heart motifs. *Outer guard band*: A wavy floral scroll with lilylike blossoms and rosettes.
PUBLISHED: Dimand, *Persian Rugs*, no. 18, pl. II.
Bequest of Horace Havemeyer, The H. O. Havemeyer Collection
56. 185. 4

23   FIGURE 90

Silk floral rug, probably Isfahan, second half of XVII century

6′ 7¼″ × 6′ ½″
WARP: Silk
WEFT: Silk; 2 shoots after each row of knots
KNOTTING: Silk. Senna knot, about 210 knots per square inch
COLORS: 10. *Ground*: red (field), green (border), yellow (inner guard band), gray brown (outer guard band). *Pattern*: white, tan, yellow, salmon, red, light blue, blue, green, gray brown, black.
DECORATION: *Field*: A symmetrical design of floral scrolls

bearing palmettes, blossoms, and lanceolate leaves intersecting with arabesque bands. The arabesque bands, overlaid with cloud motifs and bearing half-palmettes, issue from each side of the field and from a central rosette, which is surrounded by an arabesque device forming a lozenge. *Border*: A wavy floral scroll bearing composite palmettes with curving lanceolate leaves. *Guard bands*: Interlaced floral scrolls bearing lilylike blossoms and rosettes.

PUBLISHED: Dimand, *Persian Rugs*, no. 26, pl.v.

Mr. and Mrs. Isaac D. Fletcher Collection, Bequest of Isaac D. Fletcher

17. 120. 143

24   FIGURE 91

Silk medallion rug (so-called "Polish"), Kashan, first half of XVII century, period of Shah Abbas

7′ 9″ × 4′ 9″

WARP: Silk

WEFT: Silk and metal thread (silver and silver-gilt strips wound around a silk core)

TECHNIQUE: Tapestry; 26–27 warp threads per inch

COLORS: 13. *Ground*: gold (field, portions of border, outer guard band), silver (corner medallions), dark blue (portions of border), light green (portions of inner guard band). *Pattern*: white, salmon, red, light blue, blue, dark blue, yellow green, light green, gray brown, black, silver, gold.

DECORATION: *Field*: In the center, a lobed lozenge medallion containing a design of stylized cloud bands and interlaced arabesques; at each end of the medallion in the long axis, a small pendant. In each corner of the field, a quarter of a lobed medallion containing arabesques, cloud bands, and a portion of the central pendant. The rest of the field has a pattern of floral scrolls bearing palmettes, peony palmettes, lanceolate leaves, and rosettes. *Border*: A wavy scroll of lanceolate leaves bearing pomegranate palmettes and rosettes. *Inner guard band*: Cartouches containing a floral scroll alternating with quatrefoils. *Outer guard band*: A wavy scroll with rosettes and leaves. *Outer edging*: Saw-tooth motif.

PUBLISHED: Dimand, *Handbook*, fig. 200.

EX COLL. Royal House of Saxony

Rogers Fund

31. 70

25   FIGURE 92

Silk medallion rug (so-called "Polish"), Kashan, first half of XVII century, period of Shah Abbas

7′ 7″ × 4′ 7″

WARP: Silk

WEFT: Silk and metal thread (silver and silver-gilt strips wound around a silk core)

TECHNIQUE: Tapestry; 26–27 warp threads per inch

COLORS: 11. *Ground*: gold (field, lozenge-shaped panel, corner medallions, portions of border, outer guard band), red (lobed medallion), light orange (small medallion, inner guard band), blue (portions of border). *Pattern*: white, yellow, light orange, red, light blue, blue, light green, light brown, black, silver, gold.

DECORATION: *Field*: In the center, a lobed eight-pointed medallion enclosing a lozenge-shaped panel filled with stems bearing trefoils, palmettes, and leaves surrounding a small central medallion. At each end of the medallion in the long axis, a small trefoil pendant. In each corner of the field, a quarter of a medallion filled with stems, trefoils, and palmettes. The rest of the ground is patterned with floral scrolls bearing composite palmettes, lanceolate leaves, and other floral motifs. *Border*: A wavy floral scroll with buds and leaves bearing carnations and palmettes. *Inner guard band*: Cartouches containing a floral scroll alternating with quatrefoils. *Outer guard band*: A wavy floral scroll bearing rosettes and leaves. *Outer edging*: Saw-tooth motif.

PUBLISHED: Dimand, *Persian Rugs*, no. 19, pl. III; Erdmann, *Oriental Carpets*, fig. 91.

Gift of Horace Havemeyer, The H. O. Havemeyer Collection

51. 197

26   FIGURE 93

Silk medallion rug (so-called "Polish"), Kashan, first half of XVII century, period of Shah Abbas

7′ 1/2″ × 4′ 10 1/2″

WARP: Silk

WEFT: Silk and metal thread (silver and silver-gilt strips wound around a silk core)

TECHNIQUE: Tapestry, 28–29 warp threads per inch

COLORS: 10. *Ground*: gold (field, guard bands), silver (central panel, border), blue (cartouches, corner medallions, octofoils of border), red (escutcheon-shaped pendants), salmon pink (border cartouches). *Pattern*: white, yellow, salmon pink, red, light blue, blue, pale green, brown black, silver, gold.

DECORATION: *Field*: In the center, a lobed medallion containing six flying cranes placed symmetrically around a central crane with cloud motifs interspersed among them. At either end of the medallion, a cartouche and an escutcheon-shaped pendant, each containing a pair of ducks. In each corner of the field, a quarter of a lobed medallion containing a pair of cranes and cloud motifs and a portion of a pendant containing a bird. The rest of the field is filled with blossoming trees and shrubs, most of which grow transversely, and a variety of animals appearing singly or in combat, including running hares, tigers attacking stags, foxes, dragons fighting bull ch'i-lins, antelopes, and panthers attacking ibexes. *Border*: Cartouches alternating with lobed medallions formed by interlacing bands. The cartouches contain a pair of animals in combat flanked by two single animals, or, in the two central cartouches, two pairs of fighting animals. In the medallions, a flying crane and small cloud motifs. *Guard bands*: A wavy floral scroll bearing palmettes and buds.

PUBLISHED: Pope, *Early Oriental Carpets*, no. 28; Sarre-Trenkwald, II, pl. 46.

EX COLL. Robert Woods Bliss

Rogers Fund

43.84

27   FIGURE 95

Floral rug, Herat, second half of XVI century

25′ 1″ × 9′ 10″

WARP: Cotton

WEFT: Cotton; 3 shoots after each row of knots

KNOTTING: Wool. Senna knot, about 208 knots per square inch

COLORS: 11. *Ground*: blue green (field), white (border), tan (inner guard band), red (outer guard band). *Pattern*: white, tan, yellow, orange, pink, red, light blue, dark blue, blue green, light green, green.

DECORATION: *Field*: An allover symmetrical floral pattern consisting of two systems of scrolls forming circular convolutions. From the imaginary center of the field the scrolls issue in four directions, corresponding to the four quarters of the field, each scroll forming three circular spirals. The underlying scroll system bears leaves, rosettes, and palmettes; the overlying one bears leaves and fan-shaped and composite palmettes, with two or three forms combined. Cloud bands and birds, including birds of paradise, are arranged symmetrically amidst the scrolls. *Border*: Interlaced arabesque bands overlaid with floral scrolls bearing palmettes; the bands send out lobed medallions, each containing a palmette and floral scroll. In the intervening spaces are cloud bands. *Inner guard band*: Cartouches with cloud bands alternating with quatrefoil medallions containing blossoms. *Outer guard band*: Interlaced arabesque scrolls.

PUBLISHED: McMullan, no. 14; Pope, *Early Oriental Carpets*, no. 14; Pope, *Survey*, VI, pl. 1186.

EX COLL. Dikran Kelekian

Gift of Joseph V. McMullan

59.59

28   FIGURE 96

Floral rug, Herat, second half of XVI century

9′ 6″ × 6′ 4″

WARP: Cotton

WEFT: Cotton; 2 shoots after each row of knots

KNOTTING: Wool. Senna knot, about 255 knots per square inch

COLORS: 9. *Ground*: red (field), green (border), white

(inner guard band), yellow (outer guard band). *Pattern*: white, tan, yellow, orange, red, light blue, dark blue, yellow green, green.

DECORATION: *Field*: A symmetrical design of two systems of intersecting floral scrolls with stems curling in spirals and bearing leaves, blossoms, peony palmettes, and fan-shaped composite palmettes. Cloud bands are placed symmetrically among the scrolls. *Border*: A broad arabesque band overlaid with floral scrolls sending out leaf-shaped panels containing composite palmettes, on a ground covered with floral stems. *Inner guard band*: A floral scroll bearing blossoms and rosettes interlaced with an arabesque scroll. *Outer guard band*: Intersecting floral scrolls bearing rosette blossoms and palmettes.

PUBLISHED: Breck-Morris, no. 5; Dimand, *Handbook*, fig. 195.

Gift of James F. Ballard, the James F. Ballard Collection

22.100.77

29   FIGURE 97

Floral rug, Herat, second half of XVI century

26′ 6″ × 10′ 6″

WARP: Cotton

WEFT: Cotton; 3 shoots after each row of knots

KNOTTING: Wool. Senna knot, about 120 knots per square inch

COLORS: 14. *Ground*: red (field, outer guard band, edging), dark blue green (border), light blue (inner guard band). *Pattern*: white, tan, yellow, orange, pink, red, light blue, blue, dark blue, dark blue green, light green, green, dark green, black brown.

DECORATION: *Field*: An allover symmetrical floral pattern consisting of two systems of intersecting floral scrolls that issue from the center of the field and extend toward both ends of the rug, spiraling and sending off shoots curling in similar fashion. Each scroll forms three spirals in each quarter of the field. The stems bear leaves, buds, blossoms, a variety of composite palmette, and fan-shaped palmettes characteristic of Herat rugs. At intervals appear cloud bands. *Border*: Floral scrolls bearing composite, fan-shaped, and leafy palmettes. *Inner guard band*: Cartouches containing a floral scroll alternating with circular medallions with blossoms. *Outer guard band*: Intersecting floral scrolls bearing rosette blossoms and palmettes. *Edging between border and inner guard band*: A geometrical scroll.

EX COLL. Henry G. Marquand

Gift of Mr. and Mrs. David M. Levitt

57.133

30   FIGURE 99

Floral rug, Herat, first half of XVII century, period of Shah Abbas

13′ 8″ × 5′ 10″

WARP: Cotton

WEFT: Cotton; 3 shoots after each row of knots

KNOTTING: Wool. Senna knot, about 168 knots per square inch

COLORS: 9. *Ground*: red (field, outer guard band), dark blue (border), light blue (inner guard band). *Pattern*: white, yellow, orange, pink, red, light blue, dark blue, light blue green, green.

DECORATION: *Field*: An allover symmetrical floral pattern consisting of a double system of floral scrolls that form oval spirals and end in a variety of palmettes, blossoms, and feathery lanceolate leaves. The center is indicated by stems bearing small palmettes that form a lozenge, each point of which terminates in either a regular palmette or a composite fan-shaped palmette. *Border*: Intermittent interlaced floral scrolls bearing alternately palmettes, blossoms, and lanceolate leaves. *Guard bands*: A wavy floral scroll with leaves and blossoms.

PUBLISHED: Dimand, *Handbook*, fig. 196; Erdmann, *Oriental Carpets*, fig. 81; Valentiner, no. 45.

Bequest of Benjamin Altman

14. 40. 711

31   RIGHT

Floral rug, Herat, early XVII century, period of Shah Abbas

21′ 3″ × 10′ 4½″

WARP: Cotton

WEFT: Cotton; 3 shoots after each row of knots

KNOTTING: Wool. Senna knot, about 132 knots per square inch

COLORS: 12. *Ground*: red (field, outer guard band), dark blue (border), green (inner guard band), *Pattern*: white, yellow, orange, pink, red, light blue, blue, dark blue, blue green, light green, green, black.

DECORATION: *Field*: An allover design of floral scrolls. Two systems of scrolls intersect each other and send off palmettes including fan-shaped ones, blossoms, and leaves. Cloud bands appear amidst the scrolls. *Border*: Intersecting floral scrolls bearing large leafy palmettes, small palmettes, and blossoms. *Guard bands*: Intersecting floral scrolls bearing rosette blossoms and palmettes.

NOTE: Probably originally longer.

Gift of Mrs. Carl Tucker

51. 177. 1

32   NEXT PAGE

Floral rug, Herat, early XVII century, period of Shah Abbas

8′ 1½″ × 4′ 8¼″

WARP: Cotton

WEFT: Wool; 3 shoots after each row of knots

KNOTTING: Wool. Senna knot, about 156 knots per square inch

COLORS: 12. *Ground*: red (field), dark blue green (border), light green (inner guard band), yellow, orange (portions of outer guard band). *Pattern*: white, yellow, orange, pink, red, light blue, blue, dark blue, dark blue green, light green, green, black.

DECORATION: *Field*: A symmetrical floral pattern of two intersecting floral scrolls issuing from a central lozenge configuration, and extending toward both ends of the field. The spiraling stems bear leaves, blossoms, palmettes, and leafy palmettes. Cloud bands are placed upon this floral background. *Border*: Leaves and lotus blossoms. *Guard bands*: A wavy floral scroll bearing rosette blossoms and leaves.

EX COLL. Henry Walters

Gift of Ralph Dudley

53.214

33   FIGURE 100

Floral rug, Herat, end of XVII century

6′ 6½″ × 4′ 7½″

WARP: Cotton

WEFT: Wool; 2 shoots after each row of knots

KNOTTING: Wool. Senna knot, about 120 knots per square inch

COLORS: 10. *Ground*: red (field, outer guard band), green, blue (portions of border), yellow (inner guard band). *Pattern*: yellow, pink, light blue, blue, dark blue, light green, green, light brown, brown black.

DECORATION: *Field*: A symmetrical floral pattern consisting of floral scrolls forming curling and angular convolutions. From a central rosette the scrolls issue in four directions forming one spiral in each quarter of the field. The stems send off palmettes, some of them flanked by lanceolate leaves, rosettes, and a variety of other leaves. Cloud bands are placed amidst the scrolls. *Border*: A wavy floral scroll bearing large palmettes flanked by lanceolate leaves. *Inner guard band*: Forklike motifs. *Outer guard band*: Small rosettes.

Mr. and Mrs. Isaac D. Fletcher Collection, Bequest of Isaac D. Fletcher

17.120.141

34   FACING PAGE, TOP

Floral rug, Herat, second half of XVII century

5′ 3″ × 4′ 2″

WARP: Cotton

WEFT: Wool; 3 shoots after each row of knots

KNOTTING: Wool. Senna knot, about 129 knots per square inch

COLORS: 12. *Ground*: rose red (field), blue green (border), white (inner guard band), golden yellow (outer guard band). *Pattern*: white, tan, golden yellow, pink, rose red, light blue, blue, blue green, yellow green, light green, green, brown.

DECORATION: *Field*: A symmetrical design of floral scrolls; the center indicated by a lozenge configuration with four small rosettes surrounded by four palmettes. The scrolls send off regular and leafy palmettes, small rosettes, and leaves with cloud bands placed amidst them. *Border*: A wavy floral scroll with two types of large palmettes in alternation, small palmettes, and leaves. *Guard bands*: A wavy floral scroll with rosettes and leaves.

PUBLISHED: Hawley, pl. 18.

Rogers Fund

08.173.12

35   FACING PAGE, BOTTOM

Floral rug (fragment), Herat, first half of XVII century

8′ 2″ × 7′ 5½″

WARP: Wool

WEFT: Wool; 3 shoots after each row of knots

KNOTTING: Wool. Senna knot, about 120 knots per square inch

COLORS: 10. *Ground*: red (field). *Pattern*: white, yellow,

orange gold, red, blue, dark blue, light blue green, dark blue green, green, black brown.

DECORATION: *Field*: An allover pattern of floral scrolls bearing leaves, palmettes, and rosettes. The floral scrolls, overlaid at intervals with cloud bands, form circular convolutions terminating in lanceolate leaves or palmettes.

Theodore M. Davis Collection, Bequest of Theodore M. Davis, 1915

30.95.228

36   FIGURE 102

Floral and arabesque rug, Isfahan, early XVII century, period of Shah Abbas

15′ 9″ × 6′ 11″

WARP: Cotton

WEFT: Cotton; 2 shoots after each row of knots

KNOTTING: Wool. Senna knot, about 195 knots per square inch

COLORS: 12. *Ground*: red (field, outer guard band), dark blue (border), reciprocal red and light blue (inner guard band). *Pattern*: white, yellow, orange, red orange, pink, red, light blue, dark blue, blue green, light green, green, black.

DECORATION: *Field*: Scrolling arabesque bands in four main and four secondary units intersect with each other. The bands end in several places in seminaturalistic, double lanceolate leaves. At one end and at each side, near the center, small lanceolate leaves are attached to the large leaves forming a pointed arch. The bands are overlaid at intervals with fan-shaped leaf palmettes, lotus palmettes, pomegranates, small lanceolate leaves, and cloud motifs. Delicate floral scrolls bearing palmettes of various sizes and leaves run parallel to the main bands. Undulating Chinese cloud bands are placed symmetrically over the field. *Border*: Intersecting floral scrolls with pomegranate palmettes, lotus palmettes, and leaves. Large fan-shaped composite leaf palmettes appear at intervals. *Inner guard band*: Reciprocal trefoils. *Outer guard band*: A floral scroll with rosettes, interlaced with an arabesque scroll.

PUBLISHED: Dimand, *Kevorkian Foundation*, pl. IV; Dimand, in *Islamic Art*, fig. 9 and color plate.

Rogers Fund

69.244

37   FIGURE 104

Vase rug, probably Isfahan, end of XVI century, period of Shah Abbas

26′ 8″ × 9′ 6″

WARP: Cotton

WEFT: Wool; 3 shoots after each row of knots

KNOTTING: Wool. Senna knot, about 238 knots per square inch

COLORS: 13. *Ground*: red (field), dark blue (border), yellow (inner guard band), reciprocal red and green (outer guard band). *Pattern*: white, yellow, orange, salmon, red, purple, light blue, dark blue, blue green, light green, green, light brown.

DECORATION: *Field*: A triple system of floral stems running from end to end, alternately parting and coming together, forming intersecting lozenges. At one end the stems terminate in arabesque fashion and bear half-palmettes. The stems are overlaid with large composite palmettes of great variety, including a stylized lilylike palmette characteristic of vase rugs, and with Chinese vases filled with sprays of peach blossoms. Thinner stems placed between the principal ones bear, in addition to palmettes, more naturalistic blossoms such as carnations and lilies, and lanceolate leaves. *Border*: Two interlacing arabesque scrolls on a background of delicate floral scrolls bearing rosettes. *Inner guard band*: A wavy floral scroll bearing blossoms and leaves. *Outer guard band*: Reciprocal trefoils.

PUBLISHED: Pope, *Early Oriental Carpets*, no. 16; Pope, *Survey*, VI, pls. 1219, 1219 A–C.

EX COLL.: Austrian Museum of Applied Art, Vienna; Mrs. Edith Rockefeller McCormick

Rogers Fund

43. 121. 2

38   RIGHT

Vase rug (fragment), probably Isfahan, early XVII century, period of Shah Abbas

12′ × 7′ 2″

WARP: Cotton

WEFT: Cotton; 3 shoots after each row of knots

KNOTTING: Wool. Senna knot, about 208 knots per square inch

COLORS: 12. *Ground*: red (field), dark blue (border), yellow (inner guard band), reciprocal red and light green (outer guard band). *Pattern*: white, tan, yellow, pink, red, light blue, blue, dark blue, blue green, yellow green, light green, dark brown.

DECORATION: *Field*: A triple system of floral stems that part and come together forming lozenges. The stems are overlaid with palmettes of various types seen in many other vase rugs. The intervening spaces are filled with thinner stems bearing blossoms and leaves. *Border*: Two interlacing arabesque scrolls on a background of delicate floral scrolls bearing rosettes. *Inner guard band*: A wavy floral scroll with leaves and rosettes. *Outer guard band*: Reciprocal trefoils.

PUBLISHED: Breck-Morris, no. 8; Dimand, *Handbook*, fig. 197.

Gift of James F. Ballard, the James F. Ballard Collection

22. 100. 68

39   FIGURE 105

Floral compartment rug, probably Isfahan, early XVII century, period of Shah Abbas

16′ 5″ × 10′ 8″

WARP: Cotton

WEFT: Wool; 3 shoots after each row of knots

KNOTTING: Wool. Senna knot, about 272 knots per square inch

COLORS: 12. *Ground*: white, yellow, orange, salmon, pink, rose red, light blue, blue, dark blue, blue green, green (compartments), reciprocal blue and dark blue (border). *Pattern*: white, yellow, orange, pink, rose red, blue, dark blue, blue green, light green.

DECORATION: *Field*: An allover pattern of cartouches divided into compartments, each compartment con-

taining floral scrolls bearing blossoms or large composite palmettes, some of a type familiar from vase rugs.
The shape of one of the floral motifs, formed by curling
leaves, suggests a vase. *Border*: A wavy arabesque
scroll.

PUBLISHED: Bode-Kühnel, fig. 93; Dimand, *Oriental Rugs*,
fig. 6; Dimand, *Handbook*, fig. 247; Erdmann, *Oriental
Carpets*, fig. 78; Pope, *Survey*, VI, pl. 1223.
EX COLL. Dikran Kelekian
Bequest of Horace Havemeyer, The H. O. Havemeyer
Collection
56.185.1

40   FIGURE 110

Tree rug, probably northwestern Persia, second half of XVI century

6′ 10″ × 5′ 1½″
WARP: Silk
WEFT: Wool and cotton; 3 shoots after each row of knots
KNOTTING: Wool. Senna knot, about 156 knots per square
inch
COLORS: 12. *Ground*: red (field), dark blue green (border),
white (inner guard band), orange (outer guard band).
Pattern: white, tan, yellow, orange, pink, red, blue,
light blue green, dark blue green, light green, green,
black brown.
DECORATION: *Field*: In the center, a pond with fish from
which spring four pairs of flowering trees with birds
perched on their branches. Other flowering trees with
birds appear in the field and parts of others in the
corners. Several large palmettes are placed along the
vertical and transverse axes filling the intervening
spaces. *Border*: Cartouches and lobed medallions containing cloud bands, floral scrolls, palmettes, leaves,
and blossoms, bordered by two rows of half-medallions
and half-cartouches, interspersed with floral scrolls.
Guard bands: A wavy scroll bearing rosettes and buds.
Mr. and Mrs. Isaac D. Fletcher Collection, Bequest of
Isaac D. Fletcher
17.120.142

41   FIGURE 111

Tree rug, probably Isfahan, early XVII century, period of Shah Abbas

8′ 11″ × 5′ 10″
WARP: Cotton
WEFT: Wool; 3 shoots after each row of knots
KNOTTING: Wool. Senna knot, about 208 knots per
square inch
COLORS: 10. *Ground*: red (field), dark blue (border), white
(guard bands). *Pattern*: white, yellow, orange, pink, red,
light blue, dark blue, light green, green, dark green.

DECORATION: *Field*: Six horizontal rows of flowering
shrubs, including iris, carnations, roses, and pomegranates, growing from patches of ground. *Border*:
Two interlacing arabesque scrolls with palmette devices
placed upon a background of floral scrolls bearing
rosettes. *Guard bands*: A wavy floral scroll with blossoms and leaves.

PUBLISHED: Breck-Morris, no. 10; Dilley, pl. VII; Pope,
Survey, VI, pl. 1231.
Gift of James F. Ballard, the James F. Ballard Collection
22.100.76

42   FIGURE 113

Tree rug, Kurdistan, end of XVII century

21′ 4″ × 7′ 2″
WARP: Cotton
WEFT: Cotton; 3 shoots after each row of knots
KNOTTING: Wool. Senna knot, about 131 knots per square
inch
COLORS: 11. *Ground*: dark blue green (field), light tan, blue
(large medallions), red (small medallions, border),
white (small medallions) yellow (guard bands).
Pattern: white, light tan, yellow, pink, red, light blue,
blue, dark blue, light blue green, brown.
DECORATION: *Field*: Rows of lobed medallions alternating
with larger elongated polylobed medallions and connected by small octagons containing cross-shaped
motifs. From every other one of the smaller lobed
medallions issue diagonally four blossoming fruit
trees. The small medallions are filled with floral scrolls
and arabesques; the large ones with floral scrolls and
palmettes of various types. *Border*: Palmettes linked by
stylized arabesque bands overlaid with floral scrolls.
Guard bands: A wavy floral scroll with rosettes and
leaves.
PUBLISHED: McMullan, no. 26.
EX COLL. William H. Vanderbilt
Gift of Joseph V. McMullan
60.32

43   NEXT PAGE

Tree rug, Kurdistan, end of XVIII century

17′ 5″ × 9′ 6″
WARP: Cotton
WEFT: Cotton; 2 shoots after each row of knots
KNOTTING: Wool. Senna knot, about 169 knots per
square inch
COLORS: 9. *Ground*: dark blue (field), salmon (border),
blue (guard bands). *Pattern*: white, salmon, brick red,
light blue, dark blue, light green, green, dark brown.
DECORATION: *Field*: Staggered rows of medallions prob-
ably representing pools, each medallion containing a

COLORS: 13. *Ground*: dark blue (field), dark salmon (central pool), red (garden plots, corner medallions), blue (garden plots), light green, yellow green (canals), cream white (small pools, guard bands). *Pattern*: cream white, pink, dark salmon, red, purple, light blue, blue, dark blue, light green, green, olive green, brown.

DECORATION: *Field*: A vertical and a horizontal canal radiate from a central pool enclosing a garden pavilion, represented by a flower-filled octagon, dividing the field into four garden sections. Both the pool and canals, indicated by angular parallel lines, contain stylized fish and plants. Each quarter section of the garden has two small plots and two pools, bordered on two sides by a band containing trees. One of the plots has flowering shrubs and plants; the other, an octagonal medallion with a palmette, leaves, and buds. In each corner of the field, a portion of a medallion with geometrical arabesques. *Border*: Reciprocal trefoils. *Guard bands*: Rosettes.

PUBLISHED: Breck-Morris, no. 4; Dimand, *Handbook*, fig. 199; Martin, pl. xxiv.

EX COLL. Carl Robert Lamm

Gift of James F. Ballard, the James F. Ballard Collection
22. 100. 128

45   FIGURE 116

Garden rug, Kurdistan, about 1800

18′ 3″ × 7′ 8″

WARP: Cotton

WEFT: Cotton; 2 shoots after each row of knots

KNOTTING: Wool. Ghiordes knot, about 50 knots per square inch

COLORS: 12. *Ground*: dark blue green (field, border), red (canals, pools, garden plots), white (garden plots, guard bands), light blue (garden plots). *Pattern*: white, yellow, orange, pink, red, purple, light blue, dark blue, light green, green, brown.

DECORATION: *Field*: A main canal in the vertical axis and three secondary horizontal canals divide the field into rectangular garden plots. The water, represented by diagonal parallel lines, contains stylized fish. At each of the three juncture points of the canals is a basin containing peach trees. Each garden plot, bordered by trees, is divided into two square plots; one contains a star-shaped medallion with palmettes, the other is filled with leafy branches of trees which issue from the two end basins. At one end of the rug, the garden plots contain one square plot each. *Border*: Rosettes alternating with plants. *Guard bands*: A wavy floral scroll with leaves.

PUBLISHED: Dimand, *Peasant and Nomad Rugs*, no. 13.

Gift of William R. Pickering
67. 156

floral scroll of four rosettes. From every other medallion a pair of flowering trees issues, a cypress tree between them. From the alternate medallions issue floral scrolls with blossoms and palmettes. *Border*: Floral scrolls bearing palmettes, rosettes, and leaves. *Guard bands*: Two interlaced scrolls with leaves and blossoms.

PUBLISHED: Pope, *Survey*, VI, pl. 1110.

Bequest of Benjamin Altman
14. 40. 710

44   FIGURE 115, PAGE 146

Garden rug, Kurdistan, first half of XVIII century

10′ 5″ × 6′ 2″

WARP: Cotton

WEFT: Cotton; 2 shoots after each row of knots

KNOTTING: Wool. Ghiordes knot, about 176 knots per square inch

46 FIGURE 117

Garden rug (fragment), Kurdistan, XVIII century

14′ 2″ × 8′ 9″

WARP: Cotton

WEFT: Cotton; 2 shoots after each row of knots

KNOTTING: Wool. Ghiordes knot, about 84 knots per square inch

COLORS: 10. *Ground*: dark blue (field), white (water, garden plots), red, green (garden plots), reciprocal dark blue and yellow (border), reciprocal red and white (inner guard band), reciprocal red and green (outer guard band). *Pattern*: white, yellow, light red, red, light blue, dark blue, light green, green, black brown.

DECORATION: *Field*: A main water canal, the water indicated by parallel zigzag lines, divides the field into two garden sections. On each side of the canal is a row of cypress trees separated by floral shrubs and pairs of birds. Each of the two garden sections has a central octagonal pavilion with canals radiating from it and dividing the section into four quarters, which are further subdivided by bands of flowers and shrubs into two garden plots filled with conventionalized trees or palmette devices. *Border*: Reciprocal trefoils. *Guard bands*: Heart motifs.

PUBLISHED: Dilley, pl. V; Valentiner, no. 46.

Theodore M. Davis Collection, Bequest of Theodore M. Davis, 1915

30.95.150

47 FIGURE 119

Arabesque rug, probably Kurdistan, middle of XVII century

19′ 10″ × 8′ 2″

WARP: Cotton

WEFT: Cotton; 3 shoots after each row of knots

KNOTTING: Wool. Senna knot, about 225 knots per square inch

COLORS: 16. *Ground*: red (field), white, blue green (arabesque bands), light green, yellow green (border), brown (edging). *Pattern*: white, tan, yellow, orange, salmon, pink, red, light blue, blue, dark blue, blue green, light green, green, brown, black.

DECORATION: *Field*: Several systems of interlaced arabesque bands defining areas of various shapes and sizes. The bands are overlaid with small cloud motifs and floral scrolls bearing rosettes, palmettes, and pomegranates. At intervals along the bands and at their junctures are lotus palmettes, composite palmettes, or leaves enclosing palmettes. The areas between the bands are filled with floral scrolls with palmettes of various sizes and occasionally with large animals including deer, lions, and dragonlike ch'i-lins. *Border*:

Palmettes, blossoms, and buds connected by stems. *Inner edging*: Forklike motif.

PUBLISHED: Bode-Kühnel, fig. 81.

EX COLL. Stefano Bardini

Gift of Mrs. Harry Payne Bingham

59.75

48 FIGURE 121

Prayer rug, Tabriz, first half of XVI century, period of Shah Tahmasp

5′ 3½″ × 3′ 6½″

WARP: Cotton

WEFT: Silk; 3 shoots after each row of knots

KNOTTING: Wool. Senna knot, about 552 knots per square inch

BROCADING: Silver strips wound around a silk core

COLORS: 12. *Ground*: red (niche, outer guard band), ivory (border), green, blue green (inner guard band). *Pattern*: ivory, yellow, orange, light rose, red, light blue, dark blue, blue green, light green, black, silver.

DECORATION: *Field*: A prayer niche with a curved arch ending in a finial and outlined by a band of Koranic inscription. Within the niche, floral scrolls bearing palmettes, leaves, and blossoms, large cloud bands, and, at the apex of the arch, a cartouche with an Arabic inscription. The spandrels are filled with Arabic inscriptions arranged in irregular compartments. *Border*: Lower half: intersecting floral stems curling in spirals and bearing palmettes, blossoms, and leaves, overlaid with a spiraling arabesque with half-palmettes; upper half: cartouches containing Koranic inscriptions on a ground of floral scrolls, separated by four circles enclosing squares bearing the name of Allah in angular Kufic writing. *Inner guard band*: Lower half: an arabesque scroll interlaced with a floral scroll bearing palmettes; upper half: Koranic inscriptions. *Outer guard band*: Lower half: a wavy floral scroll with palmettes and blossoms; upper half: Koranic inscriptions.

PUBLISHED: Dilley, pl. XV; Dimand, *Handbook*, fig. 190; Pope, *Survey*, VI, pl. 1167; Sarre-Trenkwald, II, pl. 51.

Mr. and Mrs. Isaac D. Fletcher Collection, Bequest of Isaac D. Fletcher

17.120.124

49 FIGURE 122

Prayer rug, probably Kashan, second half of XVI century

5′ 3¾″ × 3′ 2¼″

WARP: Cotton

WEFT: Silk; 3 shoots after each row of knots

KNOTTING: Wool. Senna knot, about 342 knots per square inch

COLORS: 9. *Ground*: blue green (niche, border), red (spandrels), yellow (guard band). *Pattern*: white, yellow, orange, pink, red, olive green, light green, black.

DECORATION: *Field*: An elaborately curved prayer niche, whose outline is formed by cloudlike motifs. Within the niche, two blossoming trees rising from the lower edge; between them, two shrubs bearing blossoms. In the apex of the arch is a bulbous vase decorated with sprays of blossoms, containing floral stems, blossoms, and palmettes. The spandrels are filled with floral scrolls and arabesques. *Border*: Lower portion: four cartouches filled with floral scrolls and cloud bands and two lobed medallions containing rosette devices; upper portion: five cartouches containing Koranic inscriptions alternating with lobed medallions bearing monograms of Allah in angular Kufic. *Guard band*: Lower portion: intermittent interlaced arabesque scrolls bearing palmettes; upper portion: Arabic and Persian inscriptions. At the top of the rug is a band of Arabic inscriptions.

PUBLISHED: Sarre-Trenkwald, II, pl. 52.

EX COLL. Stefano Bardini

Bequest of Benjamin Altman

14. 40. 720

50   FIGURE 123

Prayer rug, probably Isfahan, second half of XVII century

7' 7" × 3' 4"

WARP: Cotton

WEFT: Cotton; 2 shoots after each row of knots

KNOTTING: Wool. Senna knot, about 184 knots per square inch

COLORS: 7. *Ground*: blue green (upper niche), dark blue (lower niche, outer guard band), red (spandrels, border), gray green (inner guard band). *Pattern*: yellow, pink, red, dark red, dark blue, gray green.

DECORATION: *Field*: Two arched niches with curved stepped outline, one above the other. The lower niche is filled with an allover pattern of small plants with three blossoms. The upper niche is filled with a symmetrical pattern of floral scrolls bearing blossoms, palmettes, and lanceolate leaves; a similar pattern fills the spandrels of both niches. *Border*: Two angular scrolls bearing rosette blossoms. *Guard bands*: Blossoms and stems.

PUBLISHED: Bode-Kühnel, fig. 116; Breck-Morris, no. 11.

Gift of James F. Ballard, the James F. Ballard Collection

22. 100. 72

51   BELOW

Floral rug, Shiraz, second half of XVIII century

8' 3½" × 4' 5"

WARP: Cotton

WEFT: Wool; 2 shoots after each row of knots

KNOTTING: Wool. Senna knot, about 168 knots per square inch

COLORS: 6. *Ground*: dark blue (field), red (border), white (guard bands). *Pattern*: white, pink, red, light lavender, light blue, dark blue.

DECORATION: *Field*: A lozenge diaper formed by delicate stems connected by large and small rosettes. The diaper is further subdivided into rectangular compartments by lengthwise and horizontal stems. Tendrils bearing peach blossoms, carnations, roses, and other flowers grow from the stems of the lozenges and fill the field. *Border*: Lozenges formed by thin stems and filled with palmettes. *Guard bands*: A wavy floral scroll. *Edgings*: A wavy scroll.

PUBLISHED: McMullan, no. 33.
Gift of Joseph V. McMullan
67. 267

PUBLISHED: McMullan, no. 27.
Gift of Joseph V. McMullan
68. 219

52 FIGURE 108

Floral rug, Kurdistan, early XIX century

22′ 10″ × 8′ 10″

WARP: Wool

WEFT: Wool; 2 shoots after each row of knots

KNOTTING: Wool. Ghiordes knot, about 56 knots per square inch

COLORS: 12. *Ground*: dark blue (field), red (border), white (guard bands). *Pattern*: white, light tan, yellow, red, light blue, blue, dark blue, blue green, light green, green, light brown, brown.

DECORATION: *Field*: An allover pattern of floral scrolls bearing palmettes, small rosettes, leaves, and buds. The scrolls, overlaid with large palmettes and rosettes, form lozenges and other angular compartments. Along the lengthwise axis large composite palmettes formed by serrate leaves that enclose lotus palmettes alternate with large composite rosettes and floral devices consisting of small palmettes surrounding a central rosette. The floral devices are flanked on either side by large palmettes composed of three floral motifs that alternate with rosette-filled cartouches placed diagonally. *Border*: Cartouches containing arabesques and floral devices alternate with lobed medallions containing a floral device with buds. *Guard bands*: A wavy arabesque scroll.

53 FIGURE 125

Floral rug, Kurdistan, early XIX century

18′ 4″ × 8′ 5″

WARP: Cotton

WEFT: Cotton; 2 shoots after each row of knots

KNOTTING: Wool. Ghiordes knot, about 121 knots per square inch

COLORS: 12. *Ground*: dark blue (field), tomato red (border), off-white (guard bands). *Pattern*: white, off-white, yellow, orange, pink, rose red, tomato red, blue, dark blue, blue green, light green, green.

DECORATION: *Field*: An allover pattern of floral scrolls forming lozenges overlaid with large palmettes, rosettes, and a great variety of blossoms. The large composite palmettes with "flaming" contours are formed by serrate leaves that enclose a lotus palmette. Also present are large palmettes composed of three floral motifs and a split half-palmette. *Border*: Wavy floral scrolls bearing palmettes and rosettes flanked by lanceolate leaves. *Guard bands*: A wavy floral scroll with leaves and rosettes.

PUBLISHED: Breck-Morris, no. 6.
Gift of James F. Ballard, the James F. Ballard Collection
22. 100. 71

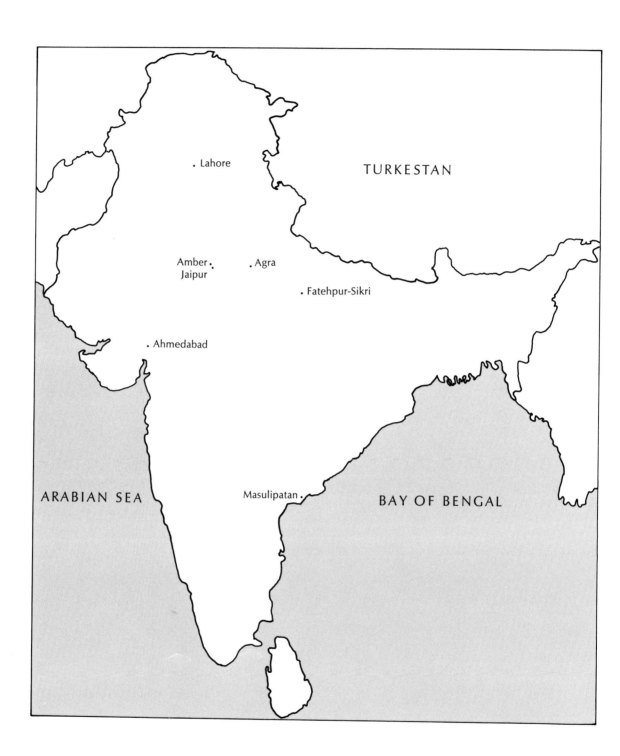

TURKESTAN

. Lahore

Amber . . Agra
Jaipur

. Fatehpur-Sikri

. Ahmedabad

ARABIAN SEA

Masulipatan .

BAY OF BENGAL

Six:

RUGS OF MUGHAL INDIA

The Mughal dynasty of India was founded by Babur (1526–1530), a fifth-generation descendant of the Mongol ruler Timur. (The name Mughal, or Mogul, is a corruption of the name Mongol.) Setting out from his minor kingdom in Afghanistan in 1526, Babur defeated the Sultan of Delhi and his Hindu army at Panipat, and made himself master of Hindustan. Babur brought Persian culture and art to India. Like his Timurid ancestors he was greatly interested in the art of painting. He had a collection of illuminated Persian manuscripts illustrated by painters of the Herat school, including the famous Bihzad and his pupils. The few known paintings of Babur's time[1] are direct copies of paintings of the Herat school. The court rugs of this period, about which almost nothing is now known, were doubtless imported from Persia.

Babur's son and successor, Humayun (1530–1556), as the result of an Afghan revolt in 1540, sought refuge in Sind and later in Persia. A portion of his exile was spent in Tabriz at the court of Shah Tahmasp. Here Humayun became acquainted with some of the most famous Persian painters of the time. Moving to Kabul, Afghanistan, in 1549, and subsequently returning to India, he invited two of them, Mir Sayyid Ali and Abdus Samad, to join his court. As the emperor's protégés, these masters were the founders of the Mughal school of painting. Bestowing the title Nazir al-Mulk (Marvel of the Realm) upon Mir Sayyid Ali, Humayun commissioned him to illustrate the Persian *Dastan i-Amir Hamza* (*Romance of Amir Hamza*), the story of the uncle of the Prophet. The book consisted of twelve large volumes, and its illustrations were painted on cotton cloth. This ambitious work[2] was not completed until the time of Humayun's son and successor, Akbar the Great. Many of its paintings depict contemporary Mughal rugs.

Akbar (1556–1605) was an extraordinary personality who not only consolidated the political power of the Mughal empire but deeply influenced Indian art and culture. He was interested in religions other than Islam, namely Hinduism and Christianity, and in 1578 he requested the Portuguese authorities of Goa to send him missionaries and copies of the Gospels. In March, 1580, a party of Jesuits led by Father Rodolfe Aquaviva and Antonio Monserrate arrived at Akbar's court at Fatehpur-Sikri and presented him with paintings of Christ and the Virgin as well as a copy of Plantin's Bible illustrated with engravings by Flemish artists.

The palace-city of Fatehpur-Sikri, which Akbar began building in 1569 and finished in 1584, survives today as one of the great monuments of Mughal architecture. The years during which it was Akbar's capital—he abandoned it in favor of Agra in 1584—saw remarkable activity in the arts. The palaces were sumptuously decorated with mural paintings by both Persian and Indian artists. A library was established as well as ateliers for painting, goldwork, weaving, and the manufacture of arms. More than a hundred painters worked at illustrating Persian, Hindu, and Mughal historical works, particularly the *Akbar Namah* (*Book of Akbar*), written by Abul Fazl, the emperor's minister and friend.

It was during this time, too, that the massive *Amir Hamza*, commissioned by Humayun, was completed.

FIGURE 127   Painting from an *Amir Hamza*, about 1575. The Brooklyn Museum, New York

In many of its miniatures, as well as those of other manuscripts of the period, we find representations of Indian court rugs covering floors, terraces, or thrones. They are entirely Persian in style, reminding us of Safavid floral rugs and medallion rugs (figure 127). Supplementing this evidence is the testimony of Abul Fazl, who tells us that Akbar "caused carpets to be made of wonderful varieties and charming textures; he has appointed experienced workmen, who have produced many masterpieces. The carpets of Iran and Turan [Turkestan] are no more thought of, although merchants still import carpets from Jushagan, Khuzistan [in western Persia], Kerman, and Sabzawar [in Khurasan]. All kinds of carpet-weavers have settled here, and drive a flourishing trade. These are to be found in every town, but especially in Agra, Fatehpur, and Lahore." Despite the minister's claim that the rugs of Persia were "no more thought of," many of the Mughal rugs that have survived from this period are direct copies of Herat and other Persian floral rugs. A number, known today as "Indo-Persian" or "Indian Isfahans," are in museums and private collections. They are easily recognized by their color scheme, since it includes a reddish brown and a deep orange that are unknown in Persian rugs of Herat. The collection of the Maharaja of Jaipur,[3] which is today in the Jaipur Museum, contains not only Mughal copies but some of the Persian originals.

Akbar's court artists attempted to develop a national Mughal style. This style is apparent not only in their painting but in their decorative arts, including rugs. The Hindu weavers introduced into their rug designs naturalistic Indian plants, animals, and human figures, deriving these from contemporary miniature paintings. To the early period of Akbar can be assigned fragments of animal rugs that are now widely dispersed in public and private collections, including the Louvre, the Burrell Collection of the Glasgow Art Gallery and Museum, the Musée des Arts Décoratifs, Paris, the Textile Museum, Washington, and the collection of Joseph V. McMullan.[4] All of these pieces are the remains of at least two rugs that were decorated with plants and fantastic creatures of land and sea on wine red grounds. Some scholars have dated them to 1500, but the style of the plants and animals indicates that they should be assigned to the second half of the sixteenth century. Sea monsters are depicted in several contemporary Mughal paintings.

Akbar's son Jahangir (reigned 1605–1628) was as eminent a patron of the arts as his father. He collected Persian manuscripts, albums of individual miniatures, and European paintings, some of the last acquired for him abroad by his agents. The father's interest in religions continued in the son, and among the frescoes decorating Jahangir's palace at Agra were some representing Christian scenes. A great lover of beauty in nature, the emperor traveled extensively in India, always taking with him two or three of his court painters to record events of importance. At his orders the artists Mansur, Manohar, and Murad painted beautiful specimens of Indian birds, animals, and flowers. Kashmir, which he called "the garden of eternal spring," was one of the emperor's favorite regions, and here he spent many happy days. Here, too, Mansur produced more than a hundred paintings of flowers for his patron. From this interest developed the fashion of decorating the borders of Mughal miniature paintings with rows of naturalistic plants, painted either in gold or polychrome.

Representative of the style of the Jahangir period is a large rug patterned with animals and birds amid flowering shrubs (figure 128). The pattern is derived from a Safavid animal rug, although there is evident a greater freedom in the composition and a more realistic rendering of the landscape. The artist also introduced many naturalistic plants unknown in Persian rugs, including palm trees, often represented in Mughal paintings. In another rug representative of this period there is a balanced symmetrical design of floral scrolls with large palmettes (figure 129, page 148), recalling the early seventeenth-century Herat rugs. However, added to the Persian motifs we see many flowers that are found only in Mughal rugs. Prominent among these are the racemes of wisteria-like blossoms that alternate with lanceolate leaves. Like the field design, the border design is known from Persian rugs. In both, however, the rendering of the flowers is more naturalistic than it is in Persian rugs. We also find in these and other Mughal rugs (figure 130) colors and tints, such as madder red, that are typically Indian. The design of the rugs in figures 28 and 29 recalls the design of a well-known floral and armorial rug belonging to the Girdlers' Company of London.[5] According to the company's records, it was presented in 1634 by Sir Robert Bell, a director of the East India Company, and it was woven in the imperial factory at Lahore in the time of Jahangir.

Three well-known rugs of the Jahangir period show the influence of Mughal miniature painting. One, an animal rug in the Widener Collection of the National Gallery of Art, Washington,[6] has a red field covered with floral scrolls upon which are

FIGURE 128 Animal and tree rug, Lahore, early
XVII century. Catalogue no. 54

placed various animals, singly or in groups, running
in various directions. Among them are deer, a winged
lion, a dragon, and Chinese ch'i-lins—all familiar
from Persian rugs. In addition there are other animals
known from Mughal paintings: a crocodile, a tiger, a
rhinoceros, and elephants. The second of these rugs,
sometimes known as the "Peacock Rug," is in the
Austrian Museum of Applied Art, Vienna.[7] Its composition is purely pictorial, without symmetry, having three rows of trees and shrubs with a variety of
birds in their branches. The middle of the rug is
occupied by a large plane tree under which are a pair
of peacocks and a cock and hen with chicks. Two
cranes are placed below the top row of trees. The

FIGURE 130 Floral rug, beginning of XVII century.
Catalogue no. 56

style, with its realistic shading, recalls the animal and bird paintings of Mansur, and it is quite probable that he was responsible for the design of this beautiful rug. The pictorial style is even more pronounced in the third of these rugs (figure 131). Here various mythological scenes, figures, and animals are placed in the field without any apparent relationship to one another. The lower area, purely Hindu in conception, shows a winged elephant-monster seizing seven black elephants and being itself attacked by a phoenix. In the center of the field is a representation of a hunting party returning from the chase. At the top are several scenes, including a garden party and a group of people in a house, derived both from Mughal and Rajput (native Indian) paintings of the Jahangir period.

To this period also belong a rug with birds, floral motifs, and a unique decoration of interlaced bands forming swastikas (figure 132). The general design connects this rug with Mughal illuminations.

The Mughal style was fully developed in the time of Shah Jahan (1628–1658). To his reign belongs the Taj Mahal, built during the years 1632–1647 as a tomb and monument for his wife, Mumtaz Mahal. Built entirely of white marble, it is decorated with sumptuous and colorful inlays of precious stones such as onyx, jasper, and carnelian, in the technique known as *pietra dura*. The floral motifs of these inlays and of the openwork marble screens[8] around the cenotaph recall contemporary velvets and rugs.

The largest collection of rugs of this period is in the Jaipur Museum, where, indicating their origin, they are called "Lahore carpets." They were made originally for Rajah Jai Singh I (1622–1668), for his palace at Amber, built in 1630. In a fine rug of this period (figure 133) the design was obviously inspired

FIGURE 131   Pictorial rug, early XVII century. Courtesy, Museum of Fine Arts, Boston

FIGURE 132   Geometrical floral rug, early XVII century. Catalogue no. 57

FIGURE 133   Floral rug, first half of XVII century.
Catalogue no. 58

by that of a Persian rug of the Herat type, but modi-fied by the introduction of plants and flowers of India. The floral stems, forming an allover pattern, bear not only multiple palmettes and lanceolate leaves of Persian origin but such Indian flowers as roses, lilies, iris, bellflowers, violets, and peonies, rendered in a more naturalistic manner than in Persian rugs. The border, entirely Mughal in style, has a row of flower-ing plants, including roses, iris, carnations, lilies, and peonies. Such plants, as mentioned earlier, are com-mon in the borders of the miniature paintings of this time. The influence of painting is also to be seen in the delicate color shading of the flowers, a technique un-known in Persian rugs. Such flowering plants, ar-ranged in rows, usually on a red ground, comprise the sole decoration of many rugs that were made for Shah Jahan and his courtiers. Examples are in the Jaipur Museum, the Kevorkian collection,[9] and the Metropolitan, probably the earliest of this group (figure 134, page 150). Some of these rugs have inset contours on one side,[10] indicating that they were made to fit around the base of a fountain in palace rooms.

A unique tree rug of the Shah Jahan period (figure 135) has, on a wine red ground, a design of trees in three transverse rows with foliage trees and flowering trees alternating. Between the trees grow various flowers, including tulips and carnations. Like the trees, the flowers are rendered realistically. This rug came originally from the shrine of Shaikh Safi at Ardabil, Persia, to which it had probably been sent as a gift.

A popular type of rug made in Shah Jahan's time has a trellis framework containing floral scrolls with large palmettes and blossoms or else single flowering plants. There are several varieties, and the rugs were made in both large and small sizes. The compart-ments are usually formed either by slender leaves or by a series of curving bands. In some examples the compartmental division is itself the dominant motif, as seen in a fragmentary rug in the Victoria and Albert Museum[11] and a rug in the Metropolitan (figure 136). The pattern of the Metropolitan's rug may be traced to Persian prototypes, but its naturalistic plants are Mughal. So, too, is the border, with its row of pines, azaleas, and other growth in a hilly landscape. In the variety of rug where the trellis is composed of con-nected curving bands, the compartments are filled with floral scrolls with large palmettes and blossoms (figure 137). In this variety the diaper and the elements it contains are often of equal interest. In still another variety the trellis is formed by acanthus leaves and the compartments contain naturalistic flowers (figure 138). Such trelliswork, very popular in the time of Shah Jahan, is also found in the Taj Mahal.

Prayer rugs were made in the time of Shah Jahan, but only a few have survived. A fine specimen in the collection of Joseph V. McMullan has a niche filled with a large white-flowered chrysanthemum plant and tulips growing on a hill (figure 139). Another, with an elaborate floral design, was formerly in the Aynard collection.[12]

The Mughal weavers of Shah Jahan often sur-

passed the weavers of Persia in the fineness of their materials and techniques. A number of their wool rugs have as many as 780 knots to the square inch, while one exceptional rug, that of figure 136, has 1258. The wool of these rugs is so fine that it is often mistaken for silk.

Silk rugs were made in India, but only a few have been preserved. A fragment of a silk prayer rug (figure 140) indicates a niche resting on columns and containing a hilly ground with small flowering plants and a large central plant with thistlelike leaves. The decoration, of the period of Shah Jahan, originally must have resembled that of figure 139. The knotting of this piece is so fine, approximately 2552 knots per

FIGURE 135   Tree rug, first half of XVII century. Copyright The Frick Collection, New York

FIGURE 136   Floral rug with trellis pattern (fragment), first half of XVII century. Catalogue no. 60

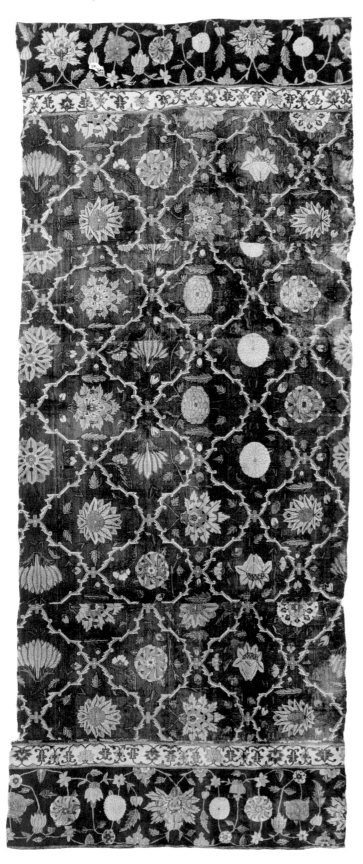

FIGURE 137 Floral rug with trellis pattern (fragment), early XVII century. Catalogue no. 61

square inch, that the texture approaches that of velvet. Prayer rugs with similar decorations were also made of velvet and of silk brocade.

The manufacture of fine rugs continued in the time of Shah Jahan's successor, Aurangzib (1658–1707). To the end of the seventeenth century can be assigned a fine millefleurs prayer rug in the Austrian Museum of Applied Art, Vienna.[13] Its niche, formed by cypress trees, is filled with a huge bouquet of assorted flowers. The design recalls some of the designs of printed and painted cottons of contemporary Indian manufacture, made chiefly in Ahmedabad,

FIGURE 138 Floral rug with trellis pattern (fragments), early XVII century. Catalogue no. 62

FIGURE 139 Prayer rug, first half of XVII century. Collection of Joseph V. McMullan, New York

FIGURE 140 Silk prayer rug (fragment), first half of XVII century. Catalogue no. 63

FIGURE 141 Floral rug, end of XVII century.
Catalogue no. 65

Lahore, and Masulipatan.[14] Also assignable to the end of the seventeenth century are two rugs in which dense floral patterns cover the entire field (figures 141, 142). The borders of these rugs have an unusual floral design of lotus buds, blossoms, and leaves.

In the eighteenth and nineteenth centuries many rugs were produced in India for the European market. These show a gradual decline in quality, both as to design and workmanship.

FIGURE 142 Floral rug (fragment), end of XVII century. Catalogue no. 66

Notes to Chapter Six

1 Ernst Kühnel and Hermann Goetz, *Indische Buchmalereien aus dem Jahângîr—Album der Staatsbibliotek zu Berlin* (Berlin, 1924), pls. 3, 31.

2 C. Stanley Clarke, *Victoria and Albert Museum. Indian Drawings*, Portfolio I (London, 1921); Heinrich Glück, *Die indischen Miniaturen des Haemzae-Romanes im Österreichischen Museum für Kunst und Industrie in Wien, und in anderen Sammlungen* (Zurich, 1925).

3 T. H. Hendley, *Asian Carpets: XVI and XVII Century Designs from the Jaipur Palaces* (London, 1905).

4 Gaston Migeon, *L'Orient musulman*, Musée du Louvre, I (Paris, 1922), pl. 38, no. 128; Kurt Erdmann, *Oriental Carpets*, figs. 170, 171; Stuart C. Welch, *The Art of Mughal India* (New York, 1963), pl. 21; Joseph V. McMullan, *Islamic Carpets*, no. 8.

5 A. F. Kendrick and C. E. C. Tattersall, *Hand-Woven Carpets*, II, pl. 33.

6 Arthur Urbane Dilley, *Oriental Rugs and Carpets*, pl. xxxv.

7 Friedrich Sarre and Hermann Trenkwald, *Old Oriental Carpets*, I, pls. 35, 36.

8 Vincent A. Smith, *A History of Fine Art in India and Ceylon*, 2d ed. rev. by K. de B. Codrington (Oxford, 1930), pls. 142, 140.

9 Maurice S. Dimand, *The Kevorkian Foundation: Collection of Rare and Magnificent Oriental Carpets*, pl. xii.

10 Kendrick-Tattersall, II, pl. 31.

11 Ibid., pl. 32.

12 F. R. Martin, *A History of Oriental Carpets before 1800*, fig. 213.

13 Sarre-Trenkwald, I, pl. 37.

14 Geo. P. Baker, *Calico Painting and Printing in the East Indies in the XVIIth and XVIIIth Centuries* (London, 1921), pl. 25.

CATALOGUE

54 FIGURE 128

Animal and tree rug, Lahore, early XVII century, period of Jahangir

27′ 4″ × 9′ 6″
WARP: Cotton
WEFT: Cotton; 3 shoots after each row of knots
KNOTTING: Wool. Senna knot, about 110 knots per square inch
COLORS: 13. *Ground*: red (field, border), pale yellow (guard bands). *Pattern*: white, pale yellow, yellow, ochre, salmon, pink, red, blue, dark blue, dark blue green, light green, green, black brown.
DECORATION: *Field*: A pattern consisting of a naturalistic landscape with birds and animals repeated three and a half times, each unit reversing the direction of the preceding one. The unit includes a palm tree, flowering trees, shrubs, and plants. Amid the branches are small birds; below stand larger birds. The animals include ibexes, tigers, and lions, some of them with the flames or streamerlike shoulder attachments of Chinese ch'i-lins. A lion is shown attacking an ibex. *Border*: Elongated angular panels containing slender floral stems and an arabesque scroll interlaced with a cloud band; the panels alternate with a six-pointed star containing a composite palmette. *Guard bands*: A wavy floral scroll bearing palmettes, blossoms, and buds. *Edgings*: A zigzag band.
PUBLISHED: Dimand, *Handbook*, fig. 201; Sarre-Trenkwald, II, pl. 55.
EX COLL. Lady Sackville
Gift of J. Pierpont Morgan
17. 190. 858

55 FIGURE 129, PAGE 148

Floral rug, Lahore, beginning of XVII century, period of Jahangir

30′ 3″ × 11′ 1″
WARP: Cotton
WEFT: Cotton; 3 shoots after each row of knots
KNOTTING: Wool. Senna knot, about 130 knots per square inch
COLORS: 11. *Ground*: red (field, outer guard band), dark blue (border), white (inner guard band). *Pattern*: white, yellow, salmon, pink, red, light blue, dark blue, blue green, light green, brown, black.
DECORATION: *Field*: A symmetrical floral pattern of wavy stems bearing large composite palmettes of the leaf type and lotus type, small leaves, large lanceolate leaves, and racemes of wisterialike flowers. The lanceolate leaves frame the palmettes in one row, the racemes

of flowers frame the palmettes in the next row. *Border*: A succession of shield-shaped panels, lobed medallions, and cartouches, the intervening spaces filled with cloud bands. In the central row, the medallions contain a composite leaf palmette surrounded by rosettes, the shield-shaped panels contain a composite leaf palmette and floral scrolls, and the cartouches contain arabesques and a floral scroll. *Inner guard band*: An intermittent floral scroll interlaced with an arabesque. *Outer guard band*: A wavy floral scroll bearing palmettes, leaves, and small blossoms. *Edgings*: A geometrical scroll; crosses alternating with a hexagonal panel.
PUBLISHED: Dilley, pl. XXXII; Erdman, *Oriental Carpets*, fig. 169; Sarre-Trenkwald, II, pl. 56.
EX COLL. Lady Sackville
Gift of J. Pierpont Morgan
17. 190. 857

56 FIGURE 130

Floral rug, beginning of XVII century, period of Jahangir

10′ 8½″ × 7′ 6″
WARP: Cotton
WEFT: Cotton; 3 shoots after each row of knots
KNOTTING: Wool. Senna knot, about 132 knots per square inch
COLORS: 11. *Ground*: red (field), dark blue (border), cream white (guard bands). *Pattern*: cream white, tan, yellow, pink, red, light blue, dark blue, blue green, light green, green, dark green.
DECORATION: *Field*: An allover floral design of stems balanced from side to side, forming lozenges along the long axis. The stems curl in spiral fashion, sending off large palmettes, composite leaves, lanceolate leaves, and wisterialike blossoms. *Border*: Palmettes, rosettes, and composite leaves, on a scrolling stem bearing naturalistic leaves. *Guard bands*: A floral scroll bearing leaves, buds, and palmettes. *Edgings*: A geometrical scroll; a cross alternating with a hexagonal panel.
Bequest of George Blumenthal
41. 190. 264

57 FIGURE 132

Geometrical floral rug, early XVII century, period of Jahangir

6′ × 4′ 2″
WARP: Cotton
WEFT: Cotton; 3 shoots after each row of knots
KNOTTING: Wool. Senna knot, about 132 knots per square inch

COLORS: 11. *Ground*: red (field, outer guard band), blue green (border), cream white (inner guard band). *Pattern*: cream white, yellow, orange, pink, red, light blue, dark blue, blue green, light green, green, dark brown.

DECORATION: *Field*: An allover geometrical pattern of interlacing bands, forming two swastikas and various polygonal compartments; in the spaces between the bands are floral scrolls. In the center of the field is a hexagon containing a bird and a floral stem; parts of similar hexagons containing birds, and star-shaped compartments containing floral scrolls and palmettes appear along the edges of the field. *Border*: A wavy floral scroll bearing large palmettes, large and small leaves, and blossoms. *Inner guard band*: A cross motif alternating with a stylized lotus bud. *Outer guard band*: A scrolling stem with alternating rosettes and blossoms.

PUBLISHED: Breck-Morris, no. 15.

Gift of James F. Ballard, the James F. Ballard Collection

22. 100. 73

58   FIGURE 133

Floral rug, first half of XVII century, period of Shah Jahan (1628–1658)

13′ 4″ × 5′ 6″

WARP: Silk

WEFT: Silk; 2 shoots after each row of knots

KNOTTING: Wool. Senna knot, about 462 knots per square inch

COLORS: 14. *Ground*: red (field), blue green (border), yellow (guard bands). *Pattern*: white, yellow, salmon pink, rose, wine red, red, light violet, dark violet, light blue, dark blue, blue green, light green, olive green, light brown.

DECORATION: *Field*: In the center, a vertical row of cartouches alternating with lobed eight-pointed stars, both motifs containing ornamental floral devices of seminaturalistic blossoms and leaves. Between the cartouches and stars are large composite palmettes. Along the sides of the field are portions of similar cartouches and stars, separated from the center by a pattern of wavy stems bearing large lanceolate leaves arranged in pairs around large rosette blossoms, palmettes, small naturalistic leaves, buds, roses, tulips, irises, lilies, peonies, violets, and bellflowers. *Border*: Naturalistic plants with leaves and blossoms, including roses, iris, carnations, lilies, and peonies. Between each plant, a pair of small cloud motifs. *Inner guard band*: A double wavy scroll with rosettes and blossoms. *Outer guard band*: Wavy scrolls with blossoms.

PUBLISHED: Dilley, pl. XXXII; Dimand, *Handbook*, fig. 202; Sarre-Trenkwald, II, pl. 57.

Bequest of Benjamin Altman

14. 40. 725

59   FIGURE 134, PAGE 150

Floral rug, early XVII century, period of Shah Jahan

14′ × 6′ 7″

WARP: Cotton

WEFT: Cotton; 3 shoots after each row of knots

KNOTTING: Wool. Senna knot, about 156 knots per square inch

COLORS: 11. *Ground*: crimson red (field, border), white (guard bands). *Pattern*: white, yellow, pink, red, light blue, dark blue, blue green, light green, green, brown.

DECORATION: *Field*: Seven rows of plants with blossoms and leaves, including carnations, lilies, tulips, iris, and roses. *Border*: A floral scroll bearing lanceolate leaves, blossoms, palmettes, and rosettes. *Guard bands*: Wavy scroll with small leaves.

PUBLISHED: Dimand, *Kevorkian Foundation*, pl. XIII.

EX COLL. Maharajah of Jaipur and Hagop Kevorkian

Purchase, Bequest of Florance Waterbury and Rogers Fund

1970. 321

60   FIGURE 136

Floral rug with trellis pattern (fragment), first half of XVII century, period of Shah Jahan

9′ 8″ × 4′ 6″

WARP: Silk

WEFT: Silk; 3 shoots after each row of knots

KNOTTING: Wool. Senna knot, about 1258 knots per square inch

COLORS: 12. *Ground*: wine red (field), yellow (border), dark blue green (guard bands). *Pattern*: white, cream white, yellow, pink, rose, wine red, light blue green, blue green, dark blue green, light green, light brown, black.

DECORATION: *Field*: An allover trellis formed by slender curved leaves; at the intersections, either a large composite rosette blossom or a leaf palmette. The trellis frame is superimposed on a background of floral scrolls whose spiraling stems bear leaves, blossoms, and at the center of each ogee-shaped compartment, a palmette or a composite blossom. *Border*: A sequence of naturalistic trees growing in a hilly landscape. The trees include pines and azaleas. Between each tree, a flowering plant and cloud motifs. *Guard bands*: A continuous wavy floral stem bearing leaves and blossoms.

PUBLISHED: Dilley, pl. XXXIV; Sarre-Trenkwald, II, pl. 58.

Bequest of Benjamin Altman

14.40.723

61   FIGURE 137

Floral rug with trellis pattern (fragment), early XVII century, period of Shah Jahan

9′ 11″ × 4′

WARP: Silk

WEFT: Silk; 3 shoots after each row of knots

KNOTTING: Wool. Senna knot, about 702 knots per square inch

COLORS: 10. *Ground*: red (field), blue green (border), white (guard bands). *Pattern*: white, cream white, tan, pink, rose, red, light purple, blue green, green, light brown.

DECORATION: *Field*: An allover trellis of curving bands forming a lozenge diaper. The background consists of slender curving stems bearing leaves and buds, with a large palmette or a blossom centered in each compartment. *Border*: Two intersecting floral scrolls bearing palmettes, blossoms, and leaves. *Guard band*: A wavy floral scroll bearing palmettes and leaves.

NOTE: Another fragment of this rug is in the Metropolitan: The Michael Friedsam Collecton, 32.100.457.

PUBLISHED: Dilley, pl. XXXI.

Bequest of Benjamin Altman

14.40.712

62   FIGURE 138

Floral rug with trellis pattern (fragments), early XVII century, period of Shah Jahan

4′ 11½″ × 1′ ¾″

WARP: Silk

WEFT: Silk; 3 shoots after each row of knots

KNOTTING: Wool. Senna knot, about 728 knots per square inch

COLORS: 8. *Ground*: red (field), blue green (border). *Pattern*: cream white, yellow, pink, red, dark blue, light green, light brown.

DECORATION: *Field*: A trellis pattern of acanthus leaf scrolls, each compartment enclosing a naturalistic blossoming plant. *Border*: Leaves and lotus blossoms.

Bequest of Benjamin Altman

14.40.713

63   FIGURE 140

Silk prayer rug (fragment), first half of XVII century, period of Shah Jahan

2′ 1½″ × 6″

WARP: Silk

WEFT: Silk; 2 shoots after each row of knots

KNOTTING: Silk. Senna knot, about 2552 knots per square inch

COLORS: 13. *Ground*: gray white (field), green (border), light tan (guard bands). *Pattern*: light tan, yellow, orange gold, rose, red, light blue, blue, dark blue, olive green, light green, green, dark green.

DECORATION: *Field*: Originally a prayer niche with two columns; the base of one is visible at the left. The niche contained a large plant in the center, probably a chrysanthemum with thistlelike leaves, with an irislike

plant at either side and a series of small flowering plants, all growing from a hilly ground. *Border*: Two intersecting scrolls with serrate leaves.

PUBLISHED: Sarre-Trenkwald, II, pl. 60.

Bequest of Benjamin Altman

14.40.722

64   BELOW

Floral rug (fragment), first half of XVII century, period of Shah Jahan

10′ 2″ × 2′ 10″

WARP: Silk

WEFT: Silk; 3 shoots after each row of knots

KNOTTING: Wool. Senna knot, about 780 knots per square inch

COLORS: 10. *Ground*: red (field), blue green (border), cream white (guard band). *Pattern*: white, cream white, yellow, pink, light red, red, light blue green, blue green, green, light brown.

DECORATION: *Field*: A pattern of floral scrolls bearing large leaf palmettes, large and small blossoms, and leaves. *Border*: A floral design of blossoms and leaves on stems, the stems overlaid with cloud motifs. *Guard band*: A wavy scroll bearing leaves and blossoms.

Bequest of Benjamin Altman

14. 40. 719

65   FIGURE 141

Floral rug, end of XVII century, period of Aurangzib

12′ 2″ × 8′ 7″

WARP: Cotton

WEFT: Cotton; 2 shoots after each row of knots

KNOTTING: Wool. Senna knot, about 240 knots per square inch

COLORS: 10. *Ground*: red (field), dark blue (border), cream white (guard bands). *Pattern*: cream white, tan, yellow, pink, red, light blue, dark blue, light green, green, brown.

DECORATION: *Field*: An allover millefleurs pattern of floral scrolls bearing palmettes and blossoms, including roses, carnations, violets, lilies, and iris. At intervals

the blossoms are grouped into symmetrical forms, chiefly a repeated oval compartment. *Border*: Intertwining lotus buds, blossoms, and leaves. *Guard bands*: A wavy floral scroll with leaves and blossoms. *Edgings*: A scroll.

Bequest of Benjamin Altman

14. 40. 714

66   FIGURE 142

Floral rug (fragment), end of XVII century, period of Aurangzib

8′ 7″ × 8′ 5″

WARP: Cotton

WEFT: Cotton; 2 shoots after each row of knots

KNOTTING: Wool. Senna knot, about 225 knots per square inch

COLORS: 10. *Ground*: red (field), dark blue (border), cream white (guard bands). *Pattern*: cream white, yellow, orange, pink, red, light blue, dark blue, light green, green, black.

DECORATION: *Field*: An allover millefleurs pattern of leafy stems bearing various palmettes and blossoms, including roses, carnations, violets, lilies, and iris. Many of the blossoms are grouped into symmetrical forms, chiefly a repeated oval compartment. *Border*: Intertwining lotus buds, blossoms, and leaves. *Guard bands*: A wavy floral scroll with leaves and blossoms. *Edgings*: A scroll.

Gift of F. H. Hirschland

44. 70

COLOR PLATES

Discussions of the nineteen rugs
illustrated in color in the following pages
will be found elsewhere in the book.

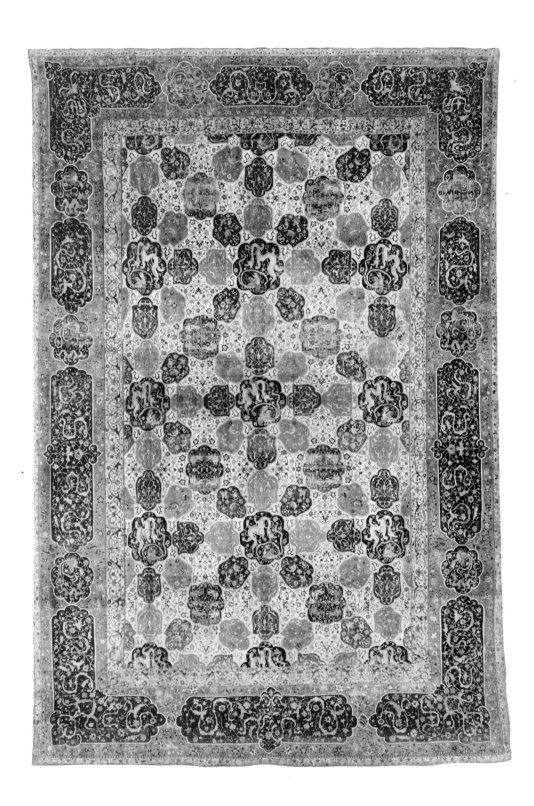

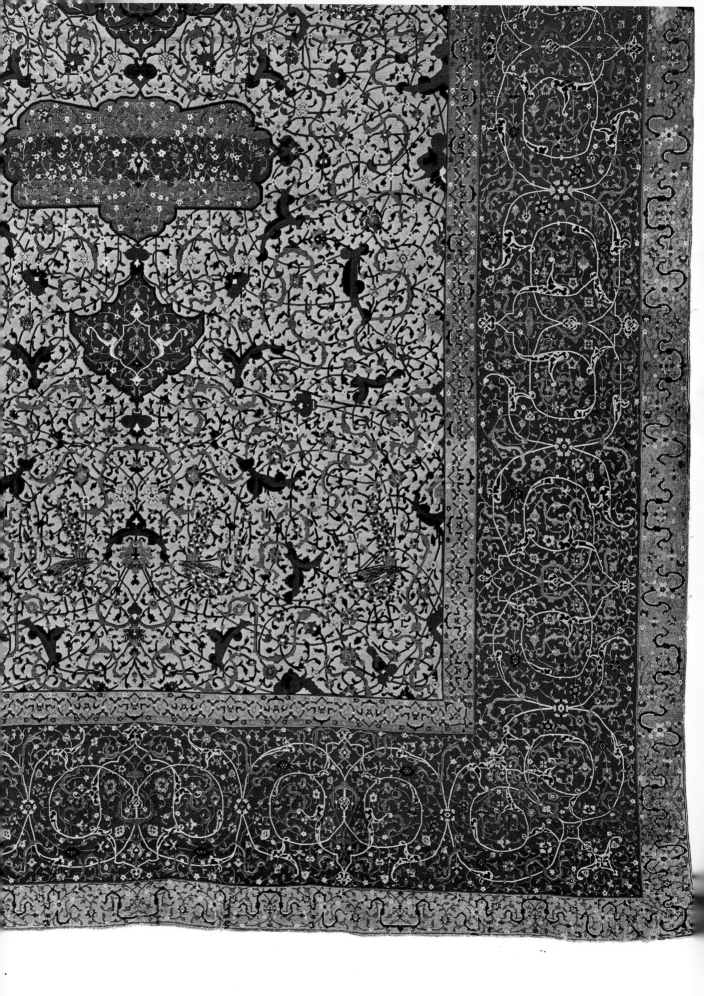

FIGURE 69

Medallion rug, Tabriz, Persia,
second half of XVI century.
Catalogue no. 7

FIGURE 71   Pair of medallion animal rugs with figure subjects,
probably Herat, Persia, second half of XVI century.
Catalogue nos. 9a (color), 9b

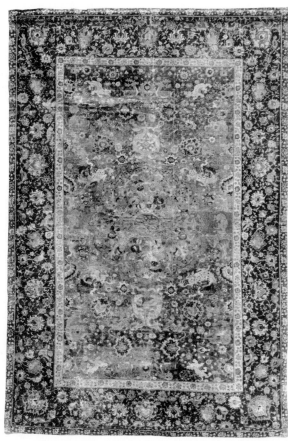

FIGURE 76

Animal and floral rug, Herat,
Persia, middle of XVI century.
Catalogue no. 12

FIGURE 79   Silk animal rug, Kashan, Persia, second half of XVI century.
Catalogue no. 13

FIGURE 87 Pair of silk compartment rugs ("Polish"), Isfahan, Persia,
first quarter of XVII century.
Catalogue nos. 20a (color), 20b

FIGURE 115 Garden rug, Kurdistan, Persia, first half of XVIII century.
Catalogue no. 44

FIGURE 129   Floral rug, Lahore, India,
beginning of XVII century.
Catalogue no. 55

FIGURE 134

Floral rug, India,
first half of XVII century.
Catalogue no. 59

FIGURE 163   Arabesque and floral rug with star medallions,
Ushak, Turkey, end of XVI century.
Catalogue no. 72

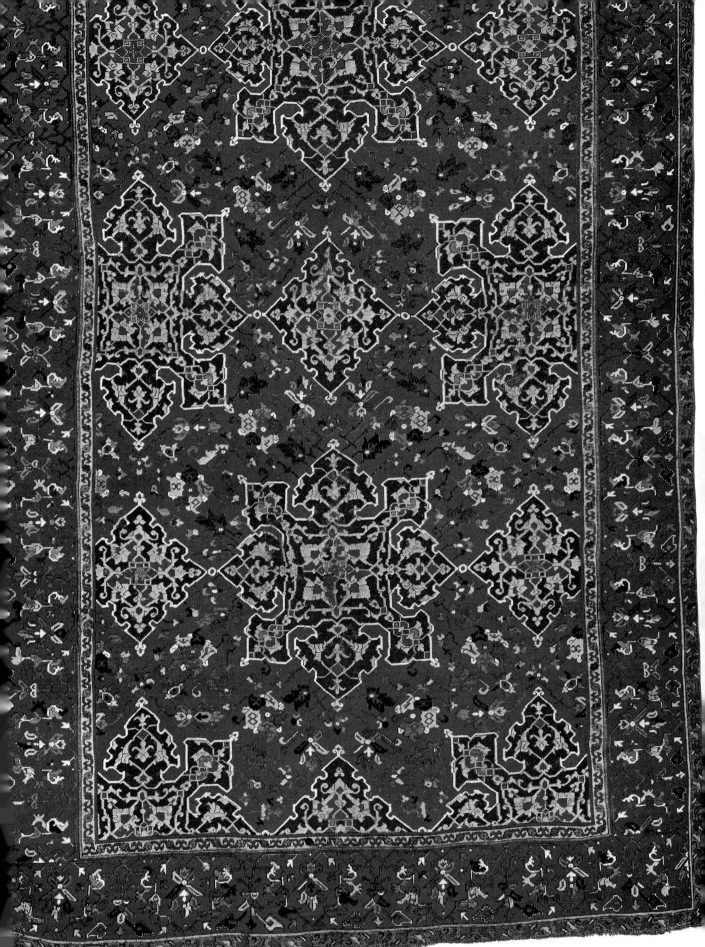

FIGURE 181　Geometrical rug, so-called Mamluk, probably Cairo, beginning of XVI century. Catalogue no. 97

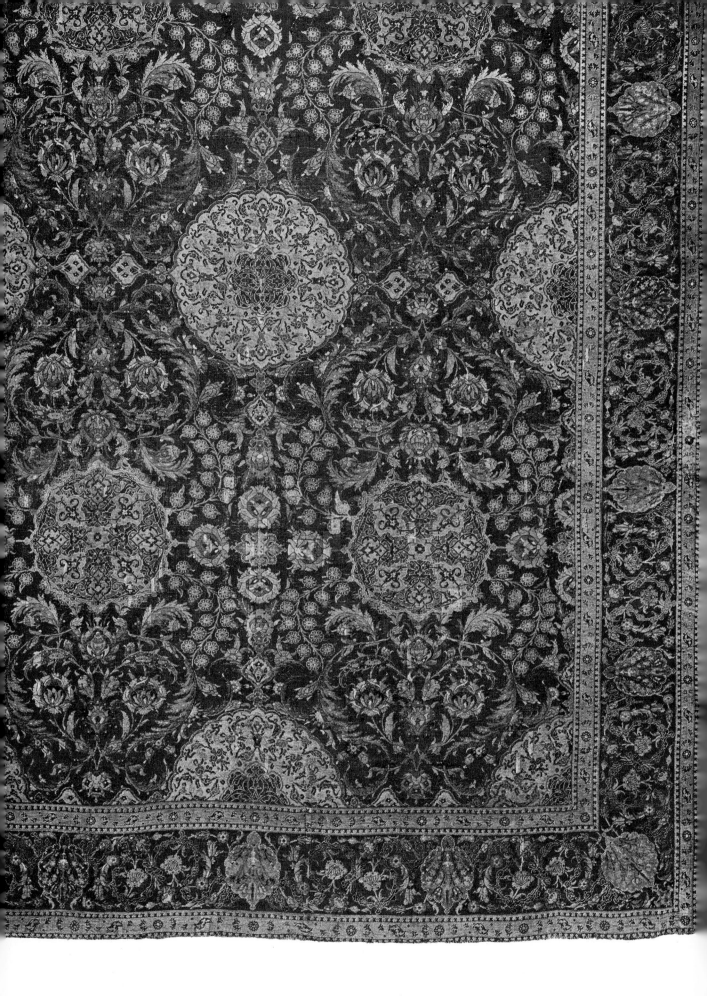

FIGURE 184

Floral rug, court manufactory,
Brusa or Istanbul,
Turkey, middle of xvi century.
Catalogue no. 103

FIGURE 222 Arabesque rug,
Alcaraz, Spain, end of xv century.
Catalogue no. 153

FIGURE 231 Floral compartment rug,
probably Kuba, the Caucasus,
first half of XVII century.
Catalogue no. 164

FIGURE 268   Rug, Ming style, China, XVII century.
              Catalogue no. 199

FIGURE 285   Rug, China, Ch'ien-lung period (1735–1795).
            Catalogue no. 207

FIGURE 294   End border of rug, China, early XIX century.
Catalogue no. 220

FIGURE 306   Rug, Chinese Turkestan, late XVIII–early XIX century.
             Catalogue no. 231

Seven:

OTTOMAN RUGS OF TURKEY

In the second half of the thirteenth century, after nearly two hundred years of dominance in Asia Minor, the Seljuks of Rum were made the vassals of the Mongols of Persia. Ten petty dynasties then succeeded the Seljuks, and the rulers of these dynasties divided the kingdom of Rum among themselves. One of these dynasties, that of the Othmanli or Ottoman Turks, whose founder was Othman (1299–1326), gradually absorbed the other nine and eventually inherited the religious power of the caliphate. Pushing back the Byzantine frontiers, the Ottomans made the Byzantine city of Brusa (or Bursa), in Asia Minor, their capital in 1326. By 1366 the Ottoman flag and that of Islam had been carried into Europe, and the Ottoman capital was Adrianople (present-day Edirne). In 1453, under Sultan Mehmet II, the Ottomans took Constantinople, renamed it Istanbul, and made it their capital. In 1516–1517 the Ottoman empire was extended to the south, Selim I overrunning Syria, taking the cities of Aleppo and Damascus, then conquering Egypt. Under Selim's son and successor, Suleiman the Magnificent, the Turks resumed their advance in Europe, capturing Belgrade in 1521 and laying siege to Vienna in 1529. A second attempt to take Vienna was made in 1683. With the termination of this campaign the Turks abandoned their tents, leaving behind them many fine silks, velvets, and rugs. A number of these rugs, which were of Persian as well as Turkish manufacture, are known today, including those of figures 69 and 91.

The Ottomans were great patrons of the arts and crafts, and the many splendid mosques and palaces of Brusa, Edirne, and Istanbul are vivid monuments to the development of Islamic art under Ottoman patronage. Many centers for ceramic and textile production were established, beginning in the fourteenth century. The looms of Brusa produced magnificent brocades and velvets for the garments of the sultans. In various centers in Asia Minor, chiefly in the province of Anatolia, wool rugs were manufactured, the industry based to a great extent on the Seljuk tradition. Western Europe, which had imported Anatolian rugs as early as the end of the thirteenth century, imported the Ottoman rugs in quantity, chiefly through Venice and Genoa.

ANATOLIAN ANIMAL RUGS (FOURTEENTH AND FIFTEENTH CENTURIES)

Two main types may be differentiated among early Ottoman rugs: one with animal decoration, the other with a geometrical pattern only. It is quite probable that the production of animal rugs had begun earlier, in the Seljuk period. Animal decoration was popular in Seljuk art of the twelfth and thirteenth centuries, particularly in silk textiles, metalwork, and ceramics. Although only fragments of the Ottoman animal rugs have survived, the rugs themselves are represented in numerous Italian and Spanish paintings, in which they appear in use as

173

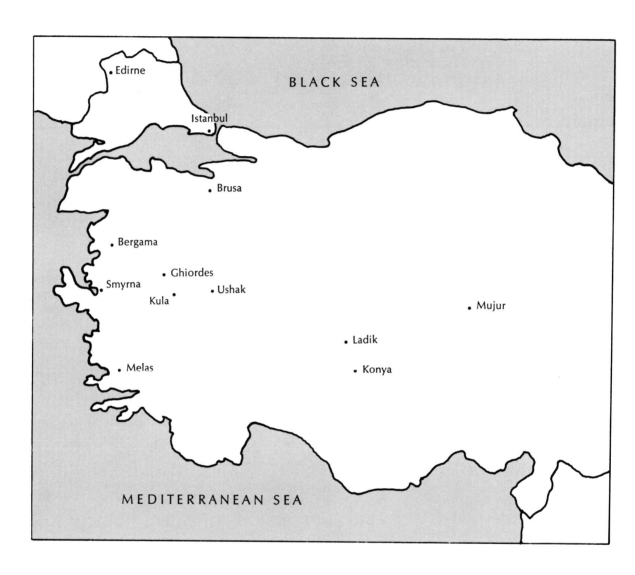

BLACK SEA

Edirne

Istanbul

Brusa

Bergama

Ghiordes

Smyrna
Ushak

Kula

Mujur

Ladik

Konya

Melas

MEDITERRANEAN SEA

FIGURE 143   The Madonna and Child, by Giovanni di Paolo, xv century. The Metropolitan Museum of Art, Bequest of George Blumenthal, 41.190.16

floor or table coverings, on the steps of thrones of the Madonna or altars, or hung from windows and balconies on festive occasions. These representations, which have been carefully studied,[1] yield valuable information. All of the rugs, the actual fragments as well as the painted likenesses, have strongly stylized birds or animals within square or octagonal compartments. Rugs with single birds appear in several fourteenth- and fifteenth-century Italian paintings—for example, a Marriage of the Virgin by Nicolo di Buonaccorso (about 1348), in the National Gallery, London, and an early fifteenth-century fresco of the Annunciaton in the church of Santa Annunziata, Florence.[2] Other paintings show rugs with pairs of birds, usually eagles, separated by trees—for example, a Madonna by Sano di Pietro in the Pinacoteca Vaticana, Rome, a Madonna by Lippo Memmi (about 1350) in the Staatliche Museen, Berlin,[3] and a Madonna and Child by Giovanni di Paolo (figure 143). Still other paintings show rugs in which single, angularly stylized beasts of prey, possibly lions, appear in rectangles or octagons of various colors—a painting by Giovanni di Paolo in the Galleria Doria, Rome, and several paintings by Ambrogio Lorenzetti (active 1323–1348), notably a Madonna and Child in the Academy of Fine Arts, Siena.[4]

Of the surviving fragments of these rugs, what is perhaps the earliest one—it was found at Fustat, Egypt, and can be dated to the fourteenth century—has a single geometrically stylized bird in tan, green, and red within a blue green octagon (figure 144). It is tied with the Ghiordes knot. A fragment datable to the fifteenth century, found in an Italian church and now in the Staatliche Museen, Berlin,[5] has two octagonal compartments, each containing a dragon and phoenix in combat. The ground color is yellow. The animals, strongly stylized, are rendered in blue with red edging, white details, and dark brown outlines. The hook motifs that adorn the animals became a characteristic feature of many peasant rugs of Asia Minor in the eighteenth and nineteenth centuries. The pattern of this rug appears in a fresco by Domenico di Bartolo in the hospital of Santa Maria della Scala in Siena, painted between 1440 and 1444,[6] and it is echoed in another of the fragments found in

FIGURE 144   Geometrical animal rug (fragment), Anatolia, xiv century. Catalogue no. 67

FIGURE 145   Madonna and Child with Saints
(detail), 1455–1456, by Jaume Huguet. Museo de Arte
de Cataluña, Barcelona

Fustat, datable to the fifteenth century.[7] Still another
fragment, also datable to the fifteenth century, was
found in a church at Marby, Sweden, and is now in
the Statens Historiska Museum, Stockholm.[8] It has
two octagonal compartments, each containing two
confronted geometrically stylized birds separated by
a palmette tree. The ground is yellow, the colors of
the pattern yellow, blue, red, and green. This piece
and the Berlin fragment both have the remains of a
long nap at the back, a technical feature indicating,
according to one writer,[9] that the rugs came from
the same workshop.

Anatolian rugs with geometrically stylized birds,
known in Spain, were depicted by the fifteenth-
century Catalonian artist Jaume Huguet. In one of
his paintings the birds are not enclosed in octagons,
as they are in the Marby rug, but arranged in rows
(figure 145). Even so, the stylization of the birds is
strongly reminiscent of the Marby fragment. This
painting and others offer proof that Spain was familiar with Anatolian animal rugs by the mid-fifteenth
century. Geometrically stylized cocks or peacocks
similar to those of the Huguet painting occur in a
Turkish rug in the Mevlana Museum, Konya. The
birds, arranged in ten rows, are rendered in various
colors on a bright red ground. This rug has been

dated to the fifteenth century,[10] and also, because of
its similarity to the Huguet rug, to the end of the
fifteenth or the early part of the sixteenth century.[11]
However, my examination of the actual rug convin-
ces me that both these datings are much too early. Its
design, colors, and material all point to a later period,
probably not much earlier than the seventeenth
century. Accordingly, it may be regarded as a copy of
a fifteenth-century Anatolian rug.

GEOMETRICAL RUGS, INCLUDING "HOLBEINS" (FOURTEENTH CENTURY TO SIXTEENTH)

Contemporary with the animal rugs of the fourteenth and fifteenth centuries were those with geometrical patterns—patterns that assumed a wide
variety of forms. In two fourteenth-century paintings
of the Giotto school, one in the Santo Spirito, Prato,
the other in Assisi,[12] rugs with diapers of squares are
depicted. In the first there is a swastika meander
within the squares, in the second a lozenge containing
a square. A fresco of the Annunciation in the church
of Santa Maria Novella, Florence,[13] has a rug with
square compartments in various colors containing

FIGURE 146   Virgin and Child with Saints and a
Donor (detail), by Jan van Eyck (1422–1441).
Copyright The Frick Collection, New York

cruciform medallions with hook motifs. Moving on from this simple division of the field into squares, we find in paintings by Jan van Eyck rugs with lozenge diapers formed by bands. His Madonna and Child in the Gemäldegalerie Alte Meister, Dresden,[14] and his Virgin and Child in the Frick Collection (figure 146) depict rugs with such diapers enclosing rosettes. Lozenge diapers, already known in thirteenth-century Seljuk rugs (figures 25, 26), continued to be popular in the sixteenth and seventeenth centuries, as seen in several rugs attributed to the district of Ushak (figure 171). In another painting by van Eyck, the Madonna of Canon van der Paele (finished 1436) in the Groeninge Museum, Bruges,[15] there appears a rug in which interlacings form various angular compartments filled with large star motifs and rosettes.

A number of the fifteenth-century fragments found in Fustat have allover patterns in which various kinds of polygons are arranged in staggered rows.[16] This decoration, not then new, had occurred in Seljuk rugs (figures 28, 29).

During the fifteenth century, as geometrical gradually replaced animal rugs, their designs became more complicated. Some of the geometrical rugs are now called, for convenience' sake, "Holbeins," because they are represented in several sixteenth-century paintings by Hans Holbein the Younger. Actually, such rugs were known in Europe well before Holbein's time, for they appear frequently in Italian, Flemish, and Spanish paintings of the fifteenth century—for example, a Madonna and Child by Ghirlandaio in the Uffizi Gallery, Florence, a fresco of 1485 by Vincenzo Foppa in the Brera, Milan, and a painting of the Annunciation by Carlo Crivelli, in the National Gallery, London.[17] As depicted, the rugs are usually of small size and vigorous color scheme, with white, red, blue, and yellow predominating. In the paintings of Hans Memling there occur a number of interesting geometrical rugs whose designs survived in eighteenth- and nineteenth-century rugs of Turkey and the Caucasus. Memling's Madonna Enthroned, in the Uffizi Gallery,[18] shows a rug with lozenges formed by arabesques in white, red, and blue, arranged in staggered rows as in some of the Fustat fragments mentioned above. His Madonna of about 1470 (figure 147) has a rug with squares containing octagons filled with cross-shaped polygons, with a series of angular hooks adorning the polygons. This pattern continued for centuries in Turkey and the Caucasus, surviving in Bergama-type rugs of the eighteenth and nineteenth centuries in Turkey, and in

Kazaks and other types of Caucasian rugs (figure 240). To a certain extent it is also seen in Turkoman rugs of the nineteenth century (figure 247).

Other paintings by Memling show variations of the pattern of octagons within squares, related to the so-called "Holbeins." One, the octagons of which are filled with an elaborate design, appears in his Betrothal of Saint Catherine, of 1479 (figure 148). The rug

FIGURE 147 Madonna and Child with Angel and Donor (detail), about 1470, by Hans Memling. Kunsthistorisches Museum, Vienna

FIGURE 148 Design of an octagon rug in the Betrothal of Saint Catherine, 1479, by Hans Memling. Hospital of Saint John, Bruges

FIGURE 149   Saint Ursula and the Prince Taking Leave of their Parents (detail), 1495, by Vittore Carpaccio. Gallerie dell' Accademia, Venice. Photograph: Anderson-Art Reference Bureau

shows two squares in its width; it probably had three in its long dimension. Each square contains an octagon. The octagon has trefoils along its exterior sides and contains a star and interlacings. These in turn form an octagonal device whose points end in palmettes. The border of the rug, decorated with a meander in squares, also appears in a fifteenth-century rug fragment from Beyshehir mosque, now in the Mevlana Museum, Konya.[19] Similar rugs, among other Anatolian types, are represented in paintings by Carpaccio, particularly in his Ursula series. Two of the rugs in his Departure of Saint Ursula, dated 1495, have octagons with central stars, interlacings and palmettes (figure 149), not unlike those in one of the Memling rugs. In a late fifteenth-century painting by an unknown Flemish master a geometrical "Holbein" is depicted in detail (figure 150). Holbein himself depicted such a rug in his painting of the Two Ambassadors in the National Gallery, London.[20] An actual rug of this type is in the McIlhenny Collection of the Philadelphia Museum of Art (figure 151). For some time this piece was wrongly regarded as Hispano-Moresque, despite its Ghiordes knot and other characteristics of early Anatolian rugs. Its red field has three squares containing double octagons. In the center of each octagon is a star surrounded by eight palmettes in blue and green. Surrounding this is an elaborate framework of bands containing geometrical S-motifs, rectangles, and red stars. Along the outer edge of this framework are trefoils, as in other "Holbeins" of this type, and in the spandrels of the squares are interlacings in red and green. The inner blue border of the rug has an intermittent scroll with trefoils in red. The red outer border is decorated with simulated Kufic whose verticals are connected by ovals, alternating with four-petaled rosettes. Identical borders appear in "Holbeins" depicted by Domenico Ghirlandaio and other fifteenth-century Italian painters. The McIlhenny "Holbein," probably the earliest extant example of this type of Anatolian geometrical rug, can be dated to the second half of the fifteenth century. Perhaps of nearly the same date is a "Holbein" in the Museum

FIGURE 150 The Mass of Saint Giles (detail), by the Flemish Master of Saint Giles, end of xv century. Courtesy of the Trustees, The National Gallery, London

of Turkish and Islamic Art, Istanbul (figure 152); another "Holbein" dating to the beginning of the seventeenth century is in the same museum.[21] A "Holbein" of about the sixteenth century, in the Staatliche Museen, Berlin, has been assigned to the district of Bergama.[22] Rugs with similar octagons were made here as late as the nineteenth century, and it is quite possible that the "Holbeins" with octagons were made in Bergama. In Spain, during the fifteenth

century, such rugs were copied by the Moorish weavers of Alcaraz (page 254).

In addition to the "Holbeins" with a large-scale design of geometrical octagons within squares, there is a type with a small design consisting of interlaced arabesques forming lozenge-shaped devices. Each compartment contains an octagon whose outline forms a series of heart-shaped knots. In the center of the octagon is a star motif, and smaller star motifs appear in the intervening spaces. The ground color of the field is usually blue or red, occasionally green. The colors of the design are yellow, blue, green, red, and white. A rug of this type is depicted by Holbein

FIGURE 151   Geometrical "Holbein" rug, Anatolian, second half of xv century. Philadelphia Museum of Art, McIlhenny Collection

FIGURE 152   Geometrical "Holbein" rug, Anatolian, second half of xv century. Museum of Turkish and Islamic Art, Istanbul

in his portrait of Georg Gisze (1532) in the Staatliche Museen, Berlin (figure 153). An especially fine example, known as the Wulff rug after its former owner,[23] is in the collection of Mrs. Walter Rosen, New York. Other examples are in the Museum of Turkish and Islamic Art, Istanbul (a fifteenth-century rug), the Williams Collection in the Philadelphia Museum of Art, and the City Art Museum, St. Louis; another was formerly in the Staatliche Museen, Berlin.[24] In some of these the squares are defined by a change of color, such as green alternating with red, a treatment also found in Persian rugs of the fourteenth and fifteenth centuries, as represented in Mongol and Timurid miniature paintings (figures 45, 55). The borders of this second type of "Holbein" have several kinds of ornament derived from Kufic writing. One has interlacings, another Kufic letters ending in half-palmettes interlaced with ovals, alternating with four-petaled rosettes. The latter border can be seen in the fifteenth-century rug in the Museum of Turkish and Islamic Art, mentioned above, and in rugs in several paintings by Domenico Ghirlandaio, including a Madonna and Child in the Museo Nazio-

nale, Naples, and a fresco in the Church of Ognissanti, Florence.[25] Other fine examples of this type of "Holbein" rug occur in a Madonna and Child (1480) by Lorenzo di Credi in the Cathedral of Pistoia, a Madonna and Child by Mantegna in the church of San Zeno, Verona, and a portrait by Dosso Dossi in the National Gallery, Rome.[26]

In a small group of these rugs large-scale and small-scale "Holbein" designs are combined. One such rug is in the Museum of Turkish and Islamic Art in Istanbul (figure 154).

A frequent feature in the "Holbeins" with small-scale designs is the arabesque. Although arabesques were popular in Seljuk textiles of the twelfth and thirteenth centuries, they did not appear, so far as is known, in Seljuk rugs. Apparently they were first used in rugs in the Ottoman period.

Still another type of geometrical rug was made, one in which there are five octagons in the field—a large central one with four smaller surrounding ones—and in which large-scale and small-scale patterns are combined. Such a rug appears in a painting by Carpaccio representing the Embassy of Hippolyta, in the Musée Jacquemart-André, Paris.[27] In a fine rug of this type (figure 155), blue octagons filled with geometrical interlacings in white, yellow, and brown appear on a red field, along with a pattern of cypresses alternating with palmettes. The red border has interlaced Kufic with half-palmettes, as do some of the "Holbeins." Several scholars have classified this rug and similar ones as Egyptian, but their design, including the typically Anatolian Kufic border, and their Ghiordes knot technique show that this attribution could not be correct.

The cypresses and palmettes of the field constitute a link with still another type of early seventeenth-century geometrical rug with eight-pointed stars. Such a rug appears in Lorenzo Lotto's portrait of the Protonotary Juliano (figure 156). A fragment of one of the actual rugs is in the Textile Museum, Washington.[28] Despite the fact that the rugs of this particular group are tied with the Senna knot, their design clearly indicates that they should be assigned to the looms of Anatolia, not Egypt.

Related to the Anatolian rugs just discussed and also to the geometrical "Mamluk" rugs to be discussed further on is a group of sixteenth-century compartment rugs whose red fields are usually

FIGURE 153   Portrait of Georg Gisze, 1532, by Hans Holbein. Staatliche Museen, Berlin

FIGURE 154   Geometrical "Holbein" rug, Anatolian, XVI century. Museum of Turkish and Islamic Art, Istanbul

FIGURE 155   Geometrical rug, Anatolian, XVI century. Philadelphia Museum of Art, photograph by
A. J. Wyatt, staff photographer

FIGURE 156   Portrait of the Protonotary Juliano, by
Lorenzo Lotto (1480–1556). Courtesy of the Trustees,
The National Gallery, London

similarities to the Anatolian "Holbeins." As for the
term "Rhodian," it may well be that this was simply
a commercial designation for Anatolian rugs that
were exported via Rhodes.

USHAK RUGS (SIXTEENTH CENTURY THROUGH EIGHTEENTH)

In the sixteenth and seventeenth centuries several
types of Anatolian rugs were imported to Europe
under a variety of names: Damascus (or Damascene)
carpets, Smyrna carpets, and Turkey carpets. None
of these names points specifically to the rugs' place
of origin. Damascene, especially as it was used in
Venetian inventories, meant any Turkish rug of
brilliant color, while Smyrna denoted simply that the
rugs were shipped from this port in western Asia
Minor. The particular types of rugs were distinctive
in a number of ways from the rugs so far discussed,

FIGURE 157   Geometrical rug, Anatolian, XVI
century. Catalogue no. 96

divided into squares containing either hexagons or
octagons, with central eight-pointed stars and crosses
the hexagons or octagons surrounded by cypress
trees. Such a rug may be seen in a painting of the
second half of the sixteenth century by Il Moro, the
Circumcision of Christ in the Academy, Venice.[29]
The number of compartments in these rugs varies
greatly. An example in the City Art Museum, St.
Louis, has but three, one in the Metropolitan has
nine (figure 157), one of several examples in the
Textile Museum, Washington, has twenty-eight, and
one in the Bardini Museum, Florence, has thirty-
two.[30] The borders of these rugs, usually blue, have
either a floral design of the type to be found in
sixteenth- and seventeenth-century rugs attributed to
Ushak (see below), or a series of cartouches and
rosettes such as appear in other Anatolian rugs of this
time. All the rugs of this group are tied with the
Senna knot rather than the Ghiordes. Despite this
technical difference, the rugs should be assigned to
some unknown center in Anatolia. In the past, called
"compartment rugs in the Egyptian manner,"[31] they
have been linked with the "Rhodian" rugs that are
mentioned in old records. However, this ignores their

and all may be attributed to the district of Ushak. There is documentary evidence that such rugs reached England as early as the first quarter of the sixteenth century. According to the report of Sebastian Giustiniani, Venetian ambassador to England, Cardinal Wolsey was anxious in 1519 to obtain one hundred "Damascene" carpets from the Signory in Venice. In October, 1520, the cardinal received from Venice sixty rugs of the Ushak variety. Such rugs are to be seen in several contemporary English paintings, in use both as table covers and floor covers.

Because the arabesque, star, and medallion Ushaks were the first oriental rugs imported to England, all such rugs, including Persian ones, became known there as "Turkey" carpets.

The arabesque rug attributed to Ushak usually has, upon a vermillion field, an overall pattern of angular arabesques in yellow, forming a series of quatrefoils and polygons. As in the "Holbeins," the patterns are arranged in rows. The borders, particularly of sixteenth-century examples, have simulated Kufic writing with the verticals of the letters ending in half-palmettes (figure 158). In other rugs the borders have geometrical interlacings derived from Kufic. In still others the border may have a floral pattern,

FIGURE 158   Arabesque rug ("Lotto"), Ushak, end of xvi century. Catalogue no. 68

FIGURE 159   Detail of arabesque rug ("Lotto"), Ushak, xvi century. Courtesy of The Art Institute of Chicago

as in a painting by Girolamo dai Libri in the Museo Civico, Verona, or a series of interlacings with cartouches, as in a painting by Evaristo Baschenis in Bergamo.[32] The borders of other arabesque Ushaks have cloud bands.

The arabesque Ushaks have sometimes been called "Holbeins," although they are not to be found in any of that master's paintings. In the United States they have for some time been known as "Lottos," for the reason that they appear in paintings by Lorenzo Lotto (1480–1556), for example, a painting of a family group (about 1515) in the National Gallery, London.[33] They are also to be found in other Venetian paintings and in Flemish paintings from the early sixteenth century to the end of the seventeenth. Although most "Lottos" are of small size, larger pieces are known. One such is in the Art Institute of Chicago (figure 159), another was formerly in the Staatliche Museen, Berlin.[34]

The finest of these rugs belong to the sixteenth century. In seventeenth century examples the angularity of the half-palmettes increases, and the design of the border changes from Kufic to large cartouches with lilylike blossoms (figure 160). Vermeer depicts a similar rug in his Lady Sleeping (figure 161). Other seventeenth-century arabesque rugs have cloud bands in their borders. In the late seventeenth-century examples the design is even coarser, and

FIGURE 160   Arabesque rug ("Lotto"), Ushak, first half of XVII century. Catalogue no. 70

FIGURE 161   Girl Asleep, by Jan Vermeer (1632–1675). The Metropolitan Museum of Art, Bequest of Benjamin Altman, 14.40.611

the borders are often too large in relation to the fields.

Some of the "Lottos" have coats of arms of European families, indicating that they were woven to the order of Western patrons. A rug bearing the alliance arms of the Genoese families of Doria and Centurione (figure 162) is one of three so decorated; the others are in the state collection of Poland,

Wroclaw, and the Museum für Kunst und Gewerbe, Hamburg.[35] All have the same floral border and may be dated to about 1600. Other "Lottos" with coats of arms may be seen in two paintings of the seventeenth century: one by Volterrano, in the Uffizi Gallery, Florence, the other by G. B. Crespi, in the Tesoro del Duomo, Milan.[36]

The so-called star Ushaks constitute an important group of Anatolian rugs. Most of them have dark red fields decorated with star-shaped, eight-pointed, lobed medallions in dark blue, alternating with smaller lozenge-shaped panels. Both the medallions and the panels are filled with interlaced arabesques bearing half-palmettes in yellow (figure 163, page 152). The rest of the field is covered with angular floral scrolls bearing palmettes and leaves in white, yellow, blue, red, and green. The blue borders usually contain floral scrolls similar to those in the field. In composition and design these rugs were influenced in many ways by Persian designs. The star medallions recall the star-shaped tiles in Persian faïence mosaics of Tabriz and Ardabil, while the floral scrolls and palmettes resemble those of early Safavid rugs, known to the Ottomans in the first half of the sixteenth century as a result of their conquests in Persia. In 1514 Selim I took Tabriz, and in 1534 Suleiman the Magnificent occupied the city again. On both occasions Persian art objects, including rugs, were removed to Istanbul, as were also Persian artists and craftsmen.

The star Ushaks, exported to Europe since early in the sixteenth century, were popular there for a long period, as we know from their representations in Italian, Spanish, Dutch, and English paintings from the middle of the sixteenth century to the end of the seventeenth. An early instance is a painting of 1535 by Paris Bordone, in the Academy, Venice, showing a fisherman restoring a ring to the doge, who is enthroned on a star Ushak.[37] A portrait of Henry VIII and Jane Seymour at Hampton Court includes a star Ushak with a Kufic border, and a portrait of Henry VIII at Belvoir Castle shows him standing upon a star Ushak.[38]

In the collection of the Duke of Buccleuch are three rugs of the star Ushak type bearing the coat of arms of his ancestor, Sir Edward Montagu. Two of these rugs bear dates: 1584 and 1585.[39] There has been disagreement as to the origin of these rugs. A number of German authorities held that they were made in Anatolia, whereas English authorities, in particular Tattersall, advanced reasons for regarding them as of English make. The letters E. B. and A. N.

FIGURE 162 Arabesque rug ("Lotto") with coat of arms, Ushak, late XVI or early XVII century. Catalogue no. 69

FIGURE 164 Arabesque and floral rug with star medallions, Ushak, beginning of XVII century. Catalogue no. 74

FIGURE 165 Arabesque rug with star medallion, Ushak, end of XVII century. Catalogue no. 75

woven into various parts of the borders and fields are, according to Tattersall, initials of English weavers. Furthermore, the designs of the rugs, although copied rather faithfully from Turkish originals, appear elongated. Finally, the warp is of hemp, not wool as in Turkish rugs. According to this evidence, we must regard these rugs as English copies of Turkish originals. These were perhaps made in Norwich, famous for its wool weavings.

There are star Ushaks of small size whose fields contain only two stars, or even only one. These rugs, which usually have inferior designs (figures 164, 165), are probably of a later period and should be dated to the seventeenth century, some perhaps even to the eighteenth.

Another type of Ushak usually has a large central oval medallion, the rest of the field filled with star-shaped medallions and portions of medallions (figure 166). In some examples two smaller medallions may be centered on the long axis (figure 167). The medallions, usually red, sometimes blue, are filled with arabesques intertwined with floral scrolls with

FIGURE 166   Medallion rug, Ushak, first half of XVII century. Catalogue no. 76

FIGURE 167   Arabesque and floral medallion rug, Ushak, middle of XVII century. Catalogue no. 77

stylized leaves and flowers, usually in yellow, with the addition of other colors. A great number of these rugs, most of them of large size, found their way into Italian, Spanish, and Portuguese churches during the sixteenth and seventeenth centuries. And like the star Ushaks and arabesque Ushaks, these rugs appear in Flemish and Spanish paintings from the second

half of the sixteenth century through the seventeenth.

The medallion Ushaks range in date from the sixteenth century through the eighteenth, with a gradual deterioration in design and colors. Such changes help in the dating of various specimens. For example, the rug of figure 166 may be assigned to the first half of the seventeenth century, while the rug of figure 167 may be assigned to the mid-seventeenth century. A medallion Ushak with a Polish coat of arms, dated by Ernst Kühnel to about 1700, is in the Staatliche Museen, Berlin.⁴⁰ Rugs like these, often known in the trade as Smyrna carpets, continued to be popular throughout the eighteenth century in Holland, France, and England. An eighteenth-

palmettes in blue and red (figure 168). They should be dated to the second half of the eighteenth century or the beginning of the nineteenth.

Related in design to the Ushak rugs is a group of small Anatolian rugs, most of which have a small central medallion with a prayer niche symmetrically balanced at either end. In some of these rugs an

FIGURE 168   Palmette rug, Smyrna, end of XVIII or beginning of XIX century. Catalogue no. 82

FIGURE 169   Prayer rug, Ushak, beginning of XVII century. Catalogue no. 83

century example occurs in a portrait of Maria Luisa of Parma by Laurent Pécheux (1765), in the Metropolitan.

To the looms of Smyrna are usually assigned rugs with a different design. Made for the Dutch market, these show, on a yellow ground, a design of large

ornament in one of the niches indicates a mosque lamp (figure 169). Such rugs appear in European paintings from the middle of the sixteenth century to the middle of the seventeenth. Arabesques or cloud bands appear in the spandrels of these rugs, and the borders have either cloud bands or a floral

FIGURE 170 Prayer rug with palmette design, Ushak, beginning of XVII century. Catalogue no. 84

FIGURE 171 Geometrical rug, Ushak, XVII century. Catalogue no. 85

decoration familiar from other Ushak rugs. The colors are usually deep: the fields red, the borders blue, the spandrels blue, red, or green.

In some of the rare examples of small Ushaks the field has an allover pattern of palmettes. In a prayer rug of this type (figure 170) the red field is covered with rows of slender vertical stems that send off palmettes horizontally. Stems also form the niche. The deep blue border has arabesques and palmettes, a design seen in other Ushak rugs. A rug with similar decoration, though without a prayer niche, is in the McMullan collection.[41] Another small Ushak (figure 171) has a lozenge diaper of stems with stars enclosing smaller stars at each intersection. Each lozenge contains a large, leafy, star-centered rosette.

Two related groups of rugs distinguished chiefly by their having cream white grounds are usually assigned to the Ushak district. The better-known are the so-called "bird rugs." In these, large blossom rosettes, alternating with pairs of arabesque palmette devices that suggest double-headed birds, form a sort of square diaper filled with rosettes, buds, and leaves. The borders have either cloud bands (figure 172) or stylized palmettes (figure 173). The colors are usually limited to tan, orange or brown, blue, and olive green. Such rugs appear in European paintings from the middle of the sixteenth century to the first half of the seventeenth, one of the earliest representations occurring in a portrait of about 1557 by Hans Mielich (figure 174).

FIGURE 172 "Bird rug," probably Ushak, end of XVI century. Catalogue no. 86

FIGURE 173 "Bird rug," probably Ushak, about 1600. Catalogue no. 87

In the second group of rugs with cream white grounds there appears a repeat pattern of three balls above two wavy bands. In Turkish inventories these bands are called tiger stripes, while the balls and bands as a unit are sometimes referred to as the Badge of Timur. Known also as the ball-and-lightning motif, this decoration appeared not only in Ushak rugs but in brocades and velvets of Brusa from the fifteenth century on. The rugs, some of which are of large size, are to be found in the Williams Collection in the Philadelphia Museum of Art, the collection of Prince Schwarzenberg, Vienna, the Bardini Museum, Florence, and (one with a red background) in the Museum of Turkish and Islamic Art, Istanbul.[42]

BERGAMA RUGS (SEVENTEENTH CENTURY TO NINETEENTH)

Two types of small Anatolian rugs, one a prayer rug, the other geometrical, are usually attributed to the looms of Bergama (Pergamon). Along with other types of Anatolian rugs these were found in Transylvania after this region was won back from the Ottomans. For this reason they are often called Transylvanian or Siebenbürgen (the German for Transyl-

FIGURE 174   Portrait, about 1557, by Hans Mielich. Collection of Mrs. Rush H. Kress, New York

FIGURE 175   Arabesque rug, Bergama, end of xvi or beginning of xvii century. Catalogue no. 88

vania).[43] Many of them came from Transylvanian churches and are now in the Hungarian National Museum of Applied Arts, Budapest.

A unique geometrical rug, perhaps the earliest existing Bergama rug, has an allover design of angular arabesques in blue green on a red ground (figure 175). Although this color combination occurs frequently, the arabesque design does not appear in any other known Bergama rug. The border of this rug has the trefoil pattern to be found in the guard bands of nearly all Bergama prayer rugs.

The Bergama prayer rugs have either one niche (figure 176) or two, one at either end of the field (figure 177), with hanging mosque lamps. The spandrels of the arches are decorated either with arabesques or floral motifs in vivid colors. The characteristic border has angular cartouches containing arabesques alternating with star-shaped compartments,

FIGURE 176 Prayer rug, Bergama, XVII century. Catalogue no. 89

FIGURE 177 Prayer rug, Bergama, second half of XVII century. Catalogue no. 90

the guard bands having a reciprocal trefoil pattern. Such rugs were popular in Europe, and may be found in Dutch paintings of the seventeenth century—for example, in a portrait of Abraham Grapheus by Cornelis de Vos (1620), in the Royal Museum of Fine Arts, Antwerp.[44] They also appear in European and American paintings of the eighteenth century. A portrait of Isaac Royall and his family painted by Robert Feke in 1741 (figure 178) shows an eighteenth century type of Bergama, large rosettes in the border being combined with the cartouches of the earlier rugs.

FIGURE 178 Isaac Royall and Family, 1741, by Robert Feke. Harvard University, Law School Collection

FIGURE 179   Geometrical rug, Bergama, end of XVIII or beginning of XIX century. Collection of Joseph V. McMullan, New York

FIGURE 180   Geometrical rug, so-called Mamluk, probably Cairo, middle of XVI century. Catalogue no. 99

FIGURE 182   Geometrical rug (fragment), so-called Mamluk, probably Cairo, end of XVI century. Catalogue no. 98

The geometrical rugs attributed to Bergama are usually of small size, with one or two squares containing octagons, lozenges, and cornerpieces. The designs of their geometrical or stylized floral motifs are bold, and the colors are vivid, reds and blues predominating. Many of these rugs,[45] dating from the seventeenth to the nineteenth century are direct descendants of the "Holbeins" with octagons. An example is in the McMullan collection (figure 179). Some have end panels with stylized lotus palmettes, similar to rugs of Melas (figure 210). These rugs are often attributed to that center.

GEOMETRICAL, SO-CALLED MAMLUK RUGS (SIXTEENTH CENTURY)

Quite unlike any rugs so far discussed is a group of geometrical rugs with several small compartments symmetrically arranged around a dominant central octagon or eight-pointed star. As we have seen, such octagons, stars, and other polygons made their appearance in art in the Seljuk period. The compartments

are filled with a complex, dense pattern of arabesques, scrollwork, lancet leaves, geometrical figures, and papyrus umbels. Other motifs seen in these rugs are candelabra, palm trees, and cypresses. In smaller examples (figure 180), there is one central motif; the larger rugs (figures 181, 182) have a more elaborate composition with a great variety of ornamental motifs. The largest and finest of this group (figure 181, page 154) has five main compartments: a central star, two lobed octagons, and two squares with inner octagons. In most of the smaller rugs the color scheme is limited mainly to light shades of red, blue, and yellow green, while in larger rugs, such as figure 182 and a silk rug in the Austrian Museum of Applied Art, Vienna,[46] additional colors and deeper shades are employed. The Austrian Museum and the Textile Museum in Washington[47] have two of the largest collections of these rugs.

For a long time these rugs were attributed to Asia Minor, to Damascus, and even to Morocco. The attribution to Damascus was based mainly on the use of the term "Damascene" in old inventories,

particularly Venetian ones, for any Turkish pile rug of brilliant colors. In 1924 Friedrich Sarre advanced a new theory—that this group of rugs was made in Cairo. He based his case chiefly on the many analogies between their designs and those of Cairene bookbindings and mosaic pavements of mosques of the Mamluk period.[48] This theory was accepted and further developed by Kühnel and Kurt Erdmann,[49] both of whom pointed out that the umbrella leaves reproduced the ancient Egyptian motifs of papyrus leaves and umbels. Other authors, doubting the Mamluk theory, continued in their opinion that the rugs were of Turkish manufacture. There is no question but that the rugs differ both in design and technique—they have the Senna knot rather than the Ghiordes—from the Anatolian rugs so far presented, with the exception of the early seventeenth-century compartment rugs discussed on page 183—a group also tied with the Senna knot but regarded even so as Turkish or "Rhodian." Both Kühnel and Erdmann were of the opinion that Persian weavers introduced the Senna knot and established an independent Mamluk rug industry in Cairo at the end of the fifteenth century. However, there is no historical or literary evidence to support such a theory. "Cairene" rugs are indeed mentioned in old European inventories, but there is never an indication whether the name designates the place of manufacture or simply a trade center. Furthermore it is not possible to link any of the surviving rugs to any of the relevant inventories.

As to the dating of these rugs, the earliest ones belong, in the opinion of Kühnel and Erdman, to the last quarter of the fifteenth century. However, some of the rugs so assigned (figures 181, 182) have a border of cartouches alternating with lobed medallions, and this border does not appear in Persian rugs before the beginning of the sixteenth century. "Mamluk" rugs with cartouche borders are depicted in frescoes by Moretto in the Salvadego Palace, Brescia.[50] Since these paintings are datable to the second quarter of the sixteenth century, it is probable that the rugs with cartouche borders are of the sixteenth, rather than the fifteenth, century. A further point in the dating is that the "Mamluk" rugs often have a floral pattern known from Turkish Ushak-type rugs of the sixteenth century. Because of this it is doubtful that any of the "Mamluk" rugs are earlier than 1517, the date of the Ottoman conquest of Egypt. Although it is possible that further evidence may one day make a revised attribution necessary, we may conclude that the "Mamluk" rugs should be classified as Ottoman. It is probable that they were woven in Cairo after 1517, both for domestic use and for export.

FLORAL COURT RUGS (SIXTEENTH AND SEVENTEENTH CENTURIES)

A class of Turkish rugs with floral decoration, including prayer rugs, forms a category quite different from the Anatolian and other geometrical rugs so far discussed. The rugs fall into two groups according to the materials used in them. In one group the warp, weft, and pile are all of wool; in the other the warp and weft are of silk and the pile is of wool and undyed cotton, the latter being used in the white parts of the pattern. Both groups, like the so-called "Mamluk" rugs and the early seventeenth-century compartment rugs described on page 183, are tied with the Senna knot rather than the Ghiordes. The rugs are decorated with arabesques and floral scrolls bearing palmettes, curving lanceolate leaves, and the naturalistic blossoms popular in Turkish art, such as plum, hyacinth, tulip, and rose, as well as such fruit as the pomegranate. While a number of these rugs have merely an allover floral pattern, most have either a central circular medallion and cornerpieces, or multiple circular medallions. Several of the rugs have a floral pattern within a lozenge diaper.

For a long time these floral rugs were called "Damascus." Then a number of authors, including Sarre, recognized them as Turkish court products and attributed them to the looms of Brusa or Istanbul. Later, both Erdmann and Kühnel attempted to establish these rugs, particularly the ones made entirely of wool, as of Egyptian rather than Turkish manufacture, dating them from the middle of the sixteenth century to the middle of the seventeenth. Their theory was that these rugs replaced the geometrical "Mamluk" rugs described in the preceding section. The rugs of the second group—those containing cotton—were called by Kühnel "Brusa rugs of Cairene workmanship," and dated by him to about 1600. It was Kühnel's contention that the rugs of the Brusa group containing cotton were made by the eleven Cairene weavers, who, together with a load of their wool, are known to have been ordered by Sultan Murad III to the Turkish court in Istanbul in 1585. In the first edition of his book *Oriental Carpets* Erdmann regarded all of the Turkish floral rugs as of Cairene workmanship, making no distinction of a Brusa group. In the second edition and later publications, having had some doubts as to the Cairene origin of these rugs, he designated some of them as "Cairo or Istanbul."

Neither from a historical nor a stylistic point of view can the dating and chronology of Erdmann and Kühnel be upheld. First of all, a wealth of stylistic and technical evidence, taken into account by neither author, shows that many of the rugs of Kühnel's "Brusa" group must be dated earlier than 1585. Second, we know from Turkish sources that the city of Brusa was an established rug center long before the arrival there of the Cairene weavers. Ever since the fifteenth century Brusa had also been the chief production center of fine Turkish brocades and velvets. A city register of Brusa, dated 1525, listed fifteen rugmakers. Even earlier, in 1474, Josafa Barbaro, the Venetian envoy to the king of Persia, reported that Brusa was a rug-producing center.

According to Kühnel, the "Brusa" rugs are of "extremely elegant design and fine knotting." However, examination of some of the rugs attributed to Cairo and made entirely of wool shows that they also are finely knotted and are equally fine in design. For example, the rug of figure 183 has a very fine texture of approximately 284 knots to the square inch. Nor is the fact that all the floral rugs are tied with the Senna knot sufficient reason for assigning them, as Kühnel does, to Persian weavers working in Cairo. As a result of the Ottomans' capture and occupation of Tabriz in 1514 and again in 1534, the weavers of Turkey must have become familiar with Persian rugs and observed that a much finer delination of design was possible when the Senna knot, rather than the Ghiordes, was used.

In Persia, both the Ghiordes and Senna knots were in use from the seventeenth century on, so that the evidence of the particular knot, of itself, is not sufficient to establish the Ottoman floral rugs as of Cairene origin. As a matter of fact, a group of Senna-knotted geometrical rugs (page 183) was regarded by Kühnel himself first as of "Rhodian" and then as of Turkish origin.

The Turks had a long tradition of rug weaving, going back, as we have seen, to the thirteenth century. Since great rugs were manufactured in Turkey in the fifteenth and sixteenth centuries, the need for the Ottoman court to order rugs in distant Cairo simply did not exist. To the Turks, Cairo was a provincial city; none of the old Turkish records, all of which are quite trustworthy in such matters, mentions Cairo as a rug-producing center.

The dating of the Ottoman floral court rugs suggested by Kühnel and Erdmann has to be completely revised. This can be done with the help of court garments and textiles of the sultans, and dated tiles in mosques and palaces. The garments, preserved in the Topkapu Seray Museum, Istanbul, were carefully labeled by court officials. Studied and classified by Tahsin Öz,[51] the garments and fabrics show the characteristic Turkish floral ornament already in use at the end of the fifteenth century. The textiles were made first in Brusa and later in Istanbul, and it is a matter of record that during the time of Suleiman the Magnificent (1520–1566) 318 looms were working for the court.

An early type of floral court rug has a dense pattern of arabesques, palmettes, and curled leaves forming four-lobed devices (figure 183). Some of the leaves are overlaid with sprays of blossoms, a device known in early sixteenth-century velvets and in a tile panel in the mausoleum of Prince Mehmet in Istanbul,[52] built in 1548. The field of this rug has a central medallion and portions of similar medallions in the corners decorated with flowers favored by Turkish artists: roses, carnations, and tulips. Many of these are overlaid with tiger stripes. This combination was known as early as the second half of the fifteenth century, as seen in a caftan of Sultan Mehmet II (1451–1481),[53] in which tiger stripes form a lozenge diaper, as in some sixteenth-century rugs. A short-sleeved velvet mantle of the same sultan has a similar lozenge pattern containing a device of six tulips and pomegranates.[54] In view of these stylistic relationships the rug of figure 183 and a similar rug in the Textile Museum, Washington,[55] should be dated to the first half of the sixteenth century, not, as suggested by Kühnel, to the middle of the century.

To the middle of the sixteenth century should be assigned a rug whose red field is decorated with yellow circular medallions containing arabesques, the rest of the field decorated with large lanceolate leaves, various composite palmettes, and floral sprays (figure 184, page 156). A Turkish rug with just such medallions is depicted in a painting by Osman, done between 1550 and 1590, in a manuscript of a *Hüner Namah* (*The Book of Accomplishments*) in the Topkapu Seray Museum. The naturalistic flowers of the rug of figure 184 are not confined to the medallions but cover the entire field, contrary to the treatment in the rugs of figure 183. Such floral patterns occur in the tile decorations of a number of Turkish buildings, among them the mausoleum of Hurrem Sultan (1558), the mosque of Rustem Pasha (1561), the mosque of Suleiman the Magnificent (1566)—all in Istanbul—and the Selimye mosque of Sultan Selim II (1562) in Edirne.

FIGURE 183
Floral medallion rug,
court manufactory,
Brusa or Istanbul,
first half of XVI
century. Catalogue
no. 102

FIGURE 185   Floral rug, court manufactory, Brusa or Istanbul, middle of XVI century. Catalogue no. 104

FIGURE 186   Silk caftan of Sultan Bayazid II
(1481–1512), Brusa. Topkapu Seray Museum,
Istanbul

Related to the rug of figure 184 and datable to the
same period are the floral rug of figure 185 and examples in the Austrian Museum of Applied Art, the
Victoria and Albert Museum, and the Musée des
Arts Décoratifs, Paris.[56] All four of these rugs, unlike that of figure 184, have cotton in their pile. Their
floral decoration is quite elaborate, including pomegranate palmettes, lotus palmettes, large curling
leaves, and sprays of plum blossoms issuing to right
and left. Such floral decoration was known in Turkish
silks of the early sixteenth century, the most magnificent examples occurring in two caftans of Sultan
Bayazid II (1481–1512) in the Topkapu Seray Museum. One has a dark brown ground, the other a
cream white ground. Upon these appears an identical
design, much like that on some of the rugs, of large
composite palmettes, stylized pomegranates, and
rosettes, separated by large curved leaves, some of
which are overlaid with blossoms (figure 186). The
large curved leaves, which also appear in other Turkish brocades, are known in Turkish as *saz*. They were
the speciality of two sixteenth-century Persian painters who worked in Istanbul: Shah Kuli, a court artist
to Suleiman the Magnificent, and Wali Jan of Tabriz,
who arrived in Istanbul in 1587. Such leaves appear
in Persian rugs later than in Turkish rugs, namely in

the time of Shah Abbas (1587–1628), suggesting that
the motif may have been introduced to Persia from
Turkey.

To this group of Turkish court rugs with floral
decoration belong a few magnificent prayer rugs,
including a particularly fine example in the Austrian
Museum of Applied Art, one in the McMullan collection,[57] and a rug in the Walters Art Gallery (figure
187). These rugs have niches and a candelabra composition of various composite palmettes surrounded
by curling leaves and sprays of plum blossoms. In the
spandrels are interlaced arabesques, and in the lower
corners of the field are interlaced Chinese cloud bands
treated in typical Turkish fashion as a series of wavy
scrolls. The central composition of all three of these
rugs, which should be assigned to the end of the
sixteenth century, it also known in splendid tile
decorations in Istanbul and other cities. Tile decorations in the mosque of Rustem Pasha and the tomb
tower of Suleiman the Magnificent in Istanbul, and
in the mosque of Sultan Selim II in Edirne, show
related floral compositions with large curved leaves.
Several of these panels are treated as prayer rugs,
showing niches and borders. Three panels in the
harem of the Topkapu Seray (1575)[58] strongly recall
the Vienna, McMullan, and Baltimore prayer rugs.
Similar floral compositions, including cloud bands,
occur in tile panels in the mosque of Takkeci Ibrahim
Aga (1592) and the mausoleum of Sultan Murad III
(1595),[59] both in Istanbul. The border of the Vienna
rug has pomegranates alternating with palmettes and
lanceolate leaves, separated by sprays of hyacinths,
tulips, carnations, and roses. A similar border occurs
in a fine prayer rug of the end of the sixteenth century
whose field has slender double columns supporting
three arches with a mosque lamp in the central one
(figure 188, page 158). A related column prayer rug in
the Staatliche Museen, Berlin,[60] should be dated to the
beginning of the seventeenth century. Another prayer
rug in the Staatliche Museen,[61] without columns and
with a less fine floral border than the rug of figure
188, is dated 1610, according to Erdmann. A unique
synagogue prayer rug with a Hebrew inscription is
in the Textile Museum, Washington.[62] The treatment
of its floral design and its coarser weave indicate that
it should be dated to the middle of the seventeenth
century. Despite Kühnel's suggestion that it was
made in Cairo, it should be attributed to Istanbul. Of
importance in determining the place of manufacture
of all these prayer rugs is a fragment of a prayer rug
in the Museum of Turkish and Islamic Art, Istanbul,[63] with a floral border similar to that of the rug

FIGURE 187 Prayer rug, court manufactory, Brusa or Istanbul, end of XVI or beginning of XVII century. The Walters Art Gallery, Baltimore

FIGURE 189 Floral rug with
medallions, court manufactory,
probably Istanbul, first half of XVII
century. Catalogue no. 106

in figure 188 and the related rug in Berlin. This rug
came originally from the mosque of Sultan Ahmet
(1617) in Istanbul, to which it was presented, according to a label, as "*Istanbul isi*," "made in Istanbul."

The manufacture of the floral court rugs continued throughout the seventeenth century. To the first
half of the century can be assigned a small multiple-
medallion rug (figure 189) and a large rug with central medallion (figure 190). In later examples the
texture coarsens and the designs become stereotyped.
A prayer rug and two other small rugs of the second
half of the seventeenth century (figures 191, 192, 193)
are tied with the Senna knot, but the number of knots
per square inch is as low as ninety. Similar rugs in the
Textile Museum, Washington, the Victoria and
Albert Museum, the Kunstmuseum, Düsseldorf, and
the Bernheimer collection, Munich,[64] have been
dated by Kühnel and Erdmann to the sixteenth or
early seventeenth century. However, their designs
and crude textures indicate that they should be dated
to the middle and second half of the seventeenth
century. Examples are small medallion rugs with
tiger stripes in the Staatliche Museen, Berlin,[65] and
the McMullan collection (figure 194). Even cruder
pieces were made in the eighteenth century, and in
the nineteenth the looms of Hereke, near Istanbul,
produced copies of the floral rugs, as well as other
types of Turkish and even Persian rugs, both for the
use of the court and for export.

In view of the available evidence, we may conclude

FIGURE 190
Floral medallion rug,
court manufactory,
probably Istanbul,
first half of XVII
century. Catalogue
no. 107

FIGURE 191   Prayer rug, court manufactory, probably Istanbul, second half of XVII century. Catalogue no. 108

FIGURE 192   Floral medallion rug, court manufactory, probably Istanbul, second half of XVII century. Catalogue no. 109

FIGURE 193   Floral rug, court manufactory, probably Istanbul, second half of XVII century. Catalogue no. 110

that the floral rugs are products of Turkish, not Egyptian, looms. Further, we must assume that the production of the floral rugs did not follow that of the geometrical "Mamluk" rugs, but was contemporary with it until at least the middle of the sixteenth century, when the geometrical patterns were replaced entirely by the floral ones.

FIGURE 194 Medallion rug, court manufactory, probably Istanbul, second half of XVII century. Collection of Joseph V. McMullan, New York

RUGS OF GHIORDES AND KULA
(EIGHTEENTH CENTURY AND NINETEENTH)

The largest known group of Anatolian rugs of the eighteenth and nineteenth centuries comprises those made by peasant weavers in the town and district of Ghiordes in western Asia Minor. Although a few large Ghiordes rugs are known, most are prayer rugs of comparatively small size. In these, floral decoration occurs in the borders and spandrels, although it occasionally fills the prayer niche as well. The flowers and fruits are those most favored by the Ottoman court designers: carnations, hyacinths, tulips, lilies, roses, and pomegranates. Adopting the floral patterns of the court rugs, the Ghiordes weavers stylized them more and more. In early examples, probably of the middle of the eighteenth century, the design of the border (figure 195) closely follows that of the court prayer rugs (compare figure 188). The borders of late eighteenth- and early nineteenth-century examples show an increasingly strong stylization of the floral motifs, chiefly of the carnations (figure 196) and pomegranates (figure 197).

The Ghiordes prayer rugs have harmonious color compositions of red and blue, with the addition of white, yellow, and other colors. Their niche usually rests upon two columns (figure 198), which in some rugs become floral festoons (figure 199). The lamp in the niche, found in many Turkish prayer rugs, is turned by the Ghiordes designers into a floral device or a jeweled piece. Further, the Ghiordes rugs usually have two transverse panels, one at either end of the field.

Although some of the Ghiordes rugs were for a time assigned to the seventeenth century, it is doubtful that any of them are earlier than the middle of the eighteenth, and the majority are of the nineteenth. One with inscriptions in Arabic, Turkish, and Persian (figure 200) bears the date 1795/96 (1210 H.).

The Ghiordes weavers also produced two other types of prayer rug: the *kis*-Ghiordes, or betrothal rug, and the cemetery rug. According to Turkish tradition the *kis*-Ghiordes rugs were woven by young women (*kis* is Turkish for maiden) as a part of their dowry. Their features include a prayer niche at either end of the field, balanced symmetrically (figure 201), an allover design of small leaves, and a color scheme of red, blue, and white. In the cemetery rugs the field is usually decorated with a series of tombs and cypress trees, and occasionally with other plants as well (figure 202).

Prayer rugs similar to those of Ghiordes were made in Kula, to the south, differing chiefly in their borders and colors. The borders are often divided into as many as seven narrow stripes and decorated with small floral motifs (figure 203). These rugs usually have only one transverse panel, occurring at the top of the field, in contrast to the two of the Ghiordes rugs. In most of the Kula rugs yellows and blues predominate. Like Ghiordes, Kula was also known for prayer rugs with cemetery patterns (figure 204).

FIGURE 195   Prayer rug, Ghiordes, probably first
half of XVIII century. Catalogue no. 111

FIGURE 196   Prayer rug, Ghiordes, end of XVIII
century. Catalogue no. 112

FIGURE 197   Prayer rug, Ghiordes, end of XVIII
century. Catalogue no. 114

FIGURE 198   Prayer rug, Ghiordes, end of XVIII
century. Catalogue no. 115

FIGURE 199   Prayer rug, Ghiordes, end of XVIII
century. Catalogue no. 116

FIGURE 200   Prayer rug, Ghiordes, dated 1210 H.
(1795/96). Catalogue no.118

FIGURE 201 Prayer rug ("kis-Ghiordes"),
Ghiordes, first half of xix century. Catalogue no. 128

FIGURE 202 Prayer rug ("cemetery rug"),
Ghiordes, xix century. Catalogue no. 129

FIGURE 203 Prayer rug, Kula, xix century.
Catalogue no. 134

RUGS OF LADIK, MUJUR, AND MELAS
(EIGHTEENTH CENTURY AND NINETEENTH)

Prayer rugs different in style from those of Ghiordes and Kula were produced in the northern town and district of Ladik. In some of the early Ladiks, known as column Ladiks, the field has a triple arch supported by slender double columns. These rugs may be dated to the beginning of the eighteenth century. In later Ladiks there is a single arch, with or without columns. When present, the columns are sometimes used purely as a decoration, as seen in a rug dated 1795/96 (1210 H.) (figure 205). Above or below the niches appear panels with arches shaped like arrowheads (sometimes called "vandykes"), from the points of which stalks issue bearing stylized tulips (a motif sometimes wrongly interpreted as a lily).

The early Ladiks have either a cream white or a red ground, and their borders have lobed cartouches in various colors, filled with floral devices, chiefly tulips. Such rugs, popular in Hungary, are still to be found in churches of Transylvania. Fine examples are in the McMullan collection (figure 206), the City Art Museum, St. Louis, and the Schmutzler collection.[66]

The borders of later eighteenth-century Ladiks, some of which bear such dates as 1771, 1795, and 1799, have a series of rosettes alternating with stylized tulips and carnations on stems (figure 207). In the nineteenth century the Ladik weavers misunderstood the traditional design and turned the stems into severe geometrical motifs.

To the looms of Mujur, a town in central Anatolia, is attributed a type of prayer rug with a pointed-arch niche and a transverse panel with a row of arches (figure 208), recalling the Ladiks. The Mujur rugs have a distinctive border, with rows of lozenges within squares enclosing either stylized rosettes or star motifs. The colors are vivid, the designs strongly stylized.

To Melas, in western Anatolia, is attributed a type

FIGURE 204 Prayer rug ("cemetery rug"), Kula, XIX century. Catalogue no. 135

FIGURE 205 Prayer rug, Ladik, dated 1210 H. (1795/96). Catalogue no. 136

FIGURE 206 Prayer rug, Ladik, XVIII century. Collection of Joseph V. McMullan, New York

FIGURE 207 Prayer rug, Ladik, end of XVIII century. Catalogue no. 139

FIGURE 208 Prayer rug, Mujur, beginning of XIX century. Catalogue no. 141

of prayer rug related to the Bergama group. Its characteristic features include an angular version of the horseshoe arch and a floral border consisting of round blossoms and leaves, the latter often forming cross devices (figure 209). Other rugs attributed to Melas have a geometrical pattern of octagons (figure 210) or star-shaped medallions (figure 211). At either end of the rug there is often a band with stylized palmettes or lotus blossoms. Rugs of this type with large stylized tulips and carnations in hexagons (figure 212) are attributed either to Melas or Konya.

There are other types of Anatolian prayer rugs that have features reminiscent of the Bergama,

FIGURE 209   Prayer rug, Melas, beginning of XIX century. Catalogue no. 142

FIGURE 210   Geometrical rug, Melas, beginning of XIX century. Catalogue no. 143

Ghiordes, or Ladik groups but are not yet attributed to specific centers. When the several hundred Turkish rugs that are now in various Turkish museums, especially the Museum of Turkish and Islamic Art in Istanbul, are systematically studied, we can expect further attributions to be made.

KILIMS (EIGHTEENTH CENTURY AND NINETEENTH)

Although tapestry-woven rugs or kilims were known in Turkey before the eighteenth century, no specimens of this early flat-surfaced weaving have

FIGURE 211 Geometrical rug with central medallion, Melas, beginning of XIX century. Catalogue no. 144

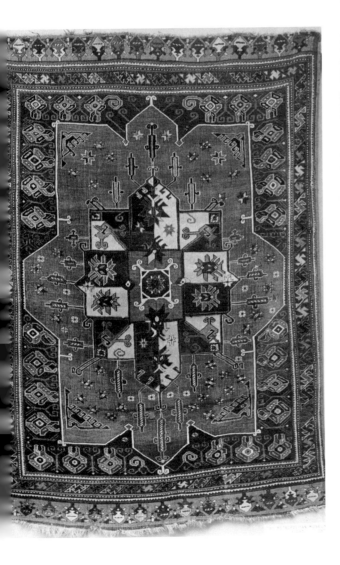

FIGURE 212 Geometrical rug, Melas or Konya, beginning of XIX century. Collection of Joseph V. McMullan, New York

FIGURE 214   Prayer rug, Ghiordes or Kula, XIX century. Catalogue no. 147

FIGURE 215   Prayer rug, Ladik, beginning of XIX century. Catalogue no. 148

survived. Toward the end of the eighteenth century and during the nineteenth peasant craftsmen in many of the Anatolian centers made prayer rugs in the tapestry technique. As with the pile rugs, regional differences may be detected in their designs. A Ladik kilim (figure 213), in which metal threads are added,

FIGURE 213   Prayer rug, probably Ladik, dated 1188 H. (1774/75). Catalogue no. 146

bears the date 1774/75 (1188 H.). Another kilim in which metal threads are added has a triple-arched niche with a floral design, and stylized carnations fill the spandrels and border (figure 214); it may have been made either in the Ghiordes or the Kula region. The border of another example, in which tulips alternate with geometrical rosettes (figure 215), shows so close a relationship to the Ladik borders that we may assume it was made in Ladik.

Kilims were also made in the district of Ushak. Their floral designs are highly stylized, their color schemes predominantly red, blue, and green.

Notes to Chapter Seven

1 Wilhelm von Bode and Ernst Kühnel, *Antique Rugs from the Near East*, pp. 22–29; Kurt Erdmann, *Jahrbuch der Preuszischen Kunstsammlungen*, 50, pp. 261–98.

2 Kurt Erdmann, *Oriental Carpets*, fig. 9; idem, *Jahrbuch der Preuszischen Kunstsammlungen*, 50, fig. 18.

3 Erdmann, *Oriental Carpets*, fig. 8; Bode-Kühnel, fig. 6.

4 Erdmann, *Oriental Carpets*, fig. 10; P. Michele Campana, *Il tappeto orientale*, pl. 7.

5 Friedrich Sarre and Hermann Trenkwald, *Old Oriental Carpets*, II, pl. 1.

6 Campana, pl. 9.

7 Kurt Erdmann, *Istanbuler Mitteilungen*, 6, pl. ix.

8 Carl Johan Lamm, *Svenska Orientsällskapets Årsbok* (1937), p. 103, pl. vii.

9 Sarre-Trenkwald, II, pl. 2; see comment by Professor Flemming.

10 Oktay Aslanapa, *Turkish Arts*, fig. 19, pl. xi, following p. 31.

11 Richard Ettinghausen, "New Light on Early Animal Carpets," in *Aus der Welt der islamischen Kunst*, pp. 108–14.

12 Erdmann, *Oriental Carpets*, figs. 17, 18.

13 Campana, pl. 10.

14 Kurt Erdmann, *Europa und der Orientteppich*, fig. 11.

15 Jacques Lassaigne, *Flemish Painting: The Century of Van Eyck* (n.p., 1957), p. 37 a.

16 Lamm, *Svenska Orientsällskapets Årsbok* (1937), pp. 117–19, figs. 22–24, and p. 121, pl. ix.

17 Erdmann, *Oriental Carpets*, fig. 19; Campana, pl. 23; Erdmann, *Europa und der Orientteppich*, fig. 14.

18 Karl Voll, *Memling* (Stuttgart, 1909), p. 116.

19 Aslanapa, pl. xii, following p. 31.

20 Erdmann, *Europa und der Orientteppich*, fig. 17.

21 Aslanapa, pl. iii, following p. 66.

22 Erdmann, *Oriental Carpets*, fig. 36.

23 Copenhagen, Museum of Decorative Arts, *A Collection of Oriental Carpets and Rugs belonging to Heinrich Wulff* (Copenhagen, 1934), pl. 9.

24 Aslanapa, pl. i, following p. 66; Wilhelm R. Valentiner, *Catalogue of a Loan Exhibition of Early Oriental Rugs*, no. 7; Maurice S. Dimand, *The Ballard Collection of Oriental Rugs in the City Art Museum of St. Louis*, pl. xiv; Bode-Kühnel, fig. 9.

25 Campana, pls. 12, 13.

26 Ibid., pls. 14, 17, 18.

27 New York, Wildenstein Gallery, *Loan Exhibition: Treasures of Musée Jacquemart-André* (New York, 1956), no. 11.

28 Ernst Kühnel and Louisa Bellinger, *Cairene Rugs*, pls. xlv, xlvi.

29 Kurt Erdmann, *Ars Islamica*, VII, fig. 23.

30 Dimand, *Ballard Collection*, pl. xv; Kühnel-Bellinger, pls. xliii, xliv; Erdmann, *Ars Islamica*, VII, fig. 22.

31 Kühnel-Bellinger, pp. 3, 65–67.

32 Campana, pls. 28, 36.

33 Ibid., pl. 30.

34 Erdmann, *Oriental Carpets*, fig. 26.

35 Breslau, Kunstsammlungen der Stadt, *Schleisischer Kulturspiegel* (Breslau, n.d.), fig. 80; Erdmann, *Oriental Carpets*, fig. 34.

36 Campana, pls. 34, 35.

37 Ibid., pl. 29.

38 Paul Ganz, *The Paintings of Hans Holbein* (London, 1956), p. 288, fig. 60, p. 289, fig. 61.

39 C. E. C. Tattersall, *A History of British Carpets* (Essex, 1934), pls. ii, iii.

40 Bode-Kühnel, fig. 21.

41 Joseph V. McMullan, *Islamic Carpets*, no. 79.

42 Valentiner, no. 12; A. F. Kendrick and C. E. C. Tattersall, *Hand-Woven Carpets*, II, pl. 46 a; Erdmann, *Oriental Carpets*, fig. 147; Aslanapa, pl. vii, following p. 66.

43 Emil Schmutzler, *Altorientalische Teppiche in Siebenbürgen*.

44 Arthur Urbane Dilley, *Oriental Rugs and Carpets*, pl. xli.

45 Erdmann, *Oriental Carpets*, figs. 37–42.

46 Sarre-Trenkwald, I, pls. 44–46.

47 Ibid., pls. 44–51; Kühnel-Bellinger, pls. i–xxi.

48 Friedrich Sarre, *Jahrbuch der asiatischen Kunst*, I, pp. 19–23.

49 Kühnel-Bellinger, pp. 5–7; Kurt Erdmann, *Ars Islamica*, V, pt. 2, pp. 179–206; idem, *Ars Islamica*, VII, pp. 55–81.

50 Erdmann, *Europa und der Orientteppich*, fig. 3.

51 Tahsin Öz, *Turkish Textiles and Velvets: XIV–XVI Centuries* (Ankara, 1950).

52 Tahsin Öz, *Turkish Ceramics* (Ankara, n.d.), pl. xxx.

53 Öz, *Turkish Textiles*, pls. viii, ix.

54 Ibid., pls. vi, vii.

55 Kühnel-Bellinger, pl. xxiii.

56 Sarre-Trenkwald, I, pl. 57; Erdmann, *Oriental Carpets*, figs. 136, 137.

57 Sarre-Trenkwald, I, pl. 56; McMullan, no. 4.

58 Aslanapa, pl. viii, following p. 108.

59 Aslanapa, pl. x, following p. 108; Öz, *Turkish Ceramics*, pl. liv.

60 Erdmann, *Oriental Carpets*, fig. 138.

61 Ibid., fig. 139.

62 Kühnel-Bellinger, pls. xxx, xxxi.

63 Aslanapa, pl. x, following p. 66.

64 Kühnel-Bellinger, pls. xxii, xxvii; Erdmann, *Oriental Carpets*, figs. 127, 128, 130.

65 Bode-Kühnel, pl. iii.

66 Dimand, *Ballard Collection*, pl. l; Schmutzler, pl. 23.

CATALOGUE

67
FIGURE 144

Geometrical animal rug (fragment), Anatolia, XIV century

10″ × 7″

WARP: Wool

WEFT: Wool; 2 shoots after each row of knots

KNOTTING: Wool. Ghiordes knot, about 80 knots per square inch

COLORS: 4. *Ground*: blue green (octagon). *Pattern*: tan, red, green.

DECORATION: An octagon containing a geometrically stylized bird, checkered lozenges, and small rosettes.

PROVENANCE: The ruins of Fustat (Old Cairo)

PUBLISHED: Erdmann, *Oriental Carpets*, fig. 11.

Rogers Fund

27.170.89

68
FIGURE 158

Arabesque rug ("Lotto"), Ushak, end of XVI century

7′ 2″ × 4′ 4″

WARP: Wool

WEFT: Wool; 2 shoots after each row of knots

KNOTTING: Wool. Ghiordes knot, about 88 knots per square inch

COLORS: 8. *Ground*: vermilion (field, outer guard band), blue green (border), blue (inner guard band). *Pattern*: ivory white, yellow, red, light blue, dark blue, blue green.

DECORATION: *Field*: Angular arabesques in rows, with palmettes and half-palmettes forming quatrefoils and octagonal devices. *Border*: Simulated Kufic writing interlaced on a horizontal bar, the tops of the letters ending in half-palmettes. *Guard bands*: An angular ribbon.

PUBLISHED: Dilley, pl. XXXVIII; Dimand, *Handbook*, fig. 207.

Rogers Fund

08.167.1

69
FIGURE 162

Arabesque rug ("Lotto") with coat of arms, Ushak, late XVI or early XVII century

7′ 7¼″ × 4′ 9″

WARP: Wool

WEFT: Wool; 2 shoots after each row of knots

KNOTTING: Wool. Ghiordes knot, about 88 knots per square inch

COLORS: 4. *Ground*: red (field, outer guard band), blue (border), yellow (coat of arms, inner guard band). *Pattern*: yellow, red, blue, brown.

DECORATION: *Field*: An allover pattern of octagonal and cross-shaped devices formed by stylized arabesques, with angular half-palmettes. In the upper left corner, superimposed, the coat of arms of Centurione and Doria (Genoa). *Border*: A wavy scroll of oval forms containing branches with leaves, the spaces filled with large double rosettes. *Inner guard band*: A floral scroll bearing leaves and small rosettes. *Outer guard band*: A geometrical scroll.

PUBLISHED: McMullan, no. 72.

Gift of Joseph V. McMullan

62.231

70
FIGURE 160

Arabesque rug ("Lotto"), Ushak, first half of XVII century

5′ 8″ × 4′

WARP: Wool

WEFT: Wool; 2 shoots after each row of knots

KNOTTING: Wool. Ghiordes knot, about 81 knots per square inch

COLORS: 6. *Ground*: red (field, guard band), dark blue (border), yellow (alternate cartouches in border), light blue (alternate cartouches). *Pattern*: yellow, orange, red, light blue, dark blue, brown.

DECORATION: *Field*: Angular arabesques in rows, with palmettes and half-palmettes forming cross-shaped motifs and octagonal devices. *Border*: Lobed octagonal cartouches filled with cross-shaped palmette devices; lilylike blossoms and angular hook motifs in the intervening spaces. *Guard band*: A scroll with stylized blossoms.

PUBLISHED: Breck-Morris, no. 37.

Gift of James F. Ballard, the James F. Ballard Collection

22.100.112

71
FACING PAGE, LEFT

Arabesque rug, Ushak, first half of XVIII century

5′ 4″ × 4′ 2″

WARP: Wool

WEFT: Wool; 2 shoots after each row of knots

KNOTTING: Wool. Ghiordes knot, about 64 knots per square inch

COLORS: 7. *Ground*: red (field, outer guard band), yellow (border), black brown (inner guard band). *Pattern*: yellow, orange, red, light blue, dark blue, dark brown.

angular floral scrolls bearing leaves and palmettes. *Border*: An arabesque scroll interlacing with a floral scroll bearing leaves and palmettes. *Inner guard band*: A wavy scroll with rosettes. *Outer guard band*: A wavy scroll with leaves and lilylike blossoms.

PUBLISHED: McMullan, no. 67.

Gift of Joseph V. McMullan

58.63

73   BELOW

Arabesque and floral rug with star medallions, Ushak, end of XVI century

9′ 1″ × 5′ 7″

WARP: Wool

WEFT: Wool; 3 shoots after each row of knots

KNOTTING: Wool. Ghiordes knot, about 56 knots per square inch

COLORS: 6. *Ground*: red (field), dark blue (medallions), blue (border), cream yellow (guard bands). *Pattern*: white, cream yellow, red, blue, dark blue, black brown.

DECORATION: *Field*: Three eight-pointed star medallions centered on the long axis, with sections of additional

DECORATION: *Field*: An allover pattern of angular arabesques, the bands of which are ornamented with small crosses and overlaid with curly leaves. *Border*: An arabesque scroll with half-palmettes, the intervening spaces filled with treelike geometrical motifs. *Inner guard band*: Leaves. *Outer guard band*: Alternating leaves and trefoils.

PUBLISHED: Riefstahl, *Art Bulletin*, XIII, figs. 14, 18.

Rogers Fund

08.171.2

72   FIGURE 163, PAGE 152

Arabesque and floral rug with star medallions, Ushak, end of XVI century

14′ × 7′ 5½″

WARP: Wool

WEFT: Wool; 2 shoots after each row of knots

KNOTTING: Wool. Ghiordes knot, about 100 knots per square inch

COLORS: 7. *Ground*: red (field, border), dark blue (stars, lozenges), yellow (inner guard band), light blue (outer guard band). *Pattern*: white, yellow, red, light blue, dark blue, green, dark brown.

DECORATION: *Field*: Four transverse rows (and portions of two more) of lobed, eight-pointed stars alternating with lozenges, both forms filled with interlaced arabesques. The ground of the field is patterned with medallions along the sides. The medallions are decorated with interlacing arabesques. The ground of the field has a pattern of angular floral scrolls bearing leaves and palmettes. *Border*: A wavy scroll on a ground of S–motifs. *Guard bands*: A wavy floral scroll with leaves and lilylike blossoms.

Rogers Fund
08. 235

74   FIGURE 164

Arabesque and floral rug with star medallions, Ushak, early XVII century

10′ 1″ × 5′ 8″

WARP: Wool

WEFT: Wool; 2 shoots after each row of knots

KNOTTING: Wool. Ghiordes knot, about 72 knots per square inch

COLORS: 11. *Ground*: brick red (field), dark blue (stars, lozenges), blue (border), yellow (guard bands). *Pattern*: white, tan, yellow, pink, red, light blue, dark blue, green, brown.

DECORATION: *Field*: An eight-pointed star medallion with a lozenge on either side along the long axis, with part of a second star medallion at one end. The medallions and lozenges are filled with interlaced arabesques. The ground of the field is patterned with angular floral scrolls bearing palmettes. *Border*: A floral scroll with palmettes and leaves. *Inner guard band*: A geometrical scroll with angular leaves. *Outer guard band*: A scroll with alternating small palmettes and leaves.

PUBLISHED: Breck-Morris, no. 26; Dilley, pl. XXXVIII.

Gift of James F. Ballard, the James F. Ballard Collection 22. 100. 110

75   FIGURE 165

Arabesque rug with star medallion, Ushak, end of XVII century

5′ 9″ × 4′

WARP: Wool

WEFT: Wool; 2 shoots after each row of knots

KNOTTING: Wool. Ghiordes knot, about 72 knots per square inch

COLORS: 10. *Ground*: brick red (field), dark blue (star, lozenge sections), black brown (border). *Pattern*: white, yellow, purple, light blue, blue, green, black.

DECORATION: *Field*: A large central four-pointed star with sections of a lozenge at either end on the long axis; all three forms filled with interlaced arabesques. The ground of the field is patterned with angular scrolls bearing leaves and palmettes. At either end, a transverse row of geometrical S-motifs. *Border*: A geometrical scroll bearing palmette leaves, the leaves bracketed with hooked arabesque motifs.

PUBLISHED: Breck-Morris, no. 27.

Gift of James F. Ballard, the James F. Ballard Collection 22. 100. 115

76   FIGURE 166

Medallion rug, Ushak, first half of XVII century

19′ 10″ × 11′ 6″

WARP: Wool

WEFT: Wool; 2 shoots after each row of knots

KNOTTING: Wool. Ghiordes knot, about 56 knots per square inch

COLORS: 10. *Ground*: red (field, center quatrefoil, outer guard band), dark blue (central medallion, border), black (star medallions), light blue (inner guard band). *Pattern*: white, yellow, red, light blue, blue, dark blue, blue green, green, greenish brown, black.

DECORATION: *Field*: In the center, an oval medallion bordered with trefoils containing palmettes. The medallion is filled with arabesques, floral scrolls, and a quatrefoil compartment containing palmettes and a small, palmette-filled, oval medallion. Issuing from the tips of the quatrefoil are arabesque devices of two types. At either end of the medallion on the long axis is an escutcheon filled with arabesques and floral scrolls. A section of the medallion, with the escutcheon, is repeated at either end of the field. Along the sides of the field are four incomplete star medallions with escutcheons at their tips, the medallions filled with arabesque devices and floral scrolls. The ground of the field is patterned with floral scrolls bearing leaves and palmettes. *Border*: A floral design of palmettes, leaves, and small star-shaped panels. *Inner guard band*: Rosettes. *Outer guard band*: A geometrical zigzag.

Rogers Fund
08. 173. 13

77   FIGURE 167

Arabesque and floral medallion rug, Ushak, middle of XVII century

9′ 10″ × 6′ 9″

WARP: Wool

WEFT: Wool; 2 shoots after each row of knots

KNOTTING: Wool. Ghiordes knot, about 72 knots per square inch

COLORS: 7. *Ground*: dark blue (field), red (medallions, border), light blue (guard bands). *Pattern*: ivory white, yellow, red, light blue, green, brown.

DECORATION: *Field*: On the long axis, two hexagonal medallions bordered with trefoils and palmettes and filled with arabesques and floral stems. In each corner of the field and along the sides are quarters or halves of medallions with jagged, irregular outlines, filled with arabesques and floral scrolls. The ground of the field is patterned with angular scrolls bearing leaves and serrate palmettes. *Border*: A wavy scroll bearing palmettes and trefoil leaves. *Inner guard band*: Small geometrical motifs. *Outer guard band* (sides only): A wavy scroll with leaves.

PUBLISHED: Breck-Morris, no. 25; Dimand, *Handbook*, fig. 206; Hawley, color pl. 11.

Gift of James F. Ballard, the James F. Ballard Collection 22. 100. 117

78   BELOW

Prayer rug, Ushak, late XVII century

5′ 9″ × 4′ 5″
WARP: Wool
WEFT: Wool; 4 shoots after each row of knots
KNOTTING: Wool. Ghiordes knot, about 110 knots per square inch
COLORS: 6. *Ground*: red (field, guard band), light blue (arches), yellow (border). *Pattern*: white, yellow, red, light blue, light green, black brown.
DECORATION: *Field*: A geometrical wavy scroll frames the field and forms an arch at either end. In each arch is a rosette and an ornamental device substituting for a mosque lamp. In the center of the field is an eight-pointed palmette-tipped star. Geometrical scroll devices appear at intervals in the field. *Border*: Stylized palmettes adorned with hooks. *Guard band*: A wavy geometrical scroll bearing leaves and blossoms.

PUBLISHED: Breck-Morris, no. 30.
Gift of James F. Ballard, the James F. Ballard Collection 22. 100. 89

79   BELOW

Prayer rug, Ushak, late XVII century

5′ × 3′ 11″
WARP: Wool
WEFT: Wool; 2 shoots after each row of knots
KNOTTING: Wool. Ghiordes knot, about 72 knots per square inch
COLORS: 7. *Ground*: red (field), light green (central medallion), blue (triangular compartments), black brown (band of niche, border). *Pattern*: white, yellow, red, blue, blue green, light green, black brown.
DECORATION: *Field*: The niche is defined by a band containing arabesque scrolls; at the bottom the band forms an arch; this contains a star motif. Above the arch are two triangular compartments, their upper sides stepped and adorned with a pole motif; the compartments are filled with geometrical scrolls. Centered in the niche is a lozenge medallion with indented sides, filled with scrolls. Above this, and in the spandrels as well, are stylized trees. *Border*: A stylized floral scroll with leafy palmettes and hooks. *Guard band*: A zigzag.

PUBLISHED: Breck-Morris, no. 29.
Gift of James F. Ballard, the James F. Ballard Collection 22. 100. 114

80   BELOW

Prayer rug, Ushak, late XVII or early XVIII century

5′ 9″ × 3′ 6″
WARP: Wool
WEFT: Wool; 2 shoots after each row of knots
KNOTTING: Wool. Ghiordes knot, about 130 knots per square inch
COLORS: 7. *Ground*: red (field, border), black brown (inner guard band). *Pattern*: white, tan, yellow, red, dark blue, blue green, black brown.
DECORATION: *Field*: The niche is defined by a band containing a geometrical scroll (top), and a wavy scroll (sides and bottom). The band is interrupted at the bottom by a narrow arch-shaped space. Centered in the niche is an eight-pointed palmette-tipped star. In the apex of the niche, substituting for a lamp, is an arabesque scroll device. *Border*: An angular scroll sending off stylized leaves and hooked stems, with squares and S–forms in the intervening spaces. *Inner guard band*: An arabesque scroll interlaced with a scroll bearing buds. *Outer guard band* (fragmentary): A geometrical scroll with leaves.

PUBLISHED: Breck-Morris, no. 28.
Gift of James F. Ballard, the James F. Ballard Collection
22. 100. 109

81   BELOW

Prayer rug, Ushak, early XVIII century

4′ 9½″ × 3′ 4½″
WARP: Wool
WEFT: Wool; 2 shoots after each row of knots
KNOTTING: Wool. Ghiordes knot, about 85 knots per square inch
COLORS: 9. *Ground*: red (field, outer guard band), yellow (medallion), dark green (spandrels), dark blue (border), gray brown (inner guard band). *Pattern*: tan, yellow, salmon, red, light blue, dark blue, green, gray brown.
DECORATION: *Field*: A niche with a lobed arch at either end. In the apex of one arch hangs a device resembling a lamp. In the spandrels are arabesque scrolls. Centered in the field is a lobed lozenge-shaped medallion containing a floral device. *Border*: A scroll bearing buds and quatrefoils, with large cloud bands alternating with leafy rosettes. *Inner guard band*: A wavy scroll with leaves and buds. *Outer guard band*: A simplified wavy scroll.

Rogers Fund
07. 116

82   FIGURE 168

Palmette rug, Smyrna, late XVIII or early XIX century

$8' 2'' \times 5' 2\frac{3}{4}''$

WARP: Wool

WEFT: Wool; 2 shoots after each row of knots

KNOTTING: Wool. Ghiordes knot, about 85 knots per square inch

COLORS: 8. *Ground*: yellow (field, guard bands), red (border). *Pattern*: white, yellow, pink, red, purple, light blue, dark blue, brown.

DECORATION: *Field*: A repeat pattern, arranged in lengthwise rows, of large pomegranate palmettes, alternating with branches bearing leaves and blossoms forming lozenges. *Border*: Lobed cartouches filled with floral scrolls; between the cartouches, halves of small octagons containing a star motif. *Guard bands*: A wavy scroll bearing leaves and buds.

Mr. and Mrs. Isaac D. Fletcher Collection, Bequest of Isaac D. Fletcher

17. 120. 131

83   FIGURE 169

Prayer rug, Ushak, early XVII century

$5' 10'' \times 3' 9''$

WARP: Wool

WEFT: Wool; 2 shoots after each row of knots

KNOTTING: Wool and cotton. Ghiordes knot, about 121 knots per square inch

COLORS: 10. *Ground*: red (field, outer guard band), dark blue (medallion, border), blue (inner guard band). *Pattern*: cream white, light tan, tan, red, light blue, blue, dark blue, blue green, green, brown.

DECORATION: *Field*: A niche with trefoil arch at either end, each spandrel containing two cloud bands. In one of the niches a "jeweled" device represents a lamp. Centered in the field is a hexagonal medallion containing a cross-shaped device of palmettes bordered by geometrical scrolls. *Border*: A floral scroll sending off palmettes, buds, and leaves, intersected by an arabesque scroll with half-palmettes, two of which form an arch over the palmettes. *Inner guard band*: A wavy scroll with rosettes and leaves. *Outer guard band*: A wavy scroll with palmettes and leaves.

PUBLISHED: Bode-Kühnel, fig. 26; Breck-Morris, no. 32.

Gift of James F. Ballard, the James F. Ballard Collection

22. 100. 111

84   FIGURE 170

Prayer rug with palmette design, Ushak, early XVII century

$5' \times 3' 5''$

WARP: Wool or goat hair

WEFT: Wool; 2 shoots after each row of knots

KNOTTING: Wool. Ghiordes knot, about 176 knots per square inch

COLORS: 7. *Ground*: red (field, guard band), dark blue (border). *Pattern*: yellow, pink, red, light blue, blue, dark blue, brown.

DECORATION: *Field*: A trefoil niche, formed by thin stems, contains three vertical rows of a floral scroll with palmettes, buds, and leaves, intersected by an arabesque scroll with half-palmettes, two of which form an arch over each full palmette. A similar design fills the spandrels. *Border*: A floral pattern of two intersecting scrolls. *Guard band*: A wavy scroll bearing palmettes and leaves.

PUBLISHED: Breck-Morris, no. 31.

Gift of James F. Ballard, the James F. Ballard Collection

22. 100. 113

85   FIGURE 171

Geometrical rug, Ushak, XVII century

$7' 2'' \times 4' 3''$

WARP: Wool

WEFT: Wool; 2 shoots after each row of knots

KNOTTING: Wool. Ghiordes knot, about 63 knots per square inch

COLORS: 7. *Ground*: red (field), light blue (border). *Pattern*: white, yellow, red, light blue, dark blue, light green, brown.

DECORATION: *Field*: A lozenge diaper formed by stems bearing trefoil leaves, with a double star at each intersection. A leafy rosette containing a star is centered within each lozenge. *Border*: A scroll sending off leafy palmettes and stylized treelike motifs, intersected by an arabesque scroll forming an arch over the palmettes.

PUBLISHED: Breck-Morris, no. 36.

Gift of James F. Ballard, the James F. Ballard Collection

22. 100. 116

86   FIGURE 172

"Bird rug," probably Ushak, late XVI century

$11' 1'' \times 5' 11''$

WARP: Wool

WEFT: Wool; 2 shoots after each row of knots

KNOTTING: Wool. Ghiordes knot, about 72 knots per square inch

COLORS: 10. *Ground*: cream white (field, border, guard bands). *Pattern*: cream white, yellow, salmon, red, deep red, blue, yellow green, green, light brown, black.

DECORATION: *Field*: A diaper of squares, the corners of which are rosette blossoms, the sides a motif of arabesque palmette devices ending in diagonal points resembling bird heads. Within each square, a floral scroll with a central blossom and branches bearing buds and leaves. *Border*: An angular scroll with six-pointed leafy rosettes and cloud bands. *Inner guard band*: Four-petaled rosettes. *Outer guard band*: Eight-pointed rosettes.

PUBLISHED: Breck-Morris. no. 35.

Gift of James F. Ballard, the James F. Ballard Collection
22.100.127

87   FIGURE 173

"Bird rug," probably Ushak, early XVII century, about 1600

14′ 7″ × 7′ 7″

WARP: Wool

WEFT: Wool; 2 shoots after each row of knots

KNOTTING: Wool. Ghiordes knot, about 56 knots per square inch

COLORS: 7. *Ground*: cream white (field, border, guard bands). *Pattern*: cream white, light yellow, salmon, red, light blue, dark blue, dark brown.

DECORATION: *Field*: A diaper of squares, the corners of which are rosette blossoms, the sides a motif of arabesque palmette devices ending in diagonal points resembling bird heads. Within each square, a floral scroll with a central blossom and branches bearing buds and leaves. *Border*: Reciprocal triangular motifs composed of arabesques and floral stems with leaves. *Guard bands*: A floral scroll.

PUBLISHED: McMullan, no. 76.

Gift of Joseph V. McMullan
63.207

88   FIGURE 175

Arabesque rug, Bergama, end of XVI or early XVII century

6′ 6″ × 4′ 1″

WARP: Wool

WEFT: Wool; 2 shoots after each row of knots

KNOTTING: Wool. Ghiordes knot, about 80 knots per square inch

COLORS: 6. *Ground*: red (field), reciprocal light brown and blue (border), tan (guard band). *Pattern*: tan, red, blue, blue green, black.

DECORATION: *Field*: A repeat pattern in lengthwise rows of angular arabesques ending in half-palmettes. *Border*: Reciprocal trefoils.

PUBLISHED: Riefstahl, *Art Bulletin*, XIII, figs. 16, 17.

Gift of W. R. Valentiner
08.208.2

89   FIGURE 176

Prayer rug, Bergama, XVII century

6′ 4″ × 4′

WARP: Wool

WEFT: Wool; 2 shoots after each row of knots

KNOTTING: Wool. Ghiordes knot, about 132 knots per square inch

COLORS: 7. *Ground*: cream white (field), red (spandrels), yellow (border), reciprocal red and black (guard bands). *Pattern*: cream white, tan, yellow, red, light blue, blue, black.

DECORATION: *Field*: A lobed niche with mosque lamp in the apex, the niche filled with angular floral scrolls sending off palmettes, rosettes, buds, and leaves. In the spandrels, interlaced arabesque bands. *Border*: Angular cartouches containing an arabesque and a floral scroll, alternating with star-shaped medallions containing a lozenge device with trefoil leaves. *Guard bands*: Reciprocal trefoils. *Inner edging*: An S-motif. *Outer edging*: A chain.

PUBLISHED: Breck-Morris, no. 45; Dimand, *Handbook*, fig. 211.

EX COLL. I. Kafanoff.

Gift of James F. Ballard, the James F. Ballard Collection
22.100.92

90   FIGURE 177

Prayer rug, Bergama, second half of XVII century

6′ 5″ × 4′ 6″

WARP: Wool

WEFT: Wool; 2 shoots after each row of knots

KNOTTING: Wool. Ghiordes knot, about 90 knots per square inch

COLORS: 7. *Ground*: yellow (field, border), violet (spandrels), reciprocal red and black brown (guard bands). *Pattern*: white, yellow, red, violet, blue, green, black brown.

DECORATION: *Field*: At either end a lobed arch with mosque lamp in the apex. The niche is filled with angular floral scrolls bearing palmettes, rosettes, and leaves. The spandrels are filled with a large rosette and stylized lanceolate leaves. *Border*: Angular cartouches containing an arabesque and a floral scroll alternating with star-shaped medallions, containing a lozenge device with trefoil leaves. *Guard bands*: Reciprocal trefoils. *Inner edging*: A wavy geometrical scroll. *Outer edging*: A chain.

NOTE: A similar rug is in the Ballard Collection of the City Art Museum, St. Louis (Dimand, *Ballard Collection*, pl. XXIII).

PUBLISHED: Breck-Morris, no. 46.

Gift of James F. Ballard, the James F. Ballard Collection
22.100.86

91   BELOW   92   BELOW

Prayer rug, Bergama, XVII century

6' 2" × 4'

WARP: Wool

WEFT: Wool; 2 shoots after each row of knots

KNOTTING: Wool. Ghiordes knot, about 100 knots per
square inch

COLORS 11. *Ground*: dark blue (field), red (spandrels,
border), dark brown (guard bands). *Pattern*: white, tan,
salmon, red, purple, light blue, dark blue, blue green,
olive green, brown, dark brown.

DECORATION: *Field*. At either end, a lobed niche with
mosque lamp in the apex. The niche is filled with symmetrically arranged angular floral scrolls bearing palmettes, rosettes, and leaves. The spandrels are filled with
angular arabesque bands. *Border*: Angular cartouches
containing a device of leaves, alternating with star-
shaped medallions containing a lozenge device with trefoil leaves. *Guard bands*: A scroll with leaves and
blossoms. *Edgings*: A chain.

PUBLISHED: Breck-Morris, no. 44.

EX COLL. I. Kafanoff

Gift of James F. Ballard, the James F. Ballard Collection

22. 100. 90

Prayer rug, Bergama, XVIII century

5' 3" × 4' 3"

WARP: Wool

WEFT: Wool; 2 shoots after each row of knots

KNOTTING: Wool. Ghiordes knot, about 100 knots per
square inch

COLORS: 12. *Ground*: red (field, border), dark blue (outer
medallion), salmon (second medallion), tan (central
lozenge), yellow (spandrels), white (guard bands).
Pattern: white, light tan, tan, yellow, orange,
salmon, red, light blue, blue, dark blue, blue green,
dark brown.

DECORATION: *Field*: A niche at either end, the spandrels
filled with rosettes and stylized lanceolate leaves;
filling the niche, a lozenge medallion in treelike form,
bordered with a garland of rosette blossoms. Centered
in the medallion is a smaller lozenge medallion filled
with floral scrolls and containing another lozenge
filled with a cross-shaped device of palmettes. The field
of the outer medallion is figured with palmettes, tulips,
and rosettes. *Border*: Large rosettes. *Guard bands*: Star-
shaped rosettes in octagons.

PUBLISHED: Breck-Morris, no. 47.

Gift of James F. Ballard, the James F. Ballard Collection

22. 100. 91

93

Geometrical rug, Bergama, early XIX century

6′ 3½″ × 5′ 4″

WARP: Wool

WEFT: Wool; 2 shoots after each row of knots

KNOTTING: Wool. Ghiordes knot, about 86 knots per square inch

COLORS: 10. *Ground*: red (field, small central octagons), light green (large central octagons), dark brown (guard bands). *Pattern*: white, tan, yellow, salmon, red, light blue, blue, dark blue, light green, dark brown.

DECORATION: *Field*: In the center, two large octagons, each containing a smaller octagon filled with a geometrical star surrounded by angular interlacings. A rectangular panel extends from each side of the inner octagon; each panel is filled with hook devices. In the triangular spaces between the panels are rosettes. The space between the large octagons contains a row of three rosettes and two large triangular hook devices. At either end of the field, a row of five rosettes, and in each corner of the field, a blossom device composed of hooks. *Border*: Octagonal panels, each containing a star. *Guard bands*: Wavy scrolls.

Gift of Mr. and Mrs. Reginald P. Rose

59. 148

94

Geometrical rug, Bergama, first half of XIX century

6′ 6″ × 4′ 11″

WARP: Wool

WEFT: Wool; 2 shoots after each row of knots

KNOTTING: Wool. Ghiordes knot, about 64 knots per square inch

COLORS: 9. *Ground*: red (field, border), dark blue (star medallion, polygons), blue (inner guard band), off-white (outer guard band). *Pattern*: white, off-white, light tan, salmon, red, blue, dark blue, blue green, brown.

DECORATION: *Field*: A central star-shaped medallion containing a lozenge surrounded by four square panels. At either end of the field, an irregular polygon. The medallion, lozenge, square panels, and polygons, as well as the field, are filled with hook motifs. *Border*: A geometrical scroll composed of hook motifs, stars appearing in its spaces. *Inner guard band*: A geometrical scroll with stylized palmettes and hooks. *Outer guard band*: A pair of triangles alternating with a leaflike form.

American Wing Installation Fund

Inst. 62. 2

95   BELOW   96   FIGURE 157

Prayer rug, Bergama, first half of XIX century

6′ 2″ × 5′ 2″
WARP: Wool
WEFT: Wool; 2 shoots after each row of knots
KNOTTING: Wool. Ghiordes knot, about 81 knots per
square inch
COLORS: 7. *Ground*: red (field), blue (spandrels), yellow
(border), brown (inner guard band), light blue (outer
guard band). *Pattern*: white, yellow, red, light blue,
blue, red brown, brown.
DECORATION: *Field*: At either end, a pointed arch with
stepped outline and mosque lamp. The niche is filled
with angular floral scrolls bearing palmettes, rosettes,
and leaves; the spandrels are filled with rosettes and
stylized lanceolate leaves. The field is edged with
carnations. *Border*: A leafy scroll sending off stems of
carnations, roses, and tulips. *Guard bands*: A curling
scroll. *Edgings*: A curling scroll.
NOTE: A similar rug is in the Ballard Collection of the City
Art Museum, St. Louis (Dimand, *Ballard Collection*,
pl. XXVIII).
PUBLISHED: Breck-Morris, no. 49.
Gift of James F. Ballard, the James F. Ballard Collection
22. 100. 88

Geometrical rug, Anatolia, XVI century

6′ × 4′ 2″
WARP: Wool
WEFT: Wool; 2 shoots after each row of knots
KNOTTING: Wool. Senna knot, about 88 knots per square
inch
COLORS: 7. *Ground*: red (field, border medallions), green
(border), blue (border cartouches), dark blue (guard
band). *Pattern*: ivory white, pink, red, light lavender,
blue, dark blue, green.
DECORATION: *Field*: Nine rectangles arranged in three
rows, each rectangle containing an octagonal compartment filled with an eight-pointed star surrounded by
stylized cypresses and rosettes. Each star is formed by
angular interlacings and has a cross at its center. The
triangular areas surrounding the octagonal compartments contain rosettes. *Border*: A succession of lobed
medallions and cartouches filled with a leaf pattern.
Guard band: A wavy scroll.
PUBLISHED: McMullan, no. 3.
Gift of Joseph V. McMullan
69. 267

97   FIGURE 181, PAGE 154

Geometrical rug, so-called Mamluk, probably Cairo, early XVI century

29′ 5″ × 7′ 10″
WARP: Wool
WEFT: Wool; 2 shoots after each row of knots
KNOTTING: Wool. Senna knot, about 100 knots per square
inch
COLORS: 7. *Ground*: red (field, border medallions, guard
bands), red, light blue, green (octagonal medallions),
light blue (border), green (border cartouches). *Pattern*:
white, light tan, yellow, red, light blue, green, brown.
DECORATION: *Field*: Five rectangular compartments, with
octagons and other shapes concentrically arranged,
divide the field vertically. The central compartment,
from the outside in, consists of an octagon, a star, two
inner octagons, a sixteen-pointed star, a small medallion,
and a small rosette. These forms are filled with a
variety of motifs: palmettes on short stems, lancet
leaves, papyrus umbels, and geometrical trefoils.
Surrounding the star and filling the outer octagon are
twenty-four small octagons, rhomboids, and triangles,
all filled with motifs including stars, rosettes and
papyrus leaves. Each corner of the rectangular compartment contains an octagon surrounded by triangles
containing stylized floral motifs.
Each of the compartments adjoining the central one,
from the outside in, consist of two octagonal medallions,
a lobed medallion, an inner octagon, and two oval

medallions. The decoration of these forms includes papyrus umbels, candelabra motifs, geometrical interlacings, arabesque motifs, and a linear arabesque design. Each corner of the rectangular compartment contains an octagon filled with candelabra motifs and arabesques. The spaces between the corners contain papyrus umbels, stylized cypress trees, and geometrical interlacings.

The end compartments consist of four concentric octagons. The innermost octagon contains geometrical scrolls with knotted motifs; the surrounding one contains angular geometrical interlacings; the next is decorated with a row of candelabra motifs. The outermost octagon is decorated by sixteen small octagons containing alternately candelabra motifs and papyrus umbels. At its two sides is a band of four squares, three with circular medallions with arabesque and floral motifs, one with papyrus umbels. Octagons and triangles with interlacings and arabesques fill the triangles between the bands and the octagon. *Border*: Cartouches filled with papyrus umbels alternating with lobed medallions containing a star motif with trefoils and palmettes attached. In the intervening spaces, wavy scrolls with papyrus. *Guard bands*: A wavy scroll with leaves.

PUBLISHED: Bode-Kühnel, fig. 46.
EX COLL. Simonetti
Fletcher Fund
1970.105

98   FIGURE 182

Geometrical rug (fragment), so-called Mamluk, probably Cairo, end of XVI century

9' 2" × 6' 3"
WARP: Wool
WEFT: Wool; 2 or 3 shoots after each row of knots
KNOTTING: Wool. Senna knot, about 144 knots per square inch
COLORS: 8. *Ground*: red (field, border medallions, guard bands adjoining border), red, blue green (central motif), blue green (border), light blue (border cartouches, guard bands adjoining field and edge of rug). *Pattern*: white, light tan, yellow, red, light blue, blue green, green, brown.
DECORATION: *Field*: A large polygonal medallion filled with geometrical interlacings and a pattern of papyrus leaves on stems, the medallion containing a circle filled with a design of geometrical interlacings and knotted motifs. Surrounding the medallion, outside a border containing candelabra motifs, a symmetrical composition of hexagons and star shapes containing palmette devices. In each corner of the field, enclosed in a triangle, an octagon filled with an arabesque device. A broad band at each side of the field is patterned with a diaper of tiger stripes and rosettes; a rectangular panel

in this band contains a palm tree flanked by cypresses. *Border*: Cartouches filled with arabesque devices alternating with round medallions containing a star tipped with trefoils. A treelike device of papyrus leaves occurs between medallion and cartouche, and above and below each medallion and cartouche there is a length of scroll bearing papyrus leaves. *Guard bands adjoining border*: A wavy scroll with leaves and palmettes. *Guard bands adjoining field and edge of rug*: A wavy floral scroll with leaves.

PUBLISHED: Breck-Morris, no. 18; Dilley, pl. XLIV; Dimand, *Handbook*, fig. 205.
Gift of James F. Ballard, the James F. Ballard Collection
22.100.52

99   FIGURE 180

Geometrical rug, so-called Mamluk, probably Cairo, middle of XVI century

7' 11" × 7' 1"
WARP: Wool
WEFT: Wool; 3 shoots after each row of knots
KNOTTING: Wool. Senna knot, about 120 knots per square inch
COLORS: 3. *Ground*: yellow green (field, border cartouches, guard bands adjoining field and edge of rug), red, light blue, yellow green (central motif), red (border medallions), light blue (border, guard bands adjoining border). *Pattern*: red, light blue, yellow green.
DECORATION: *Field*: In the center, a large eight-pointed star with indented outer border, containing a central square within three concentric octagons. Within the square, a rosette within a pattern of papyrus leaves on stems. Radiating from the sides of the square, filling the first of the octagons, are knotted motifs and hexagons. The second octagon is filled with a repeat pattern of papyrus leaves, the third with lancet leaves. The triangular points of the star and its outer border are filled with a pattern of papyrus leaves, chiefly in groups of three. In each corner of the field, an octagon within a square; the octagon, filled with lancet leaves, contains a star-shaped medallion filled with a device of papyrus leaves and trefoil leaves. Filling the field around the central star in a symmetrical arrangement are various geometrical forms: octagons, stars, squares, and triangular shapes. The triangular shapes, like the spandrels of two of the corner squares, are filled with checkering; the other forms are filled either with papyrus leaves or starlike forms of trefoils. At either end of the field is a band filled with a papyrus device. *Border*: Cartouches filled with lozenges and papyrus leaves, alternating with lobed medallions filled with a star tipped with trefoils. *Guard bands adjoining border*: A row of papyrus leaves. *Guard bands adjoining field and edge of rug*: A wavy scroll bearing papyrus leaves.

PUBLISHED: Dimand, *Oriental Rugs*, fig. 15.
Bequest of George Blumenthal
41. 190. 262

100   BELOW

Geometrical rug, so-called Mamluk, probably Cairo, XVI century

8′ 2″ × 7′ 10½″

WARP: Wool

WEFT: Wool; 2 shoots after each row of knots

KNOTTING: Wool. Senna knot, about 90 knots per square inch

COLORS: 3. *Ground*: green (field, border cartouches, outer half of double guard band), red, light blue, green (central motif), light blue (border, guard bands adjoining border), red (border medallions, inner half of double guard band). *Pattern*: red, light blue, green.

DECORATION: *Field*: In the center, a large eight-pointed star with indented outer border, containing a central square within three concentric octagons. The square contains a rosette of papyrus umbels and has radiating from its sides geometrical forms that comprise the interior of the first octagon. The second octagon is filled with a row of papyrus umbels in groups of three, the third with lancet leaves. The points of the star and its indented border are decorated with papyrus umbels.

Surrounding the medallion is an irregular sixteen-pointed compartment containing candelabra motifs with various geometrical forms including octagons, stars, and squares. The rest of the square field is filled with a diaper of rosettes. The field is framed by two bands containing rows of papyrus umbels separated by a band with a wavy papyrus scroll. *Border*: Cartouches alternating with lobed medallions. The cartouches are filled with a pattern of papyrus umbels and contain a square compartment with a lozenge within a square tipped with papyrus leaves and trefoils. The medallions contain an octagon enclosing a square with papyrus leaves radiating from its sides. *Guard bands adjoining border*: A wavy papyrus scroll. *Double guard band adjoining edge of rug*: A wavy papyrus scroll or papyrus umbels.

Bequest of George Blumenthal
41. 190. 263

101   BELOW

Geometrical rug, so-called Mamluk, probably Cairo, XVI century

6′ 8″ × 4′ 3″

WARP: Wool

WEFT: Wool; 2 shoots after each row of knots

KNOTTING: Wool. Senna knot, about 100 knots per square inch

COLORS: 4. *Ground*: red (field, border medallions), red, light blue (central motif), light blue (border, inner half of double guard band), green (border cartouches, outer half of double guard band). *Pattern*: light tan, red, light blue, green.

DECORATION: *Field*: In the center, an octagonal compartment containing a central square within two concentric octagons. Radiating from the square and filling the first of the octagons are knotted motifs and hexagons with whirl rosettes in the intervening spaces. The second octagon is filled with lancet leaves. Surrounding this octagon are eight star motifs alternating with eight whirl rosettes filling the octagonal compartment. The compartment is bordered by eight triangles containing rosettes. At either end of the field is a band containing star motifs, polygons, and rosettes, and, at one end only, a band of papyrus umbels. The field is scalloped and decorated with crosses. *Border*: Cartouches filled with papyrus umbels alternating with lobed medallions containing a star motif tipped with papyrus leaves. *Double guard band*: A wavy papyrus scroll.

Bequest of George Blumenthal
41.190.266

102   FIGURE 183

Floral medallion rug, court manufactory, Brusa or Istanbul, first half of XVI century

13′ 9″ × 8′

WARP: Silk

WEFT: Silk; 2 shoots after each row of knots

KNOTTING: Wool. Senna knot, about 210 knots per square inch

COLORS: 9. *Ground*: dark red (field, inner medallion, border), green (outer medallion), dark blue (corner medallions), light green (guard bands). *Pattern*: white, yellow, dark red, light blue, blue, dark blue, light green, green, dark green.

DECORATION: *Field*: In the center, a double medallion, the inner one containing an arabesque pattern around a rosette, the outer one floral sprays of roses, palmettes, carnations, and tulips overlaid with tiger stripes. Quarters of this medallion are repeated in the corners of the field. The field itself has an allover symmetrical floral pattern in staggered transverse rows, consisting of two units: one a design of arabesques, palmettes, including pomegranate palmettes, and leaves forming four-lobed devices; the other a cross-shaped device within a lozenge-shaped compartment formed by floral sprays with rosebuds. The units are connected by floral scrolls bearing lanceolate leaves, large rosettes, and rosebuds. *Border*: Bouquets of tulips, roses, and hyacinths between scrolls of lanceolate leaves and palmettes, overlaid with cloud bands. *Guard bands*: A

wavy scroll with palmettes. *Edgings*: Reciprocal leaf motifs.

PUBLISHED: Breck-Morris, no. 19; Dimand, *Handbook*, fig. 203.

Gift of James F. Ballard, the James F. Ballard Collection
22.100.57

103   FIGURE 184, PAGE 156

Floral rug, court manufactory, Brusa or Istanbul, middle of XVI century

18′ 8″ × 9′ 3″

WARP: Wool

WEFT: Wool; 3 shoots after each row of knots

KNOTTING: Wool. Senna knot, about 200 knots per square inch

COLORS: 9. *Ground*: red (field, lobed medallions, border), yellow (large medallions), light blue (small medallions), yellow green (guard bands). *Pattern*: white, orange yellow, yellow, red, light blue, blue, light blue green, yellow green, green.

DECORATION: *Field*: Eight large and small medallions are arranged in alternating and staggered rows, with portions of the medallions appearing along the edges of the field. The large medallions contain linear cloud bands surrounding a central lobed medallion with interlaced arabesques. The smaller ones contain arabesques forming various devices. Along the central vertical axis between the large medallions are palmettes placed in a cross formation. The rest of the field is covered with scrolls of lanceolate leaves and composite palmettes, and sprays with blossoms issuing from the smaller medallions. *Border*: Oval panels filled with tulips and hyacinths, separated by floral scrolls of lanceolate leaves and palmettes overlaid with cloud bands. *Guard bands*: Rosettes and stylized S–forms, separated by branches of hyacinths. *Edgings*: Reciprocal heart motifs.

PUBLISHED: Dimand, *Oriental Rugs*, fig. 13.

Bequest of George Blumenthal
41.190.257

104   FIGURE 185

Floral rug, court manufactory, Brusa or Istanbul, middle of XVI century

11′ 4″ × 9′ 7″

WARP: Silk

WEFT: Wool; 2 shoots after each row of knots

KNOTTING: Wool; cotton in white areas. Senna knot, about 224 knots per square inch

COLORS: 6. *Ground*: dark red (field, border, guard bands), dark blue (corner medallions). *Pattern*: ivory white, yellow, red, dark blue, olive green.

DECORATION: *Field*: Toward one end, a large floral device enclosed by four curved lanceolate leaves. This is partly repeated at either side and, in reverse position, at the other end of the field. Between these devices, a candelabra formation of large palmettes, stylized pomegranates, leaves, and sprays of plum or peach blossoms. In each corner of the field, a quarter of a round medallion with a lobed center containing arabesques, surrounded by sprays of carnations, roses, and tulips, overlaid with tiger stripes. *Border*: Floral scrolls bearing composite palmettes on stems, framed alternately by arabesque half-palmettes and cloud bands. *Guard bands*: A scroll bearing rosettes and leaves interlaced with a palmette scroll also bearing leaves. *Edgings*: An S–form alternating with a group of three balls.

PUBLISHED: Breck-Morris, no. 21.

Gift of James F. Ballard, the James F. Ballard Collection
22. 100. 55

105 FIGURE 188, PAGE 158

Prayer rug, court manufactory, Istanbul, end of XVI century

5′ 6″ × 4′ 2″

WARP: Silk.

WEFT: Silk; 2 shoots after each row of knots

KNOTTING: Wool; cotton in white areas. Senna knot, about 306 knots per square inch

COLORS: 8. *Ground*: green (center niche, guard bands), red (side niches), light blue (border). *Pattern*: white, tan, yellow, red, light blue, olive green, green, dark green.

DECORATION: *Field*: Slender double columns with capitals and bases define three niches; the columns contain an interlacing. In the apex of the center niche, a mosque lamp. The spandrels of the niches contain arabesques interlaced with floral scrolls. Above the spandrels, crenelations, and a row of four small domed towers. At the bottom of each niche, a bouquet of roses, carnations, and tulips. *Border*: Alternating large composite palmettes and rosette blossoms (probably pomegranates). A pair of curving lanceolate leaves issues from each, the direction of the leaves alternating with the unit; in the intervening spaces, stems with hyacinths, carnations, tulips, and roses. *Guard bands*: Rosettes. *Edgings*: A wavy geometrical scroll.

PUBLISHED: Bode-Kühnel, fig. 53 (here wrongly called Egypto-Ottoman); Breck-Morris, no. 24; Dilley, pl. XLVI; Dimand, *Handbook*, fig. 204.

Gift of James F. Ballard, the James F. Ballard Collection
22. 100. 51

106 FIGURE 189

Floral rug with medallions, court manufactory, probably Istanbul, first half of XVII century

13′ 2″ × 9′

WARP: Wool

WEFT: Wool; 3 shoots after each row of knots

KNOTTING: Wool. Senna knot, about 100 knots per square inch

COLORS: 7. *Ground*: red (field, border), light blue (central medallion, incomplete medallions), green (four other complete medallions). *Pattern*: white, tan, yellow, red, light blue, green, black.

DECORATION: *Field*: A pattern of lobed medallions in staggered rows, five complete, eight in halves at the sides and ends or in quarters in the corners. The medallions contain a rosette surrounded by palmettes enclosed in arabesque devices on a ground of floral scrolls. The ground of the field is patterned with floral scrolls bearing palmettes, rosettes, buds, lanceolate leaves, and simple leaves. *Border*: Wavy scrolls with palmettes and rosettes alternating. *Guard bands*: A wavy scroll with blossoms.

Bequest of George Blumenthal
41. 190. 272

107 FIGURE 190

Floral medallion rug, court manufactory, probably Istanbul, first half of XVII century

16′ 11″ × 9′ 7″

WARP: Wool

WEFT: Wool; 3 shoots after each row of knots

KNOTTING: Wool. Senna knot, about 80 knots per square inch

COLORS: 5. *Ground*: red (field, border), green (central medallion, guard bands), dark blue (corner medallions). *Pattern*: white, red, light blue, dark blue, green.

DECORATION: *Field*: A central lobed medallion containing a large rosette surrounded by floral sprays of tulips, roses, carnations, and hyacinths; quarters of this medallion are repeated in the corners of the field. The rest of the field is patterned with floral scrolls bearing lanceolate leaves, palmettes, and large rosettes. *Border*: Trilobed panels containing arabesques: between the panels, floral sprays of hyacinths, roses, carnations, tulips, and a stylized pomegranate. *Guard bands*: Rosettes. *Edgings*: Reciprocal leaf motifs.

PUBLISHED: Breck-Morris, no. 20.

Gift of James F. Ballard, the James F. Ballard Collection
22. 100. 56

108 FIGURE 191

Prayer rug, court manufactory, probably Istanbul, second half of XVII century

5′ 5″ × 3′

WARP: Wool

WEFT: Wool; 3 shoots after each row of knots

KNOTTING: Wool. Senna knot, about 100 knots per square inch

COLORS: 8. *Ground*: red (field), white (arch of niche, medallion fragments, outer guard band), green (border), yellow (inner guard band). *Pattern*: white, yellow, red, light blue, blue, yellow green, light green, green.

DECORATION: *Field*: A lobed niche containing a pattern of floral scrolls bearing palmettes, rosettes, and lanceolate leaves. In the lower corners are fragments of medallions; these and the spandrels of the arch contain interlaced arabesques. *Border*: A pattern of pomegranates and tulips, with branches of hyacinths, roses, and carnations. *Guard bands*: Rosettes.

Mr. and Mrs. Isaac D. Fletcher Collection, Bequest of Isaac D. Fletcher

17. 120. 137

109   FIGURE 192

Floral medallion rug, court manufactory, probably Istanbul, second half of XVII century

5′ 9″ × 4′

WARP: Wool

WEFT: Wool; 3 shoots after each row of knots

KNOTTING: Wool. Senna knot, about 90 knots per square inch

COLORS: 7. *Ground*: red (field, border), green (central medallion, inner guard band), light blue (corner medallions), tan (outer guard band). *Pattern*: white, tan, yellow, red, light blue, blue, green.

DECORATION: *Field*: A lobed central medallion with quarters of similar medallions repeated in the corners of the field. The medallions are filled with a wreath of palmettes around a central rosette. The rest of the field is patterned with floral scrolls bearing composite palmettes, rosettes, and curling lanceolate leaves. *Border*: A pattern of stylized pomegranates and palmettes, each with a pair of outgrowing curling lanceolate leaves. *Guard bands*: Rosettes.

PUBLISHED: Breck-Morris, no. 22.

Gift of James F. Ballard, the James F. Ballard Collection

22. 100. 54

110   FIGURE 193

Floral rug, court manufactory, probably Istanbul, second half of XVII century

6′ 2″ × 4′

WARP: Wool

WEFT: Wool; 2 shoots after each row of knots

KNOTTING: Wool. Senna knot, about 182 knots per square inch

COLORS: 8. *Ground*: red (field, border), yellow (guard bands). *Pattern*: white, tan, yellow, orange, red, light blue, blue, green.

DECORATION: *Field*: In the center, a leafy rosette surrounded by a wreath of palmettes connected by stems. The rest of the field is patterned with floral scrolls bearing curling lanceolate leaves, composite palmettes, carnations, and rosettes. In the intervening spaces, small rosettes and larger circular devices. *Border*: A pattern of stylized pomegranates and palmettes, each with a pair of outgrowing curling lanceolate leaves; some of the spaces filled with rosettes. *Guard bands*: Rosettes. *Edgings*: Reciprocal leaf motifs.

PUBLISHED: Breck-Morris, no. 23.

Gift of James F. Ballard, the James F. Ballard Collection

22. 100. 53

111   FIGURE 195

Prayer rug, Ghiordes, probably first half of XVIII century

6′ 7″ × 4′ 4″

WARP: Wool

WEFT: Wool and cotton; 2 shoots after each row of knots

KNOTTING: Wool. Ghiordes knot, about 81 knots per square inch

COLORS: 10. *Ground*: red (niche), light blue (spandrels, outer guard band), blue green (panel, inner guard band), dark blue (border). *Pattern*: white, tan, red, light blue, blue, dark blue, blue green, green, red brown, black brown.

DECORATION: *Field*: An arched niche with two columns. The columns have capitals, ewers for bases, and they contain a wavy scroll with blossoms and leaves. In the apex of the niche hangs a bouquet of carnations and tulips. The spandrels are filled with scrollwork. A panel above the niche has design of four stylized pomegranates with scrolls and rosettes between. *Border*: A pattern of composite palmettes and rosette blossoms, each with a pair of outgrowing curling lanceolate leaves; in between, stems with hyacinths, carnations, rosettes, and tulips. *Inner guard band*: A wavy scroll with blossoms. *Outer guard band*: A wavy scroll with small leaves. *Edgings*: A geometric S–motif.

PUBLISHED: Breck-Morris, no. 52; Dilley, pl. XLIII; Dimand, fig. 209.

Gift of James F. Ballard, the James F. Ballard Collection

22. 100. 85

112   FIGURE 196

Prayer rug, Ghiordes, end of XVIII century

6′ 4″ × 4′ 4″

WARP: Wool

WEFT: Wool; 2 shoots after each row of knots

KNOTTING: Wool and cotton. Ghiordes knot, about 110 knots per square inch

COLORS: 11. *Ground*: blue (niche, upper panel), red (spandrels, lower panel), white (border), greenish tan (guard bands). *Pattern*: white, greenish tan, yellow, light salmon, brick red, red, light blue, blue, light green, brown, black.

DECORATION: *Field*: A niche with pointed arch, edged all around with carnations. In the spandrels, six horizontal rows of stylized leafy blossoms with pairs of leaves. A panel above the spandrels contains a design of S–bands, palmettes, and leaves. A panel beneath the niche contains arabesque palmettes forming triangles. Both panels are edged with a geometrical scroll. *Border*: A repeat pattern of stalks bearing branches with stylized carnations. *Guard bands*: Stylized tulips. *Edgings*: Saw-tooth motif.

PUBLISHED: Breck-Morris, no. 60.

Gift of James F. Ballard, the James F. Ballard Collection
22. 100. 104

113   BELOW

Prayer rug, Ghiordes, end of XVIII century

5′ 8″ × 4′ 4″

WARP: Wool

WEFT: Wool; 2 shoots after each row of knots

KNOTTING: Wool. Ghiordes knot, about 150 knots per square inch

COLORS: 10. *Ground*: light green (niche), white (spandrels, lower panel, guard bands), dark blue (upper panel), blue (border). *Pattern*: white, tan, yellow, red, blue, dark blue, light blue green, light green, light brown, red brown.

DECORATION: *Field*: An arched niche edged with carnations. In the spandrels, horizontal rows of stylized leafy blossoms with pairs of leaves. A panel above the spandrels has a design of palmettes, carnations, and pomegranates; a panel beneath the niche has a series of S–bands, stylized blossoms, and leaves. Both panels are edged with a geometrical scroll; the lower panel is also framed by trefoils. *Border*: A repeat pattern of stalks bearing branches with stylized carnations. *Guard bands*: Stylized tulips. *Edgings*: A zigzag motif.

PUBLISHED: Breck-Morris, no. 61.

Gift of James F. Ballard, the James F. Ballard Collection
22. 100. 95

114   FIGURE 197

Prayer rug, Ghiordes, end of XVIII century

5′ 8″ × 4′ 2″

WARP: Wool

WEFT: Wool; 2 shoots after each row of knots

KNOTTING: Wool. Ghiordes knot, about 130 knots per square inch

COLORS: 12. *Ground*: dark blue (niche, upper panel), salmon (spandrels, lower panel), white (border), black brown (guard bands). *Pattern*: white, tan, light salmon, red, violet, light blue, dark blue, olive green, brown, black brown.

DECORATION: *Field*: An arched niche edged with carnations. In the spandrels, rows of stylized carnations. A panel above the spandrels contains a wavy scroll formed from a cloud band with rosettes in the intervening spaces. A panel beneath the niche contains a row of stylized tulips and carnations. Both panels are edged with a row of small crosses. *Border*: A repeat pattern of stems bearing three stylized pomegranates, the units alternating in color. *Guard bands*: A repeat pattern of pomegranates on branches. *Edgings*: A zigzag motif.

PUBLISHED: Breck-Morris, no. 59.

Gift of James F. Ballard, the James F. Ballard Collection
22. 100. 98

115   FIGURE 198

Prayer rug, Ghiordes, end of XVIII century

5′ 5″ × 4′ 1″

WARP: Wool

WEFT: Wool; 2 shoots after each row of knots

KNOTTING: Wool. Ghiordes knot, about 176 knots per square inch

BROCADING: Details in metal thread

COLORS: 11. *Ground*: red (niche), dark blue (spandrels, outer guard band), blue (panels), yellow tan (border), cream white (inner guard band). *Pattern*: white, cream white, yellow, pink, red, light blue, blue, dark blue, black, metal.

DECORATION: *Field*: An arched niche with wavy outline, the sides and bottom edged with small blossoms. The arch rests on two columns filled with a lozenge chain. At the base of the niche, a vase with a bouquet; in the apex, a floral device of carnations. In the spandrels, leafy scrollwork bearing blossoms. Panels above and below the niche contain a row of composite palmettes and V-shaped endpieces adorned with hooks. *Border*: A pattern of alternating composite palmettes and rosette blossoms, each with a pair of outgrowing curling lanceolate leaves; in the intervening spaces, stems with rosettes, carnations, and hyacinths. *Inner guard band and frame of panels*: Carnations on stems alternating with rosettes. *Outer guard band*: Rosettes. *Edgings of inner guard band*: Small leaves. *Edgings of outer guard band*: A geometrical scroll.

PUBLISHED: Breck-Morris, no. 53.

Gift of James F. Ballard, the James F. Ballard Collection 22. 100. 106

116   FIGURE 199

Prayer rug, Ghiordes, end of XVIII century

5′ 10″ × 4′

WARP: Wool

WEFT: Wool; 2 shoots after each row of knots

KNOTTING: Wool. Ghiordes knot, about 100 knots per square inch

COLORS: 10. *Ground*: white (niche), dark brown (spandrels), yellow tan (upper panels, inner guard band), light blue (lower panel, outer guard band), blue (border). *Pattern*: white, yellow tan, tan, pink, rose, light blue, blue, brown, dark brown, black.

DECORATION: *Field*: A niche with pointed arch resting upon two floral festoons in place of columns. In the apex, a floral device and an inscription in Turkish with a few words in Persian: "I come before thy throne heavily laden with sin and pray that my sins and guilt may be forgiven me." Across the bottom of the niche, a row of carnations. In the spandrels, leafy scrolls. Above the spandrels, two panels, one with arched compartments filled with arabesques, the other with an inscription (repeated in reverse): "May you be joyful and happy unto the days of the last judgment." Beneath the niche, a panel filled with palmettes alternating with an arabesque device. The field and upper panel are framed by a row of trefoils. *Border*: A large rosette alternating with a spray of hyacinths and two smaller rosettes.

Inner guard band: Carnations. *Outer guard band*: Carnations and lilylike blossoms. *Edgings*: Reciprocal triangles.

NOTE: For a Ghiordes rug with a similar inscription, see Rudolf Neugebauer and Julius Orendi, *Handbuch der Orientalischen Teppich Kunde*, 2nd ed. (Leipzig, 1920), pl. 11.

PUBLISHED: Breck-Morris, no. 57.

Gift of James F. Ballard, the James F. Ballard Collection 22. 100. 103

117   BELOW

Prayer rug, Ghiordes, end of XVIII century

5′ 10″ × 4′ 1″

WARP: Wool

WEFT: Wool; 2 shoots after each row of knots

KNOTTING: Wool. Ghiordes knot, about 117 knots per square inch

COLORS: 7. *Ground*: red (niche), light blue (spandrels), tan (panel, inner guard band), blue (border), white (outer guard band). *Pattern*: white, light tan, tan, red, light blue, black brown.

DECORATION: *Field*: A pointed niche supported by two ornamental columns edged with stylized hyacinth blossoms. The columns and spandrels are filled with

stylized tulips and carnations. A bouquet of flowers hangs in the apex. At the bottom of the niche, a row of carnations. In a panel above the spandrels, stylized blossoms and leaves. *Border*: Stylized trefoiled plants with rosettes. *Guard bands*: Stylized flowers. *Edgings of inner guard band*: Stylized flowers. *Edgings of outer guard band*: A wavy motif.

PUBLISHED: Breck-Morris, no. 68.

Gift of James F. Ballard, the James F. Ballard Collection 22. 100. 84

118   FIGURE 200

Prayer rug, Ghiordes, dated 1210 H. (1795/96)

5′ 2″ × 4′

WARP: Wool

WEFT: Wool; 2 shoots after each row of knots

KNOTTING: Wool. Ghiordes knot, about 90 knots per square inch

COLORS: 11. *Ground*: red (niche, outer guard band), blue (spandrels), white (upper panel), olive green (part of lower panel, border), light green (part of lower panel). *Pattern*: white, tan, yellow, pink, red, light blue, blue, olive green, light green, brown, black.

DECORATION: *Field*: An arched niche with wavy outline, filled with inscriptions in Arabic, Turkish, and Persian, the date appearing in the apex. The spandrels are filled with an angular floral pattern. A panel above the spandrels contains three stylized S–motifs containing an Arabic inscription: "Savagery, Syntheism, Sacredness." A panel beneath the niche contains stylized pomegranates, palmettes, and rosettes. The field and panels are framed by a geometrical scroll. *Border*: Large rosettes separated by stems with hyacinths and small rosettes. *Inner guard band*: Compartments formed by zigzag bands. *Outer guard band*: Rosettes and blossoms alternating. *Edgings*: A geometrical scroll.

INSCRIPTIONS (translation from Breck-Morris, p. 33):

Arabic: From the Grateful Ones (to God); (O God) those who engage in thy beautiful worship are delivered from the devils (evil spirits). Thou art He who bestoweth health upon, and preventeth the diseases from, the people of the two rivers (Mesopotamia) and the people of the mountains and of every habitation and locality.

Turkish: This prayer rug has been made with great skill and ornamented exquistely; it resembles the beautiful and peerless verses of virtuous Sadi. It will be defiled by the feet of a tyrant, even if in his sleep he steps on it.

Persian: It is a place for (even) the dusty foot of any blessed poor Sheikh.

PUBLISHED: Breck-Morris, no. 58.

Gift of James F. Ballard, the James F. Ballard Collection 22. 100. 96

119   BELOW

Prayer rug, Ghiordes, end of XVIII century

5′ 4″ × 4′ 5″

WARP: Wool

WEFT: Wool; 2 shoots after each row of knots

KNOTTING: Wool. Ghiordes knot, about 140 knots per square inch

COLORS: 7. *Ground*: dark blue (field, border, outer guard band), light blue (spandrels), light green (inner guard band). *Pattern*: white, red, light blue, dark blue, brown, black brown.

DECORATION: *Field*: A niche at either end, the spandrels filled with stylized tulips and carnations, the field having an allover floral pattern of large palmettes, composite rosettes, carnations, and leaves on stems. *Border*: Palmettes and rosettes alternating, a pair of stylized lanceolate leaves issuing from each; the spaces between the units filled with hyacinths and carnations. *Guard bands*: Carnations. *Edgings*: A wavy scroll with small rosettes.

PUBLISHED: Breck-Morris, no. 56.

Gift of James F. Ballard, the James F. Ballard Collection 22. 100. 100

120   BELOW

Prayer rug, Ghiordes, end of XVIII century

8′ 9″ × 5′ 9″

WARP: Wool

WEFT: Wool; 3 shoots after each row of knots

KNOTTING: Wool. Ghiordes knot, about 143 knots per square inch

COLORS: 10. *Ground*: olive tan (niche, panels, border), red (central lozenge), light blue (spandrels), blue (guard bands). *Pattern*: white, olive tan, tan, pink, red, light blue, blue, dark blue, brown, black.

DECORATION: *Field*: A niche at either end, the spandrels filled with staggered rows of pomegranates and carnations. In the center of the field, a lozenge containing a floral device of carnations and tulips. The rest of the field has a repeat pattern in transverse rows: double S–motifs and blossoms on stems alternating with a frieze of stylized carnations and pilasters. Beyond the spandrels at either end, a panel with a repeat of the stylized carnations and pilasters. The field and panels are framed by a series of trefoils. *Border*: Palmettes and rosettes alternating, a pair of stylized lanceolate leaves issuing from each; the spaces between the units filled with rosettes and carnations. *Guard bands*: Carnations. *Edgings of inner guard band*: A wavy scroll with small rosettes. *Edgings of outer guard band*: A scroll with curling leaves.

PUBLISHED: Breck-Morris, no. 55.

Gift of James F. Ballard, the James F. Ballard Collection 22. 100. 102

121   BELOW

Prayer rug, Ghiordes, about 1800

6′ 3″ × 4′ 3″

WARP: Wool

WEFT: Wool; 2 shoots after each row of knots

KNOTTING: Wool. Ghiordes knot, about 117 knots per square inch

COLORS: 9. *Ground*: red (niche), light blue (spandrels, lower panel, border), dark brown (upper panel), light tan (frame of field, outer guard band), dark blue (inner

guard band). *Pattern*: white, light tan, red, light blue, dark blue, green, light brown, black brown.

DECORATION: *Field*: A niche resting on two columns, the columns filled with stylized blossoms and edged with floral stems. The spandrels contain a diaper of hexagons filled with trefoil blossoms. In the apex, which is stepped, a bouquet of carnations and tulips. At the bottom of the niche, a row of carnations and tulips. A panel beneath the niche is filled with the pattern found in the spandrels. A panel above the spandrels contains a design of S–bands, palmettes, and leaves. The field and panels are framed by a geometrical S–motif. *Border*: A repeating unit of lilies and carnations. *Inner guard band*. A wavy scroll with blossoms. *Outer guard band*: Curly leaves. *Edgings*: A zigzag.

PUBLISHED: Breck-Morris, no. 67.

Gift of James F. Ballard, the James F. Ballard Collection 22. 100. 83

122   BELOW

Prayer rug, Ghiordes, middle of XIX century

5′ 4½″ × 3′ 8½″
WARP: Wool

WEFT: Wool; 2 shoots after each row of knots

KNOTTING: Wool. Ghiordes knot, about 105 knots per square inch

COLORS: 9. *Ground*: light blue green (field), light green (spandrels, lower panel), dark blue (upper panel, outer guard band), white (border). *Pattern*: white, tan, ochre, yellow, brick red, dark blue, light blue green, light green, light brown.

DECORATION: *Field*: A niche with pointed arch placed above two columns with floral capitals and bases, the columns filled with a lozenge chain. The sides and bottom of the niche are edged with blossoms. A floral device hangs in the apex. In the spandrels, rows of stylized pomegranates. In a panel above and beneath the niche, a design of S–bands, palmettes, and leaves. The field and panels are framed by a stylized floral motif. *Border*: A candelabra motif bearing stylized tulips and branches with leaves. *Inner guard band*: Star motifs separated by diagonal chains. *Outer guard band*: A stylized floral motif. *Edgings*: S-motifs.

PUBLISHED: Breck-Morris, no. 64.

Gift of James F. Ballard, the James F. Ballard Collection 22. 100. 97

123   BELOW

Prayer rug, Ghiordes, XIX century

5′ 3″ × 4′ 2″

240

WARP: Wool

WEFT: Wool; 2 shoots after each row of knots

KNOTTING: Wool. Ghiordes knot, about 228 knots per square inch

COLORS: 8. *Ground*: red (niche), dark blue (spandrels, outer guard band), light blue (panels), yellow (border), white (inner guard band). *Pattern*: white, yellow, pink, red, light blue, dark blue, light blue green, black.

DECORATION: *Field*: An arched niche with wavy outlines, the sides and bottom edged with small leaves. In the apex, a lamp, to the bottom of which is attached a ewer with a floral spray. At the bottom of the niche, a row of palmettes. In the spandrels, leafy scrolls. A panel above the spandrels contains a scroll with floral motifs, including palmettes. A panel beneath the niche contains palmettes and other floral motifs. The panels are framed by alternate small rosettes and blossoms. *Border*: Palmettes and rosettes alternating, a pair of stylized lanceolate leaves issuing from each; in the intervening spaces, small rosettes and sprays of hyacinths. *Guard bands*: Alternate small rosettes and blossoms. *Edgings of inner guard band*: A leaf pattern. *Edgings of outer guard band*: A geometrical scroll.

PUBLISHED: Breck-Morris, no. 54.

Gift of James F. Ballard, the James F. Ballard Collection
22. 100. 108

124   BELOW LEFT

Prayer rug, Ghiordes, XIX century

5′ 10½″ × 4′ 3″

WARP: Wool

WEFT: Wool; 2 shoots after each row of knots

KNOTTING: Wool. Ghiordes knot, about 108 knots per square inch

COLORS: 10. *Ground*: cream white (niche, outer guard band), yellow (spandrels, lower panel), dark blue (upper panel), dark brown (border), blue (inner guard band). *Pattern*: cream white, yellow, orange, red, light blue, blue, dark blue, blue green, light green, dark brown.

DECORATION: *Field*: An arched niche with wavy outline edged all around with stylized carnations. The spandrels are filled with rows of double carnations. A panel above the spandrels contains stylized pomegranates alternating with carnations. A panel beneath the niche contains triangular compartments filled with stylized tulips. The upper panel is edged with a stylized floral motif. A geometrical scroll frames the field and lower panel. *Border*: A candelabra motif bearing stylized tulips, carnations, and leaves. *Inner guard band*: A rosette alternating with a geometrical lozenge. *Outer guard band*: Carnations on stems. *Edgings*: A zigzag.

Theodore M. Davis Collection, Bequest of Theodore M. Davis, 1915
30. 95. 147

125   FACING PAGE, LEFT

Prayer rug, Ghiordes, XIX century

6′ × 4′ 4″

WARP: Wool

WEFT: Wool; 2 shoots after each row of knots

KNOTTING: Wool and cotton. Ghiordes knot, about 135 knots per square inch

COLORS: 12. *Ground*: ivory white (niche), dark blue (spandrels, outer guard band), light green (upper panel), white (lower panel), brown (border), blue (inner guard band). *Pattern*: white, tan, red, light blue, blue, blue green, light green, yellow green, red brown, brown.

DECORATION: *Field*: An arched niche with wavy outlines, resting on two columns with capitals and bases, the columns consisting of festoons of carnations. In the apex, a bouquet of carnations and roses. In the spandrels, leafy scrolls bearing carnations. A panel above the spandrels contains stylized pomegranates, rosettes, and palmettes; a panel beneath the niche contains leafy scrolls with carnations. The upper panel is edged with a zigzag line forming triangles; the lower with a scroll. *Border*: A candelabra motif bearing branches of carnations and hyacinths. *Inner guard band*: A wavy floral

scroll. *Outer guard band*: Stylized carnations and leaves. *Edgings of outer guard band*: A leafy scroll.

PUBLISHED: Breck-Morris, no. 63.

Gift of James F. Ballard, the James F. Ballard Collection
22.100.129

126   ABOVE RIGHT

Prayer rug, Ghiordes, middle of XIX century

5′ 6″ × 4′ 1″

WARP: Wool

WEFT: Wool; 2 shoots after each row of knots

KNOTTING: Wool. Ghiordes knot, about 198 knots per square inch

COLORS: 9. *Ground*: light gray green (niche, border), white (spandrels), brown (panels, inner guard band), violet (outer guard band). *Pattern*: white, yellow, salmon pink, orange red, light gray green, light green, brown, black.

DECORATION: *Field*: An arched niche with wavy outline, the sides and bottom edged with stylized tulips, the arch with carnations. In the spandrels, leafy scrolls. In a panel above the spandrels, hooked scrolls form compartments; these are filled with palmettes. A panel

beneath the niche contains a pattern of S–bands, palmettes, and leaves. The upper panel is edged with a stylized floral motif; the lower with a wavy scroll. The field is framed by a wavy scroll. *Border*: Shrubs bearing leaves, carnations, and tulips. *Inner guard band*: A row of carnations. *Outer guard band*: Rosettes. *Edgings*: A zigzag.

PUBLISHED: Breck-Morris, no. 62.

Gift of James F. Ballard, the James F. Ballard Collection
22.100.99

127   NEXT PAGE

Prayer rug, Ghiordes, middle of XIX century

4′ 8″ × 3′ 5″

WARP: Wool

WEFT: Wool; 2 shoots after each row of knots

KNOTTING: Wool. Ghiordes knot, about 150 knots per square inch

COLORS: 10. *Ground*: red brown (niche, outer guard band), blue green (spandrels), red (upper panel), white (border), light blue (inner guard band). *Pattern*: white, yellow, red, light blue, blue, light blue green, blue green, light green, red brown, dark brown.

DECORATION: *Field*: An arched niche formed by a geo-

metrical scroll, both sides of which are edged with tulips. Rising from a vase and filling the niche is a tree bearing sprays of hyacinths, tulips, roses, and carnations. In the spandrels, floral stems with stylized carnations. A panel above the spandrels contains cartouches filled with simulated script. *Border*: Palmettes and leaves on scrolling stems. *Guard bands*: A wavy floral scroll with blossoms. *Edgings*: A geometrical scroll.

PUBLISHED: Breck-Morris, no. 73.

Gift of James F. Ballard, the James F. Ballard Collection 22. 100. 78

128   FIGURE 201

Prayer rug ("kis-Ghiordes"), Ghiordes, first half of XIX century

4′ 1″ × 3′ 8″

WARP: Wool

WEFT: Wool; 2 shoots after each row of knots

KNOTTING: Wool. Ghiordes knot, about 99 knots per square inch

COLORS: 7. *Ground*: ivory white (field, border, guard bands), blue (center lozenge, spandrels, alternate triangles of border), red (alternate triangles of border). *Pattern*: ivory white, yellow, red, light blue, blue, blue green, dark brown.

DECORATION: *Field*: At either end, a niche in which hangs a jeweled device with three pendants. The spandrels are

filled with angular floral scrolls. In the center of the field, a lozenge compartment containing a four-lobed panel enclosing a rosette and four palmettes. The ground of the field is patterned with rows of small leaves or rose petals. *Border*: Reciprocal triangles containing floral scrolls. Between the triangles, a wide band containing rows of the small leaves seen in the field. *Guard bands*: A scroll with stylized blossoms.

PUBLISHED: Breck-Morris, no. 51.

Gift of James F. Ballard, the James F. Ballard Collection 22. 100. 107

129   FIGURE 202

Prayer rug ("cemetery rug"), Ghiordes, XIX century

6′ 10″ × 4′

WARP: Wool

WEFT: Wool; 2 shoots after each row of knots

KNOTTING: Wool. Ghiordes knot, about 84 knots per square inch

COLORS: 8. *Ground*: light olive green (field), light blue (border). *Pattern*: red, light purple, light blue, yellow green, green, brown, dark brown.

DECORATION: *Field*: A niche defined by a row of cypress trees that includes two stylized pomegranates, the apex containing a palmette device. In the spandrels, two leaves rising from fishbone motifs. Within the niche, a rosebush with leaves and blossoms, two tombs beneath it, two stylized blossoms on stems above it. The field is framed by a geometrical scroll bearing leaves and hook motifs. *Border*: A floral design of carnations, tulips, and lilies.

PUBLISHED: Breck-Morris, no. 72.

Gift of James F. Ballard, the James F. Ballard Collection 22. 100. 94

130   RIGHT

Prayer rug ("cemetery rug"), Ghiordes, XIX century

6′ 5½″ × 4′ 2¾″

WARP: Wool

WEFT: Wool; 2 shoots after each row of knots

KNOTTING: Wool. Ghiordes knot, about 104 knots per square inch

COLORS: 8. *Ground*: light blue (niche), tan (spandrels, lower panel), red brown (upper panel), white (border), yellow (inner guard band), black (outer guard band). *Pattern*: white, tan, yellow, red, light blue, blue, red brown, black.

DECORATION: *Field*: An arched niche filled with four transverse rows of tomb mosques with cypress and other trees. In the apex, a single large mosque lamp. In

KNOTTING: Wool and cotton. Ghiordes knot, about 99 knots per square inch

COLORS: 8. *Ground*: dark blue (niche), green (spandrels), black brown (panels, alternate stripes of border, outer guard band), white (alternate stripes of border), yellow tan (inner guard band). *Pattern*: white, yellow tan, orange, red, light blue, dark blue, green, black brown.

DECORATION: *Field*: A niche with stepped, pointed arch, edged all around with carnations. The spandrels are filled with rows of stylized carnations and leaves. A panel above the spandrels and a panel below the niche are filled with large stylized carnations on stems. The panels are framed by wavy scrolls bearing leaves; those around the lower panel are geometrically stylized. *Border*: Seven narrow stripes filled alternately with heart-shaped blossoms and buds. *Inner guard band*: Trefoil leaves and blossoms on stems. *Outer guard band*: Stylized carnations. *Edgings*: A geometrical scroll.

Theodore M. Davis Collection, Bequest of Theodore M. Davis, 1915

30.95.143

the spandrels, transverse rows of bouquets in tazzas, pointing down. In the space around the niche, a band of S–motifs. Above the spandrels, a panel filled with a row of palmettes. Beneath the niche, a panel filled with transverse staggered rows of small blossoms. The field and panels are framed by a wavy scroll with palmettes. *Border*: A floral device consisting of stylized carnations, lilylike blossoms, and roses. *Inner guard band*: Carnations on stems. *Outer guard band*: A scroll with lilylike trefoils. *Edgings*: Small blossoms.

Theodore M. Davis Collection, Bequest of Theodore M. Davis, 1915

30.95.85

131   RIGHT

Prayer rug, Ghiordes or Kula, XIX century

6′ 5″ × 4′ 4″

WARP: Wool

WEFT: Wool and cotton; 2 shoots after each row of knots

244

132 BELOW

Prayer rug, Kula, end of XVIII century

6′ × 4′ 1″

WARP: Wool

WEFT: Wool; 2 shoots after each row of knots

KNOTTING: Wool. Ghiordes knot, about 99 knots per square inch

COLORS: 7. *Ground*: dark blue (niche), light blue (spandrels, area surrounding niche), brown (panel), cream white (border), tan (guard bands). *Pattern*: cream white, tan, light blue, dark blue, red, brown, black brown.

DECORATION: *Field*: An arched niche with wavy outline, sides, and bottom. In the apex, a lamp, from which hangs a festoon of lamps and stars; a row of stars edges the sides and bottom of the niche. In the spandrels, a repeat pattern of three balls. In the area surrounding the niche a floral scroll with carnations and tulips. In a panel above the spandrels, a row of leafy palmettes. The field is framed by stylized leaves. *Border*: Three rows of stylized blossoms on stems, changing colors at intervals. *Inner guard band*: Rosettes connected by S–motifs. *Outer guard band*: Curly leaves. *Edging*: Rosettes.

PUBLISHED: Breck-Morris, no. 69.

Gift of James F. Ballard, the James F. Ballard Collection
22. 100. 80

133 BELOW

Prayer rug, Kula, about 1800

5′ 7″ × 3′ 10″

WARP: Wool

WEFT: Wool; 2 shoots after each row of knots

KNOTTING: Wool. Ghiordes knot, about 96 knots per square inch

COLORS: 6. *Ground*: dark blue (niche), light blue (spandrels), brown (panels, guard bands), cream white (border). *Pattern*: cream white, yellow, tan, light blue, dark blue, brown.

DECORATION: *Field*: An arched niche with wavy outline, sides, and bottom, filled with small stars. In the spandrels, transverse rows of rosettes. A panel above the spandrels contains geometrical motifs combined with stylized blossoms. A panel beneath the niche contains stylized pomegranates. The field and panels are framed by a geometrical S–motif. *Border*: Four rows of rosettes, changing colors at intervals. *Guard bands and edgings*: Rosettes.

PUBLISHED: Breck-Morris, no. 70.

Gift of James F. Ballard, the James F. Ballard Collection
22. 100. 81

134 FIGURE 203

Prayer rug, Kula, XIX century

6′ 1″ × 4′ 2″
WARP: Wool
WEFT: Wool; 2 shoots after each row of knots
KNOTTING: Wool and cotton. Ghiordes knot, about 110 knots per square inch
COLORS: 11. *Ground*: dark blue (niche, panels), light green (spandrels), light blue green, gray white (alternate stripes of border), red (outer stripes of inner guard band), light blue (center stripe of inner guard band), brown (outer guard band). *Pattern*: gray white, tan, yellow, salmon pink, red, light blue, light green, brown.
DECORATION: *Field*: A pointed niche, sides and bottom edged with stylized tulips, the arch with carnations. In the spandrels, a repeat pattern of carnations. A panel above the spandrels contains carnations on stems; a panel beneath the niche contains leafy scrolls with blossoms. The field and panels are framed by a wavy scroll bearing leaves. *Border*: Seven stripes, four filled with small rosebuds, the alternate three with stylized pomegranates. *Inner guard band*: Three stripes containing blossoms. *Outer guard band*: Pomegranates on stems. *Edgings*: A zigzag.
PUBLISHED: Breck-Morris, no. 65.
Gift of James F. Ballard, the James F. Ballard Collection 22. 100. 105

135 FIGURE 204

Prayer rug ("cemetery rug"), Kula, XIX century

6′ 7″ × 4′
WARP: Wool
WEFT: Wool; 2 shoots after each row of knots
KNOTTING: Wool. Ghiordes knot, about 108 knots per square inch
COLORS: 9. *Ground*: dark blue (niche), light blue (spandrels, area surrounding niche), dark brown (upper panel, alternate stripes of border), tan (alternate stripes of border, inner guard band), white (outer guard band). *Pattern*: white, tan, ochre, light yellow, red, light blue, dark blue, light brown, dark brown.
DECORATION: *Field*: A niche with a festoon of leaves hanging from the apex; the festoon ends in three blossoms. The arch is edged with small leaves. Along either side of the niche and across the bottom, a repeated decoration of tombs and cypress trees. In the spandrels, an allover pattern of stylized carnations. The area surrounding niche is filled with stylized rosebuds. A panel above the spandrels is filled with a row of leafy palmettes. The field and panel are framed by an S-motif. *Border*: Six stripes filled with buds. *Guard bands*: Swastikas. *Edgings*: A geometrical scroll.

PUBLISHED: Breck-Morris, no. 71.
Gift of James F. Ballard, the James F. Ballard Collection 22. 100. 79

136 FIGURE 205

Prayer rug, Ladik, dated 1210 H. (1795/96)

6′ 6″ × 3′ 9″
WARP: Wool
WEFT: Wool; 2 shoots after each row of knots
KNOTTING: Wool. Ghiordes knot, about 96 knots per square inch
COLORS: 6. *Ground*: white (niche), red (spandrels, lower panel, outer guard band), blue (border), violet (inner guard band). *Pattern*: white, yellow, red, violet, blue, blue green.
DECORATION: *Field*: A niche with stepped arch, bordered in the spandrels with hooks. Within the niche, two abbreviated columns filled with a lozenge chain and edged, as are the sides of the niche, with small triangles. Above the columns, two ewers. In the apex, an octagon containing the date. In the spandrels, rosettes and geometrically stylized lanceolate leaves. Beneath the niche, a band containing a wavy scroll with carnations. Beneath this, three down-pointing, arrowhead-shaped arches containing geometrical scrolls and cross motifs. Five stalks with tulips grow downward from the arches and the spaces between them. The field is framed by a geometrical scroll. *Border*: Rosettes alternating with stems bearing stylized tulips and carnations. *Guard bands*: A wavy scroll with blossoms and leaves. *Edgings*: Small rosettes.
PUBLISHED: Breck-Morris, no. 42; Dimand, *Handbook*, fig. 210.
Gift of James F. Ballard, the James F. Ballard Collection 22. 100. 61

137 NEXT PAGE, LEFT

Prayer rug, probably Ladik, late XVIII century

6′ 3″ × 4′ 6″
WARP: Wool
WEFT: Wool; 2 shoots after each row of knots
KNOTTING: Wool. Ghiordes knot, about 110 knots per square inch
COLORS: 11. *Ground*: red (niche), dark blue (spandrels), yellow tan (border), black brown (guard band). *Pattern*: white, yellow tan, salmon pink, rose, red, light blue, blue, dark blue, light green, red brown, black brown.
DECORATION: *Field*: At either end a triple arched niche with columns, the columns filled with a scroll bearing leaves and blossoms. A pair of blossoms hangs in each arch. In the spandrels, a stylized floral pattern including

large lanceolate leaves; in the center, a quatrefoil containing a rosette and four palmettes. At either side of the
niche lilylike blossoms. *Border*: Cartouches filled with
tulips on stems; in the intervening spaces, halves of a
rosette device. *Guard band*: Curly leaves. *Edgings*: Small
rosettes.

PUBLISHED: Breck-Morris, no. 40.

Gift of James F. Ballard, the James F. Ballard Collection
22. 100. 65

138   ABOVE RIGHT

Prayer rug, Ladik, end of XVIII century

    5' 8" × 4'

WARP: Wool

WEFT: Wool; 2 shoots after each row of knots

KNOTTING: Wool. Ghiordes knot, about 181 knots per
    square inch

COLORS: 6. *Ground*: red (niche, panel, outer guard band),

dark blue (spandrels, border), blue green (inner guard
band). *Pattern*: white, tan, red, dark blue, blue green,
brown.

DECORATION: *Field*: A triple arched niche resting on
short, slender, double columns with capitals and bases.
The arches are bordered in the spandrels with hooks.
In the center arch, a stylized tree; in the other arches,
growing from the bases, stylized bands with leaves. In
the spandrels, a pattern of geometrical scrolls forming
candelabra motifs, together with rosettes, hook motifs,
and S–scrolls. In a panel above the spandrels a row of
five arrowhead-shaped arches from which grow
stylized tulips on stalks; between them, stems with
leaves. *Border*: Cartouches containing scrolls with
leaves and stylized tulips; in the intervening spaces,
polygonal motifs and rosettes. *Inner guard band*: S–
motifs. *Outer guard band*: Stylized scrolls with leaves.

PUBLISHED: Breck-Morris, no. 39.

Gift of James F. Ballard, the James F. Ballard Collection
22. 100. 62

139   FIGURE 207

Prayer rug, Ladik, end of XVIII century

6′ × 3′ 10″

WARP: Wool

WEFT: Wool; 2 shoots after each row of knots

KNOTTING: Wool. Ghiordes knot, about 128 knots per
square inch

COLORS: 9. *Ground*: red (niche, panel), blue (spandrels),
yellow (border), black brown (inner guard band), tan
(outer guard band). *Pattern*: white, tan, red, light blue,
blue, light green, light brown, black brown.

DECORATION: *Field*: An arched niche, the sides and bottom
edged with small blossoms, the stepped arch bordered
in the spandrels with hooks. In the spandrels, rosettes,
tulips, stylized lanceolate leaves, and panels filled with
geometrical stems. Beneath the niche, a band containing
a wavy scroll with blossoms and leaves, a band containing chevrons, and a panel filled with three down-
pointing, arrowhead-shaped arches, each containing
a rosette and a lozenge motif. Five stalks with tulips
grow downward from the arches and the spaces
between them. The field is framed by a geometrical
S–motif. *Border*: Rosettes alternating with stems bearing stylized tulips and carnations. *Guard bands*: A wavy
scroll with blossoms and leaves. *Edgings*: Small rosettes.

PUBLISHED: Breck-Morris, no. 43.

Gift of James F. Ballard, the James F. Ballard Collection
22. 100. 63

140   RIGHT

Prayer rug, Ladik, end of XVIII century

6′ 8″ × 3′ 7″

WARP: Wool

WEFT: Wool; 2 shoots after each row of knots

KNOTTING: Wool. Ghiordes knot, about 99 knots per
square inch

COLORS: 10. *Ground*: blue (niche), orange (spandrels,
panel), dark blue (border), tan (guard bands). *Pattern*:
white, tan, yellow, orange, red, purple, light blue,
blue, brown.

DECORATION: *Field*: A triple-arched niche, in the apex of
which hangs a ewer; from the ewer grows a stylized
tree with branches ending in carnations; a second ewer
is attached at the lower end of the tree. In the spandrels,
geometrical scrolls with strongly stylized blossoms and
rosettes. Beneath the niche, a panel with three down-
pointing arrowhead-shaped arches, each filled with a
rosette blossom, hooks, and a rosette device. Five
stalks with tulips grow downward from the arches and
the spaces between them; the tops of the arches are
edged with hooks. The field and panel are framed by
geometrical S–motifs. *Border*: A rosette alternating with
tulips on stems. *Guard bands*: A wavy scroll bearing
blossoms and leaves. *Edgings*: Small rosettes.

PUBLISHED: Breck-Morris, no. 41.

Gift of James F. Ballard, the James F. Ballard Collection
22. 100. 64

141   FIGURE 208

Prayer rug, Mujur, early XIX century

5′ 5″ × 4′ 2″

WARP: Wool

WEFT: Wool; 2 shoots after each row of knots

KNOTTING: Wool. Ghiordes knot, about 56 knots per
square inch

COLORS: 10. *Ground*: red (niche), green (spandrels),
yellow (border), white (inner guard band), black
brown (outer guard band). *Pattern*: white, yellow,
orange, red, violet, light blue, blue, yellow green,
green, black brown.

DECORATION: *Field*: An arched niche with stepped outline
at the top, the sides and bottom of the niche edged with

carnations. The niche is filled with a flowering tree of carnations rising from a stylized vase. The spandrels, edged with triangles, each contain a large stylized leaf. Above the niche, a panel contains a row of arrowhead-shaped arches filled with arabesques. The field and panel are framed by a wavy scroll. *Border*: A repeat pattern of a lozenge within a square, the lozenge containing a stylized rosette. The cornerpieces of the square form two small lozenges, each containing a cross motif. *Inner guard band*: Lozenges with pairs of rosebuds on stems. *Outer guard band*: Stylized blossoms. *Inner edging*: Geometrical S–motifs. *Outer edgings*: Reciprocal triangles.

PUBLISHED: Breck-Morris, no. 74.
Gift of James F. Ballard, the James F. Ballard Collection
22. 100. 22

142   FIGURE 209

Prayer rug, Melas, early XIX century

5′ 5″ × 3′ 8″
WARP: Wool
WEFT: Wool; 2 shoots after each row of knots
KNOTTING: Wool. Ghiordes knot, about 88 knots per square inch
COLORS: 7. *Ground*: red (niche, inner stripe of inner guard band), cream white (spandrels, outer guard band), light yellow (border), purple (outer stripe of inner guard band). *Pattern*: cream white, light yellow, red, purple, blue, light green, brown.
DECORATION: *Field*: A niche with angular apex, the whole edged with small leaves. In the niche, four rosettes and three leaf-edged lozenges, the lozenges each containing a geometrical interlacing. In the spandrels, palmettes on short stems. *Border*: A blossom giving off leaves, alternating with a leaf pattern forming a cross device. *Inner guard band*: Three stripes, the inner one containing a wavy scroll, the central one trefoils, the outer one two geometrical scrolls with small panels. *Outer guard band*: Four-petaled rosettes. *Edgings*: Reciprocal triangles.

PUBLISHED: Breck-Morris, no. 75.
Gift of James F. Ballard, the James F. Ballard Collection
22. 100. 24

143   FIGURE 210

Geometrical rug, Melas, beginning of XIX century

4′ 11″ × 3′ 7″
WARP: Wool
WEFT: Wool; 2 shoots after each row of knots
KNOTTING: Wool. Ghiordes knot; about 56 knots per square inch
COLORS: 9. *Ground*: red (field, outer guard band, end panels), light blue, blue (octagon, inner guard band),

purple (spandrels), yellow (border). *Pattern*: white, yellow, orange, red, purple, light blue, blue, green, black.
DECORATION: *Field*: An octagon defined by a double band adorned with hooks. In the center and at each end in the long axis, a rosette within a lobed circular medallion. The octagon is filled with a geometrical scroll bearing hyacinths and rosettes. At each side of the central lobed medallion is a tulip. The spandrels, which are bordered with hooks, contain a stylized carnation at one end of the rug, a rosette at the other end. *Border*: A rosette on a leafy stem. *Guard bands*: Geometrical S–motifs. At either end of the rug there is a panel filled with a series of pointed arches, each containing a palmette, with a rosette in the spandrels.

PUBLISHED: Breck-Morris, no. 77.
Gift of James F. Ballard, the James F. Ballard Collection
22. 100. 23

144   FIGURE 211

Geometrical rug with central medallion, Melas, beginning of XIX century

6′ 2″ × 4′ 5″
WARP: Wool
WEFT: Wool; 2 shoots after each row of knots
KNOTTING: Wool. Ghiordes knot, about 90 knots per square inch
COLORS: 8: *Ground*: blue (field), red (panel around medallion), brown (border), brick red (end panels). *Pattern*: white, tan, red, brick red, purple, blue, dark blue, brown.
DECORATION: *Field*: A large eight-pointed panel contains a central eight-pointed medallion; this is divided into squares and triangles and contains angular palmettes. In the medallion's central square there is a rosette contained in an octagonal panel. Stylized trees grow out from the medallion's margin. The ground of the panel is figured with rosettes, stars, and a large hooked motif in each of the four principal corners. The irregular area outside the panel is filled with a geometrical blossom or fruit alternating with a geometrical flowering plant. *Border*: An angular scroll. At either end of the rug, a panel of stylized tulips.

PUBLISHED: Breck-Morris, no. 76.
Gift of James F. Ballard, the James F. Ballard Collection
22. 100. 25

145   RIGHT

Arabesque medallion rug, Konya, about 1800

10′ 1″ × 3′ 10″
WARP: Wool
WEFT: Wool; 2 shoots after each row of knots

KNOTTING: Wool. Ghiordes knot, about 90 knots per square inch

COLORS: 8. *Ground*: brick red (field), dark blue (medallions), light yellow (border), light blue (guard band). *Pattern*: white, yellow, light blue, dark blue, green, brown.

DECORATION: *Field*: On the long axis, four medallions and part of a fifth, composed of four half-palmettes and filled with roses and carnations. The rest of the field is patterned with stems bearing rosettes, carnations, and leaves. *Border*: A leafy scroll sending off stems with carnations, tulips, and roses. *Guard band*: A wavy scroll with blossoms.

PUBLISHED: Breck-Morris, no. 50.

Gift of James F. Ballard, the James F. Ballard Collection 22. 100. 82

146   FIGURE 213

Prayer rug, probably Ladik, dated 1188 H. (1774/75)

5′ 3″ × 3′ 6″

WARP: Wool

WEFT: Wool and metal threads

TECHNIQUE: Tapestry (kilim); 16 warp threads per inch

COLORS: 13. *Ground*: blue green (niche), red (spandrels), light tan (border), light blue (inner guard band), dark blue (outer guard band). *Pattern*: white, light tan, yellow, orange, red, purple, light blue, blue, dark blue, blue green, light green, brown, gold.

DECORATION: *Field*: A niche with stepped arch, the date and name "Muhammad rasul Allah" appearing in the apex. The sides and bottom of the niche are edged with small leaves, the steps of the arch with hooks. In the spandrels, rosettes and other blossoms on angular stems, together with geometrical motifs including lozenges. *Border*: Rosettes alternating with a candelabra motif bearing stylized pomegranates. *Inner guard band*: A zigzag band bearing small lozenges. *Outer guard band*: Shield-shaped compartments, each filled with a stylized plant.

PUBLISHED: Dimand, *Peasant and Nomad Rugs*, no. 6.

Anonymous Gift, 1962

62. 156

147   FIGURE 214

Prayer rug, Ghiordes or Kula, XIX century

5′ 1″ × 4′

WARP: Wool

WEFT: Wool and metal threads

TECHNIQUE: Tapestry (kilim); 17 warp threads per inch

COLORS: 10. *Ground*: white (niche), yellow green (spandrels, columns), tan (border, inner guard band), blue (outer guard band). *Pattern*: white, tan, red, light blue, blue, gray brown, dark brown, gold, silver.

DECORATION: *Field*: A triple-arched niche supported on slender columns with bases, the arches and columns edged with leaves. Filling each arch is a stylized tree. In the spandrels, stylized carnations. *Border*: Stylized carnations, growing from one long stem at either side and from short stems at the ends. *Guard band*: A wavy scroll bearing stylized hyacinths.

PUBLISHED: Breck-Morris, no. 84.

Gift of James F. Ballard, the James F. Ballard Collection 22. 100. 60

148   FIGURE 215

Prayer rug, Ladik, early XIX century

5′ 1″ × 4′

WARP: Wool

WEFT: Goat hair

TECHNIQUE: Tapestry (kilim); 14 warp threads per inch

COLORS: 8. *Ground*: gray green (niche), red (spandrels), tan (border), dark blue (guard bands). *Pattern*: white, yellow, red, blue, light green.

DECORATION: *Field*: An arched niche, the stepped apex filled with a stylized tulip tree and small rosettes. In the spandrels, cypress trees growing out of vases, tulips on stems, and rosettes. *Border*: A rosette alternating with a tulip on a leafy stem; small geometrical rosettes between them. *Inner guard band*: Geometrical rosettes.

Outer guard band: Alternate geometrical rosettes and stylized tulips.

PUBLISHED: Breck-Morris, no. 83.

Gift of James F. Ballard, the James F. Ballard Collection 22. 100. 58

149   BELOW

Prayer rug, early XIX century

5′ × 3′ 7″

WARP: Wool

WEFT: Goat hair and metal threads

TECHNIQUE: Tapestry (kilim); 15 warp threads per inch

COLORS: 9. *Ground*: red (niche), metal (spandrels), tan (border), beige (guard bands). *Pattern*: white, tan, beige, red, blue, dark blue, olive green, brown, metal.

DECORATION: *Field*: A niche with pointed arch containing a flowering tree flanked by geometrical cypress trees. The niche is edged with small leaves. In the spandrels, two geometrical cypress trees, flanked by geometrical scrolls. *Border*: At the ends, a geometrical floral device alternating with a stylized cypress; at the sides, only the floral device. *Inner guard band*: A row of shields; at the sides these alternate with a band of checkering. *Outer guard band*: A wavy scroll bearing stylized carnations.

PUBLISHED: Breck-Morris, no. 85.

Gift of James F. Ballard, the James F. Ballard Collection 22. 100. 59

Eight:

RUGS
OF
SPAIN

With the Arab conquest of Spain in the years 710–712 Muslim civilization advanced into western Europe. Spain was ruled until 756 by governors appointed by the Umayyad caliphs of Damascus. Then, when the Umayyads of Damascus were overthrown by the Abbasids, the last Umayyad ruler, Abd al-Rahman, fled to Spain. Here he became amir and founder of the Spanish Umayyad dynasty. The city of Cordova, chosen as the Umayyads' capital, soon equaled Baghdad (which in 762 succeeded Damascus as the Abbasid capital), as a center of wealth, art, and scholarship. Cordova became especially famous for its splendid Great Mosque, begun by Abd al-Rahman in 786, and later for the magnificent palace at nearby Madinat al-Zahra, built by Caliph Al-Hakim II (961–976).

The first of the Spanish rulers to adopt the title of caliph was Abd al-Rahman III, in 929. In the eleventh century Muslim Spain was ruled by a succession of minor Moroccan Berber dynasties, their rulers known as Reyes de Taifas, "Party Kings." Although Cordova continued to be Spain's chief artistic center, some of the provincial cities, notably Saragossa, now played significant parts in the development of Hispano-Moresque art. In 1090, under the Berber dynasty of the Almoravids, Muslim Spain became part of an empire that included Morocco. As a result, the culture and arts of Andalusia, the Moorish region of Spain, became influential in the Maghrib (Moorish North Africa), and many fine buildings were erected in such cities as Marrakesh (the Almoravid capital), Fez, and Tlemcen.

The Berber Almohads, the successors of the Almoravids in Africa, annexed Spain in 1145–1150. The political decline of western Islam began in 1235 with the gradual reconquest of Spain by the Christians. The last Muslim dynasty to hold out was that of the Nasrids (1232–1492), whose kingdom comprised the provinces of Almería, Málaga, and Granada, and whose capital was the city of Granada. The Nasrids revived the former splendor of Muslim Spain. The most magnificent of their monuments was the Alhambra, begun about 1245 and completed about 1345. In 1492 the kingdom of the Nasrids fell to the Castilian forces of Ferdinand and Isabella.

As early as the ninth century Spain's Moorish artists began developing the artistic forms and techniques, partly derived from eastern Islamic art, that were to be peculiar to Spain. Arabesques, geometrical interlacings, and Kufic writing became integral elements of the Hispano-Moresque decoration in stone, stucco, ivory carving, ceramics, textiles, and rugs. Under the Umayyads of the ninth and tenth centuries ivory carving was a highly developed art; the richly decorated Umayyad ivory boxes, showing court scenes with entertainers and hunters, are often inscribed with the names of contemporary rulers and court officials.

The development of ceramic art in Spain was based to a great extent on the achievements of the potters of Syria, Iraq, and to a lesser degree Persia. Among the techniques introduced in Spain by the Arabs was luster painting; this remained popular for centuries. Many Spanish ceramic centers were developed, Cor-

252

ORIENTAL RUGS

dova and Paterna being among the early ones. In the fourteenth century the potters of Málaga and Granada produced splendid lusterware with a decoration of arabesques, interlacings, and knotted Kufic writing of Persian origin. From the end of the fourteenth century through the sixteenth, Manises, in the province of Valencia, was known for its ceramics with luster decoration, many of these pieces being made for Christian rulers.

During the first half of the fifteenth century Gothic elements were gradually introduced in the patterns of the Valencian ceramics. In the middle and second half of the fifteenth century ceramic pieces were

decorated with Gothic ivy scrolls and bryony and acacia leaves combined with Spanish or Italian coats of arms.

The weaving of fine silk fabrics was another of the arts introduced by the Arabs. Hispano-Moresque silk textiles are mentioned as early as the ninth century in papal inventories. A silk veil inscribed in Kufic with the name of Caliph Hisham II (976–1009) exemplifies the early textile weaving and shows the use of Eastern motifs and techniques (figure 216). The piece is decorated with a tapestry-woven band of octagons in silk and gold. Some of the octagons contain stylized human figures, others animals or birds. Similar figures are found in Egyptian textiles of the same period, both Coptic (Christian) and Fatimid (Arabic). It is known that Coptic weavers worked in Spain during the tenth century.[1] From

Egypt, it would appear, came the techniques seen in the veil of Hisham and contemporary Moorish textiles, of using gold threads consisting of a silk core wound with gilded strips of goldbeaters' skin (called in the West, Cypriot gold). Such threads are to be seen in tenth-century silk fragments found in Egypt.[2]

The silk weaving of Spain owed much also to the importation of costly silk textiles from Baghdad. These silks, many of them lavishly brocaded with gold threads, were patterned with medallions containing figures of elephants, camels, horses, or birds. Silks of this sort are listed as having been brought from Baghdad to Cordova in 939 as presents for Caliph Abd al-Rahman III. The Spanish craftsmen not only adopted the designs of such pieces but wove direct copies of them. The copies even included the inscriptions naming Baghdad as the weaving center, as may be seen in an eleventh-century piece decorated with elephants, now in the Colegiata de San Isidoro, Leon.[3] There can be little doubt that the patterns of the Baghdad silks influenced the style of Hispano-Moresque textiles produced during the eleventh and twelfth centuries. The chief Spanish textile centers were Seville, Málaga, Granada, Almería, and the province of Murcia. Some measure of their importance may be estimated from a statement made in the twelfth century by al-Idrisi, the Arab geographer of King Roger II of Sicily, that the number of looms for the weaving of costly silks in Almería alone was eight hundred.

An important group of early Andalusian textiles is characterized by a bold pattern of human figures, birds, animals, or sphinxes in circular medallions. Some of them show a legendary figure known as the lion-strangler.[4] In the thirteenth-century silk brocades and tapestry-woven examples we find either a geometrical pattern or figure subjects, with a lavish use of gold threads.[5] Fourteenth- and fifteenth-century silks woven in Granada are decorated in the so-called Alhambra style, consisting of interlaced bands, polygons, arabesques, and Arabic inscriptions, all rendered in vivid colors.[6] In other fifteenth-century Spanish silks, favored by Christians, the Gothic style appears, featuring pomegranates and leaf patterns.[7]

The rug industry in Spain goes back to an early period. It must have been active before the twelfth century, for the Cordovan poet al-Shakundi relates early in the thirteenth century that rugs made in Chinchilla, in the province of Murcia, during the twelfth century were sent to foreign countries, including Egypt. A number of rug fragments found

FIGURE 216   Silk veil of Caliph Hisham II (976–1009). Academia de la Historia, Madrid

in the ruins of Fustat seem to confirm his statement. Some of these are in the Museum of Islamic Art, Cairo (unpublished), others are in the Textile Museum, Washington.[8] One in the Metropolitan (figure 217) has a dentelated ornament, a band of triangles, and discs in blue, yellow, green, and brown, on a red ground, bordered by a band of Kufic characters in yellow on a blue ground. The materials, colors, and type of Kufic in all these fragments suggest manufacture in Spain, and so does their knotting. All are tied with the single-warp or Spanish knot rather than with either of the knots known in rugs of the Near East, namely the Ghiordes and Senna. It seems probable that the single-warp knot reached Spain from Egypt where, as discussed on page 9, it was known to Coptic weavers of the seventh or eighth century and Arab weavers of the ninth century. Coptic weavers, as mentioned above, were active in Spain in the tenth century.

By the thirteenth century Spain's rug industry was fully developed. The products of the Moorish looms of this time were admired not only in the Muslim East but in the Christian West. A contemporary report tells us that when Eleanor of Castile, the wife of Prince Edward of England, reached London in October 1255, a great display of Spanish rugs was to be seen in the streets and in her lodgings at Westminster. And in the inventory of Gonzalo Gudial,

Bishop of Cuenca, dated 1273, small rugs of Murcia are mentioned.

From the second half of the thirteenth century on, as Christian rule was re-established in Spain, Moorish weavers continued to produce fine rugs. Often they combined Moorish and Western elements in a new style known as Mudéjar (the name signifying a Muslim living under a Christian king). In addition to the looms at Chinchilla, new weaving centers were established, notably at Letur (or Litur) and Alcaraz. Letur and Alcaraz have each been credited as the production center of the armorial rugs to be con-

FIGURE 217   Rug fragment, Moorish, probably Chinchilla, XII–XIII century. The Metropolitan Museum of Art, Purchase, Rogers Fund, 27.170.8

sidered in detail below. The making of these rugs goes back certainly to the first third of the fourteenth century, since there is documentary evidence that Pope John XXII (1315–1334) bought Spanish rugs with coats of arms for his palace at Avignon. Judging from a fresco by Matteo di Giovanetto in this palace's Chapel of Saint Martial, painted between 1344 and 1346,[9] rugs were made with patterns like those of the armorial rugs but without the coats of arms.

The only extant Spanish rug now attributed to the fourteeth century is the so-called Synagogue Rug in the Staatliche Museen, Berlin.[10] It was given this name because its decoration consists of an elaborate candelabrum whose arms end, according to Friedrich Sarre, in Torah shrines. However, the rug's Kufic border would not appear in a piece intended for a synagogue, and it is probable that the decoration represents instead a tree of life, a motif that also appears in the borders of some armorial rugs of the fifteenth century.

ARMORIAL RUGS (FIFTEENTH CENTURY)

Important Mudéjar products, made to the order of the royal house or of other prominent Spanish families, were the armorial rugs. In these, coats of arms are placed upon fields ornamented with a repeat pattern of small octagons, hexagons, or less often, stepped lozenges. Some of these compartments enclose star motifs or crosses, as well as stylized birds, animals, or human figures. The borders are divided into bands containing geometrical designs, stylized birds, animals such as bears and boars, or human figures, and Kufic inscriptions. One group of these rugs, probably commissioned by María of Castile, who married Alfonso of Aragon in 1415 and became queen of Spain in 1416, has the coat of arms of Castile and Aragon. Three of the rugs, said to have come from the convent of Santa Isabel de los Reyes, Toledo, are in the collection of the Hispanic Society of America, New York, the Detroit Institute of Arts, and the Textile Museum, Washington.[11] An old record contains the information that Juana de Mendoza left to the convent of Santa Clara, Palencia, two large rugs bearing her coat of arms and that of her husband, Alfonso Enríquez. Rugs with the coat of arms of the Enríquez family, said to have come from this convent, are in the Williams Collection in the Philadelphia Museum of Art, in Vizcaya (Dade County Art Museum), Miami, in the Dumbarton Oaks Collection, Washington, and in the Instituto de

Valencia de Don Juan, Madrid.[12] According to José Ferrandis Torres, the rug of figure 218 is another of this group. A fragment of a rug with a similar coat of arms is in the Staatliche Museen, Berlin.[13]

All of the armorial rugs have stylistic features of interest, some of oriental origin, others purely Spanish. The prototypes of the field diapers seen in the rug of figure 218 and the similar rug in Berlin appear in Anatolian rugs of the fifteenth century as we know from rugs represented in paintings by Memling. Furthermore, the stylized animals and birds of the armorial rugs recall similar figures in early Anatolian rugs. Not only did such Anatolian rugs appear in fourteenth- and fifteenth-century Italian and Flemish paintings, but several fragments of the actual rugs are known (page 173). That Anatolian animal rugs were known in Spain is evident from their representation in several Spanish paintings of the mid-fifteenth century, particularly works by the Catalan Jaume Huguet (figure 145).

Still other features of the armorial rugs may be traced to the Near East, the most prominent of these being the Kufic border. Adopting this decoration, which, as we have seen, was used in the earliest known fragments of Spanish rugs, the Moorish weavers created their own type of inscription, in which the slender verticals are often adorned with a series of hooks and the tops of the verticals are joined with stylized pine cones (figure 218). Other Islamic elements that appear in some of the armorial rugs include an inner border with a lozenge diaper containing a swastika pattern, a motif used in some Anatolian rugs of the fourteenth and fifteenth centuries, and a motif representing the right hand of Fatima, the daughter of the Prophet.

Other motifs in the armorial rugs are of Spanish origin, such as the hunting scenes that are found in some of the borders. These show wild men, bears, and boars in a Western-style tree landscape.

GEOMETRICAL RUGS (FIFTEENTH CENTURY)

Because of their resemblance to the Anatolian "Holbeins" (page 179) certain Moorish geometrical rugs are often called "Spanish Holbeins." They are usually attributed to the famous looms of Alcaraz, frequently mentioned in literary sources. A letter from Queen Isabella of Castile in which she thanks the city of Alcaraz for a gift of *alfombras*—rugs—provides evidence that the industry was thriving there in the fifteenth century. It is to the second half

FIGURE 218 Armorial rug, Letur or Alcaraz, first half of xv century. Catalogue no. 150

FIGURE 219 Geometrical compartment rug, Alcaraz, second half of xv century. Catalogue no. 151

of this century that the "Spanish Holbeins" can be dated. All of them have fields divided into large squares enclosing octagons, with the spandrels of the squares filled either with interlacings or a checkerboard pattern. The borders of the rugs often show a stylized floral motif that was referred to in Spain as a scorpion. In the inventory of King Martin of Aragon, dated 1410, rugs are mentioned with "seals of Solomon" and "scorpions"; the last term may indicate this type of border ornament.

There are three varieties of "Spanish Holbein." In one, the octagons are defined by dense interlacing and contain large many-pointed stars (figure 119),

the arms of which are divided into compartments containing lozenges, interlacings, octagons, rosettes, and small crosses. The arms of these large stars form crosses around small central stars. The colors are white, yellow, red, blue, and green. A prototype of this star pattern appears in an Anatolian rug in the painting of the Annunciation by Carlo Crivelli, cited on page 177. The cross pattern is quite pronounced in a Spanish rug formerly in the Staatliche Museen, Berlin, that Ernst Kühnel has assigned to the end of the fifteenth century.[14] Other rugs of this variety are fragments in the Textile Museum, Washington, and the Williams Collection in the Philadelphia Museum of Art, and a rug in the Victoria and Albert Museum.[15] The pattern it also to be seen in the representation of a rug in a Spanish painting of a warrior-saint that can be dated to the end of the fifteenth century.[16] This rug has features that make it Anatolian, not Moorish.

In a second variety, the color scheme of which is similar to that of the first, the design is much more elaborate. The dark blue octagons contain eight-pointed stars formed by interlaced and knotted bands, surrounded by individual knot motifs (figure 220). A companion piece to the illustrated rug was formerly in a private collection; both are said to have come from the convent of Santa Ursula, Guadalajara.

Interlacings with simple heart-shaped knots may be found in the fields of certain Anatolian rugs, particularly the "Holbeins" with small-scale patterns (page 179), but the more complicated, so-called endless knots found in the Spanish rugs are usually confined to the borders of the Anatolian rugs, where they are combined with Kufic. Such a border may be seen in an Anatolian rug represented by Jaume Huguet in his Ordination of Saint Vincent (about 1475), in Barcelona,[17] and in the fresco of 1485 by Vincenzo Foppa mentioned on page 177. Used as a field decoration the endless knot is to be found in numerous Persian rugs depicted in fifteenth-century Persian paintings (figure 53). As historical and artistic evidence testifies, a good deal of Persian influence had made its way to Spain over a period of centuries. This influence has been pointed out in the field of Hispano-Moresque ceramics,[18] and we have the word of al-Razi ("Man of Rayy"), a Persian writer of the tenth century, that many inhabitants of Rayy, one of the principal pottery centers of Persia, established

FIGURE 220   Rug with star pattern, Letur or Alcaraz, middle of xv century. The Textile Museum Collection, Washington, D.C.

themselves in Spain. In the thirteenth century, as a result of the Mongols' devastation of Persia, potters of Rayy and Kashan are known to have migrated; doubtless the Islamic centers of Spain were among those that drew them. When the Nasrids established the last great Muslim kingdom of Spain in 1232, they must have summoned the finest craftsmen and artisans to make, among other objects, the large lustered vases that adorned their palaces, including the Alhambra. That these were Persian craftsmen is suggested in two ways: by the appearance of Kufic in the vases in the form favored by Persians—with the elongated verticals of the letters interlaced and knotted—and by the use of the complicated knotted ornament, not only in the vases but in the elaborate stucco wall decorations of the Alhambra.[19] The Persian influence so seen suggests that Persian rugs may well have been known in Spain in the fifteenth century.

The third and least rare variety of "Spanish Holbein" differs from the others chiefly in the design of its octagons. This consists of eight palmettes that connect with a small central star and with the octagon frame. The spandrels of the squares surrounding the octagon are filled with a checkered pattern. In a typical piece of this group, said to have come with several other rugs from the convent of Santa Ursula, Guadalajara, eight octagons have a double frame, their outer band filled with rosettes with hooks, their inner with small squares (figure 221). The eight squares, surrounding the octagons are bordered with bands containing angular interlacing in the long direction and by bands comprised of wavy lines in the transverse direction. The rug is framed with a narrow band containing rosettes, rather than with the scorpion border popular in Alcaraz, and at either end there is a repeat pattern of lozenges framed by a double row of hook motifs. Other rugs of this variety differ in details of the design and in the number of squares. One in the Cleveland Museum of Art,[20] likewise said to have come from the Guadalajara convent, has eighteen squares. One in the Textile Museum, Washington,[21] with only four squares, has the scorpion border; at its ends it has a procession of animals and trees such as appear in some of the armorial rugs. A rug with twelve squares in the convent of Santa Clara in Medina de Pomar,[22] has a similar end decoration; its octagons are adorned with double spiral hooks forming trefoils—a motif of Anatolian origin. Two motifs seen in Anatolian geometrical rugs occur in the octagons of another example, this one having eight squares, in the City Art Museum, St. Louis[23]—angular S-motifs within

hexagons and spiral hook motifs. The squares of this rug are bordered by an archaic, simple form of Kufic. The basic design of this third variety was copied quite faithfully from Anatolian prototypes (figures 148, 149, 151).

In addition to copying "Holbeins" with geometrical patterns, the weavers of Alcaraz in some cases copied the Anatolian "Holbeins" with small-scale patterns of interlaced arabesques forming lozenge devices. Spanish rugs of this type are in the Museum

FIGURE 221 Geometrical rug, Alcaraz, second half of xv century. Catalogue no. 152

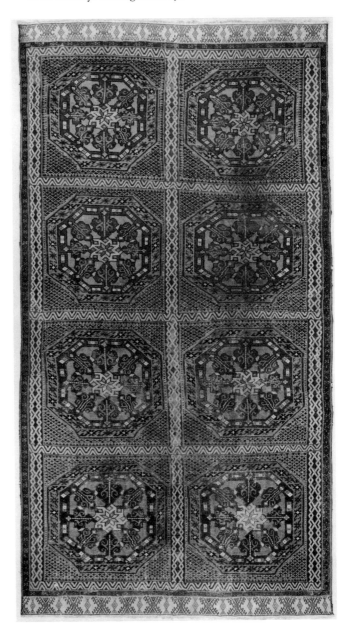

of Fine Arts, Boston, and the Textile Museum, Washington.[24]

RUGS WITH GOTHIC PATTERNS (FIFTEENTH CENTURY)

During the second half of the fifteenth century the weavers of Alcaraz and other centers, besides producing rugs with Moorish geometrical patterns, adopted Western elements, particularly floral decorations of the Gothic type. This influence was general in Spanish art, especially in ceramics and textiles, as noted earlier. One of the most popular floral motifs of Gothic silk weaves and velvets of Spain was the pomegranate,[25] a motif also popular in Italy and other countries. This ornament appears in a rug dating from about the end of the fifteenth century (figure 222, page 160). The field has an ogival diaper formed by interlaced and twisted bands. Each com-

FIGURE 223   Floral armorial rug, probably Alcaraz, second half of xv century. Catalogue no. 154

partment encloses a large leaf palmette within which appears a pomegranate stylized in Moorish fashion and decorated with heart motifs. The border has interlaced and knotted bands of a type known in Spanish textiles and ceramics of the fourteenth century. The outer guard band has a pattern resembling the scorpion motif of the Spanish geometrical rugs, and the band of trees at either end is reminiscent of the armorial rugs.

Only a few rugs of this type have survived. One in the Victoria and Albert Museum, another in the National Museum of Decorative Arts, Madrid, and two in the Textile Museum, Washington,[26] have borders with a debased Kufic resembling that of the armorial rugs. Both the Textile Museum rugs have end pieces with the stylized trees and animals found in the armorial rugs, one of them also having wild men. Two fragments of such rugs exist, one in the Metropolitan (57.170.92), the other in the Brooklyn Museum (unpublished). The latter has an atypical border, the designer having copied the interlaced Kufic decoration used in both the "Holbein" and "Lotto" rugs of Anatolia.

A Gothic floral design can be seen in a small rug with a coat of arms (figure 223). Its ogival diaper contains branches with leaves and pine cones. Its border of interlaced and knotted bands is similar to that of the "Holbein" rug of figure 221. The coat of arms is that of the Enríquez family, mentioned earlier.

A rug dating to the end of the fifteenth century may be regarded as transitional from the Gothic to the Rennaisance style. It has an ogival diaper formed by clusters of stylized floral motifs held by clasps (figure 224). The floral motifs consist of serrate leaves on stems, with both Gothic and Renaissance details. The geometrically stylized peacock and doves placed symmetrically in each compartment are known from armorial rugs. A fragment of a similar rug was formerly in the collection of Livinio Stuyck, Madrid.[27]

RUGS WITH GOTHIC AND RENAISSANCE PATTERNS (SIXTEENTH CENTURY AND LATER)

After the unification of Spain as the kingdom of Castile and Aragon, Moorish weavers, together with Christian, worked for Christian masters. Their rugs show an ever increasing use of Renaissance ornaments, some copied from textiles of Spain and Italy. Rugs formerly in the collection of Count Welczeck of Austria[28] show the continuation of the fifteenth-

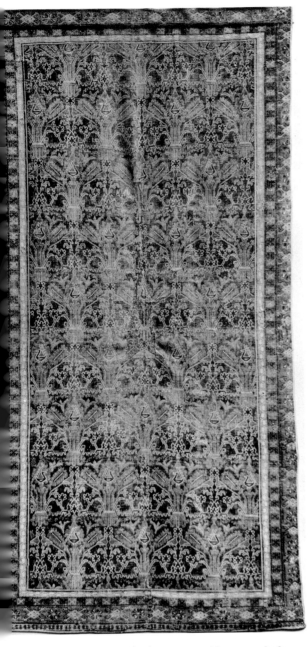

FIGURE 224 Arabesque rug, Alcaraz, end of xv century. Catalogue no. 155

FIGURE 225 Rug with wreath pattern, probably Cuenca, middle of xvi century. Catalogue no. 156

century pattern of ogival diaper with pomegranate, now treated in a more Western manner.

Popular in the sixteenth century was a Renaissance pattern of wreaths with arabesques (figure 225). The border pattern of this rug consists of a Renaissance "arabesque" made from the bodies of winged dragons. This rug and others like it, some of which are in the Textile Museum, Washington,[29] have little trace of Moorish design, and it is probable that Christian weavers, rather than Moorish, produced them. These rugs have characteristically limited color schemes, usually with two colors dominant: blue green on tan, dark green on light green, or (figure 225) blue green on red.

During the sixteenth and seventeenth centuries oriental rugs were imported to Europe in quantity,

particularly Turkish rugs of the Ushak variety. Ushak rugs were quite popular in Spain, and they influenced the design of rugs produced at Cuenca. The type known as "Holbein" or in the United States as "Lotto," with angular arabesques in yellow on a red ground (figures 158, 159), was the one most frequently imitated. Copying them, the Spanish weavers altered the color scheme, preferring blue arabesques on a golden yellow ground (figure 226). Other examples of this type are in the Textile Museum, Washington, the National Museum of Decorative Arts, Madrid, and private collections.[30] Such rugs are usually dated to the middle of the seventeenth century. Other varieties of Ushak rugs, medallion rugs, and even Turkish court rugs were copied by Spanish weavers of the seventeenth and eighteenth centuries. In addition to their Turkish designs some of these rugs have the Turkish, or Ghiordes, knot, hitherto not used in Spain.

Rugs made in Cuenca and Valencia during the eighteenth century—there are several dated examples —follow either the oriental or Western tradition, but their designs[31] are inferior to those of the sixteenth- and seventeenth-century rugs.

In the nineteenth century rugs were made in the district of Alpujarra, south of Granada, with a loop pile rather than a knotted pile.[32] The floral and animal designs of these rugs, based on traditional motifs, are often rendered in bright colors and treated broadly in conformity with their folk character.

FIGURE 226   Arabesque rug, Alcaraz or Cuenca, end of XVII century. Catalogue no. 157

Notes to Chapter Eight

1 Florence Lewis May, *Notes Hispanic*, V, p. 32.

2 Maurice S. Dimand, "Eine koptische Goldstickerei aus der Fatimidenzeit," in *Josef Strzygowski—Festschrift* (Klagenfurt, 1932), pp. 38–39.

3 Florence Lewis May, *Silk Textiles of Spain: Eighth to Fifteenth Century* (New York, 1957), fig. 14.

4 Ibid., fig. 29.

5 Ibid., figs. 43–51.

6 Ibid., figs. 89, 93, 96, 111–14, 126–31.

7 Ibid., figs. 132, 139–43.

8 Ernst Kühnel and Louisa Bellinger, *Catalogue of Spanish Rugs*, pls. I–III.

9 May, *Notes Hispanic*, V, p. 62, fig. 32.

10 Ernst Kühnel, *Maurische Kunst* (Berlin, 1924), pl. 152.

11 May, *Notes Hispanic*, V, figs. 1, 15; Kühnel-Bellinger, pls. IV–VIII.

12 May, *Notes Hispanic*, V, figs. 16, 21, 23, 26.

13 José Ferrandis Torres, *Exposición de alfombras antiguas españolas*, pl. 1.

14 Ernst Kühnel, "Maurische Teppiche aus Alcaraz," *Pantheon*, VI (1930), fig. 4.

15 Kühnel-Bellinger, pls. XIV, XV; José Ferrandis Torres, *Archivo Español de Arte*, XV, figs. 6, 4.

16 Ferrandis Torres, *Alfombras antiquas españolas*, fig. 10.

17 Benjamin Rowland Jr., *Jaume Huguet* (Cambridge, Mass., 1932), fig. 40.

18 Alice Wilson Frothingham, *Lustreware of Spain* (New York, 1951), pp. 21, 23.

19 Kühnel, *Maurische Kunst*, pls. 48–50.

20 Ferrandis Torres, *Archivo Español de Arte*, XV, fig. 10.

21 Kühnel-Bellinger, pls. XVI, XVII.

22 Ferrandis Torres, *Alfombras antiguas españolas*, pl. VI.

23 Maurice S. Dimand, *The Ballard Collection of Oriental Rugs in the City Art Museum of St. Louis*, pl. XII.

24 Kurt Erdmann, *Oriental Carpets*, fig. 175; Kühnel-Bellinger, pls. XXIV–XXV.

25 May, *Silk Textiles of Spain*, fig. 132.

26 A. F. Kendrick and C. E. C. Tattersall, *Hand-Woven Carpets*, II, pl. 79; Ferrandis Torres, *Alfombras antiguas españolas*, pl. XI; Kühnel-Bellinger, pls. IX–XI, XVIII, XIX.

27 Ferrandis Torres, *Alfombras antiguas españolas*, pl. VIII, no. 9.

28 Ibid., pls. XV, XVI.

29 Kühnel-Bellinger, pls. XXVI, XXVII, XXXIV, XXXV.

30 Ibid., pl. XXXVIII; Ferrandis Torres, *Alfombras antiguas españolas*, pls. XXXV, XXXVI.

31 Kendrick-Tattersall, II, pl. 82.

32 Kühnel-Bellinger, pls. XL, XLI.

CATALOGUE

150 FIGURE 218

Armorial rug, Letur or Alcaraz, first half of xv century

28′ 10″ × 7′ 9½″
WARP: Wool
WEFT: Wool; 1 shoot after each row of knots
KNOTTING: Wool. Spanish knot, about 132 knots per square inch
COLORS: 7. *Ground*: cream white (field at present), dark blue (outer border, inner guard bands), black brown (outer guard band). *Pattern*: cream white, orange, yellow tan, light blue, dark blue, brown, black brown.
DECORATION: *Field*: An allover diaper of stepped lozenges filled with a cross, a rosette, a stylized human figure, or a bird. Upon this diaper, three rectangular panels, the central one having a ground of parallel zigzag lines, the others having checkered grounds. In each panel, a lobed medallion containing a coat of arms. Unidentified (though according to José Ferrandis Torres, it is the emblem of the Enríquez family), it shows oak branches springing from a tree trunk. The field is framed by continuous double bands forming compartments filled with stars. *Inner border*: Rectangles containing, in no set order, a human figure with raised hands, a stylized bird, a cross, a candelabra motif, or some other geometrical ornament. *Outer border*: Pseudo-Kufic inscriptions of Moorish type, the slender letters adorned with hooks, the tops of the letters at the ends of the rug joined by stylized pine cones; between the letters at the sides of the rug, a stylized duck, a peacock, pairs of confronted cocks, an eagle, a dog, a human figure with raised hands, or a horseman. *Inner guard bands*: Transverse zigzags. *Outer guard band*: Small rosettes.
PUBLISHED: Dimand, *Metropolitan Museum of Art Bulletin*, XXII, figs, 3, 4.
Bequest of George Blumenthal
41. 190. 223

151 FIGURE 219

Geometrical compartment rug, Alcaraz, second half of xv century

9′ 3″ × 5′ 5″
WARP: Wool
WEFT: Wool; 1 shoot after each row of knots
KNOTTING: Wool. Spanish knot, about 103 knots per square inch
COLORS: 8. *Ground*: red. *Pattern*: white, yellow, orange, red, light blue, blue, dark green, brown.

DECORATION: *Field*: Six square compartments, each containing an octagon, and at one end two half-squares containing half-octagons. The octagons contain a sixteen-pointed star with a small star at the center; the arms of the larger star, formed by crosses, are subdivided into geometrical compartments filled with hooked motifs, lozenges, interlacing, or wavy lines. The spaces around the octagons are filled with interlacing. *Border* (of rug and of squares): A stylized floral motif, the so-called scorpion motif.
EX COLL. Dr. Von Buerkel
PUBLISHED: Dimand, *Handbook*, fig. 213; Dimand, *Metropolitan Museum of Art Bulletin*, XXII, fig. 6; Kühnel, *Pantheon*, VI, fig. 2.
Rogers Fund
13. 193. 2

152 FIGURE 221

Geometrical rug, Alcaraz, second half of xv century

10′ 2″ × 5′ 6½″
WARP: Wool
WEFT: Wool; 1 shoot after each row of knots
KNOTTING: Wool. Spanish knot, about 110 knots per square inch
COLORS: 8. *Ground*: red (octagons), light blue (border of squares), black brown (frame of rug), white (endpieces). *Pattern*: white, yellow, red, violet, light blue, dark blue, green, black brown.
DECORATION: *Field*: Eight squares, each enclosing an octagon with two frames. The outer frame contains rosettes with hooks; the inner frame contains squares and rectangles. The octagon has a central star within a pinwheel device. Eight stylized palmettes connect the central device to the inner frame of the octagon. The spandrels of the squares are filled with dense checkering. The squares are bordered in the lengthwise direction by bands containing angular interlacings, in the transverse direction by wavy lines. *Frame of rug*: A band of geometrical rosettes. *Endpieces*: A lozenge pattern with hooked motifs.
PROVENANCE: Said to have come from the Convent of Santa Ursula, Guadalajara.
PUBLISHED: Dimand, *Metropolitan Museum of Art Bulletin*, XXII, fig. 8; Ferrandis Torres, *Archivo español de Arte*, XV, fig. 14.
The Cloisters Collection
53. 79

153 FIGURE 222, PAGE 160

Arabesque rug, Alcaraz, end of xv century

17′ 1″ × 7′ 10″

WARP: Wool

WEFT: Wool; 1 shoot after each row of knots

KNOTTING: Wool. Spanish knot, about 120 knots per square inch

COLORS: 7. *Ground*: red (field), blue green (border), dark blue (inner guard band), white (outer guard band, end-pieces). *Pattern*: white, yellow, brick red, red, dark blue, green.

DECORATION: *Field*: An allover pattern of ogival compartments formed by interlaced and twisted bands, each compartment enclosing a large leaf-palmette within which is a stylized pomegranate containing heart motifs. *Border*: Interlaced and knotted bands forming cross-shaped compartments. *Inner guard band*: A wavy scroll with leaves. *Outer guard band*: The scorpion motif in a geometrical pattern. *Endpieces*: Stylized trees.

EX COLL. Sidney A. Charlat

PUBLISHED: Dimand, *Metropolitan Museum of Art Bulletin*, XXII, fig. 13.

The Cloisters Collection

61.49

154   FIGURE 223

Floral armorial rug, probably Alcaraz, second half of XV century

6′ 2″ × 4′ 11″

WARP: Wool

WEFT: Wool; 1 shoot after each row of knots

KNOTTING: Wool. Spanish knot, about 112 knots per square inch

COLORS: 10. *Ground*: blue (field), brick red (central square), light tan (border, guard bands). *Pattern*: white, cream yellow, light tan, tan, red, light blue, dark blue, dark brown.

DECORATION: *Field*: An allover pattern of bands forming an ogee trellis, a small leaf placed on the bands at each junction; each compartment contains a central unit of five leaves on a stem, with four pine cones on branches at the sides. Centered in the field, a square compartment containing the coat of arms of Fadrique Enríquez, Admiral of Castile, who died in 1473. *Border*: Interlaced and knotted bands. *Guard bands*: A wavy scroll with half-palmettes.

Bequest of George Blumenthal

41.190.268.

155   FIGURE 224

Arabesque rug, Alcaraz, end of XV century

9′ × 4′ 7″

WARP: Wool

WEFT: Wool; 1 shoot after each row of knots

KNOTTING: Wool. Spanish knot, about 140 knots per square inch

COLORS: 7. *Ground*: red (field), green (inner border), light blue (outer border), black brown (inner guard

bands, endpiece). *Pattern*: white, yellow, red, light blue, dark blue, green, black brown.

DECORATION: *Field*: An ogival diaper formed by rows of candelabra motifs with branches bearing serrate leaves; the central leaves are overlaid with stylized peacocks, the side stems end in stylized doves. The intervening spaces are filled with star motifs. *Inner border*: Geometrical scrolls. *Outer border*: A rosette alternating with a lozenge, the lozenge giving off trefoils. *Inner guard band*: A wavy scroll with leaves. *Endpiece*: Rosettes.

PUBLISHED: Breck-Morris, no. 127.

Gift of James F. Ballard, the James F. Ballard Collection

22.100.124

156   FIGURE 225

Rug with wreath pattern, probably Cuenca, middle of XVI century

17′ 9″ × 7′ 10″

WARP: Wool

WEFT: Wool; 1 shoot after each row of knots

KNOTTING: Wool. Spanish knot, about 110 knots per square inch

COLORS: 4. *Ground*: brick red (field), light green (border, guard bands). *Pattern*: yellow, light green, blue green.

DECORATION: *Field*: Two lengthwise rows of large wreaths composed of leaves and rosettes, and containing an arabesque device with half-palmettes issuing from a central rosette. In the spaces between the wreaths, a lozenge-shaped geometrical device. *Border*: A Renaissance scroll formed of bodies of winged dragons and leaves. *Guard bands*: A continuous line interspersed with rectangles decorated with diagonal zigzag bands.

PUBLISHED: Breck-Morris, no. 128.

Gift of James F. Ballard, the James F. Ballard Collection

22.100.125

157   FIGURE 226

Arabesque rug, Alcaraz or Cuenca, end of XVII century

11′ × 5′ 7″

WARP: Wool

WEFT: Wool; 1 shoot after each row of knots

KNOTTING: Wool. Ghiordes knot, about 56 knots per square inch

COLORS: 6. *Ground*: yellow tan (field, border, guard bands). *Pattern*: white, yellow tan, light blue, blue, dark blue, blue green.

DECORATION: *Field*: An allover pattern of arabesque devices with half-palmettes, derived from Turkish Ushak rugs. *Border*: A wavy scroll with half-palmettes and blossoms stylized in the Spanish manner. *Guard bands*: A zigzag band.

PUBLISHED: Breck-Morris, no. 129.

Gift of James F. Ballard, the James F. Ballard Collection

22.100.126

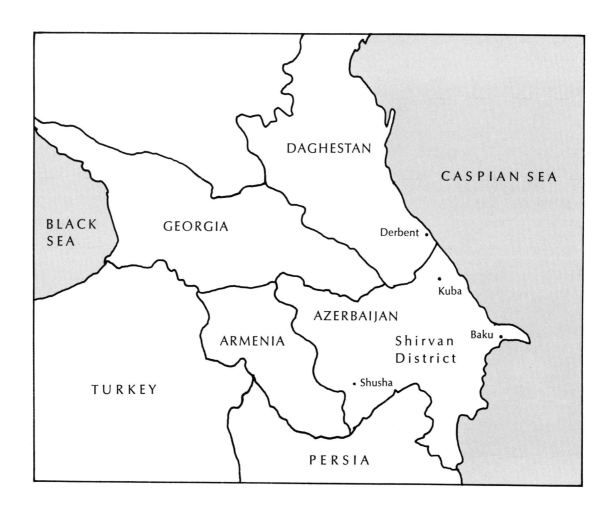

Nine:

RUGS OF
THE
CAUCASUS

The Caucasus, the region lying between the Black Sea and the Caspian, peopled by Armenians, Georgians, nomadic Tartars, and tribes of Persian and Turanian (Turkish) origin, was at an early period subject to cultural influences from Persia, to the south, and from the nomadic Scythians, who moved through the region extending from European Russia to China. As early as the third millennium B.C. the people of the Caucasus had a distinctive animal art. This was further developed by the Scythians about the eighth century B.C. and then by the nomadic Sarmatians, who controlled southern Russia and the Caucasus as late as the third century A.D. The art itself can be traced in Caucasian metalwork, sculpture, and other objects of the Islamic era.

The conquest of the Caucasus by the Arabs was gradual. By the middle of the eleventh century only Derbent, the principal town of the province of Daghestan, and a few neighboring castles were in Muslim hands. Then, in 1049, the Turkish Seljuks invaded Armenia, Georgia, and other parts of the Caucasus. Their cultural influence was soon apparent. The coins of the Georgian kings, which had at first imitated Byzantine coins, began to bear legends in Arabic. Sculpture produced in Daghestan[1] had a direct relationship to that of the Seljuks in Asia Minor. This may be seen in stone reliefs dating to the twelfth and thirteenth centuries, found in Kubatcha. These reliefs, taken from the ruined castles of local princes, were built into the houses of peasants. One such piece, an arched tympanum, now in the Metropolitan, shows a mounted warrior bordered by a typical Seljuk arabesque scroll with trefoil palmettes.[2] In the Freer Gallery of Art, Washington, is another such tympanum with a symmetrical composition of two lions bordered by a frieze of running animals against a background of arabesques, recalling Seljuk animal decoration. The Caucasian animal style also appears in twelfth- and thirteenth-century bronze braziers, their shape derived from Seljuk metalwork.

Kubatcha is also known as the place where significant quantities of Persian ceramics of the Timurid and Safavid periods (fifteenth to seventeenth century) were found.[3] These finds confirm the close relationship that existed between Persia and the Caucasus. Under the Safavids and later, into the nineteenth century, many Caucasian provinces were under Persian rule. Derbent was captured by the Russians in 1722 and Baku in 1723, and as late as 1813 Persia ceded to Russia several districts of the eastern Caucasus, from Lenkoran northward to Derbent.

DRAGON RUGS AND ANIMAL RUGS
(END OF SIXTEENTH CENTURY THROUGH
EIGHTEENTH)

The rugs of the Caucasus, made by peasants and nomads, can be divided into several groups, with features peculiar to various regions and centers. The earliest Caucasian rugs to have survived are the so-called dragon rugs. About fifty of these are known, their pattern usually consisting of a lozenge diaper of serrate leaves enclosing large palmettes and strongly stylized dragons. In some of the rugs the

horned heads large, their bodies and legs anatomically reduced (figure 227), is known from Scythian gold objects found in southern Russia and Siberia.[4]

There has been considerable difference of opinion about the provenance and dating of these rugs. Because of the archaic geometrical character of their designs, F. R. Martin dated some of them as early as the thirteenth century;[5] other writers have assigned the very same rugs to the fourteenth, fifteenth, and early sixteenth centuries, and Mehmet Aga-Oglu has assigned all of the early types to the seventeenth century.[6] In view of their differences in style, however, the rugs clearly belong to different periods, and it may be said at the outset that their production ranged from the end of the sixteenth century to the beginning of the nineteenth. The floral decoration of the group is largely based on Persian vase rugs and related floral rugs of the Shah Abbas period, for which reason the rugs cannot be earlier than the end of the sixteenth century. To this earliest group belong the rug of figure 227, a rug in the Victoria and Albert Museum, and the so-called Graf rug in the Staatliche Museen, Berlin,[7] now in fragmentary condition. To the first half of the seventeenth century belong a rug in the Metropolitan (figure 228), two rugs in the Textile Museum, Washington, and two rugs in the Philadelphia Museum of Art: one in the Williams Collection, the other formerly in the P. M. Sharples collection.[8] Toward the end of the seventeenth century there was a pronounced degeneration of the dragons and a further stylization of the floral forms, evident in a rug in the McMullan collection, another in the Detroit Institute of Arts, and two dated rugs, one a floral rug, formerly in London, dated 1679 and signed by its maker, Guhar, the other a dragon rug in the Textile Museum dated 1689.[9] In the eighteenth century the animal motifs were almost entirely transformed into geometrical devices, and the palmettes into conventional forms outlined with spiral hooks. A rug of this late period is in the Dumbarton Oaks Collection, Washington; another, till destroyed in World War II, was in the Staatliche Museen, Berlin.[10] Toward the end of the eigteenth century the number of lozenges in the field diminishes considerably, as seen in a rug now in the Staatliche Museen; an early nineteenth-century version is in the City Art Museum, St. Louis.[11]

The dragon rugs were for a long time attributed to Armenia and called "Armenian." This theory was challenged by Heinrich Jacoby and Arthur Upham Pope,[12] both of whom assigned the rugs to the region of Kuba in the eastern Caucasus. To some extent the

FIGURE 227   Dragon rug, probably Kuba, early XVII century. Catalogue no. 158

dragons appear in combat with phoenixes, a motif derived indirectly from Chinese art (page 33). In addition, some of the rugs have other animals, such as deer, gazelles, and ducks, singly or in pairs. The style is usually bold and angular, the coloring vivid. The animal decoration is partly based on an earlier Caucasian style; the treatment of the dragons, with their

FIGURE 228   Dragon rug, probably Kuba, first half of XVII century. Catalogue no. 159

FIGURE 229   Floral lozenge rug, probably Kuba, late XVII century. Catalogue no. 160

Armenian attribution was then revived by Arménag Sakisian.[13] Actually the attributions are not mutually exclusive if one uses the term "Armenian" nationally rather than geographically. Armenians dwell in the Kuba region, and it is not impossible that they, as well as the Turks who were also at home in this region, produced such rugs. Caucasian rugs with Armenian inscriptions are known; for example the floral rug, related to the dragon rugs, that bears the name of its maker, Guhar, and the date 1679. On the other hand, the late seventeenth-century dragon rug in the Textile Museum bearing the date of Muharram 1101 (October 1689) and the name of its owner, Husain Beg, has its inscription in Turkish.

Related to the dragon rugs is a rug in the Metropolitan (figure 229) whose field is occupied by large concentric lozenges in various colors, with stepped outlines, filled with floral scrolls and birds, alternating with palmettes. In the triangular corners of the field are large trees, birds, animals such as deer and elk, and monsters, all stylized in Caucasian fashion. The vivid color scheme and the stylized palmettes of the border are typical of Kuba rugs of the seventeenth and eighteenth centuries. The composition of the field is of special interest since it recalls the so-called Portuguese rugs that were made in Persia in the early seventeenth century (page 53). The resemblance again points up the close artistic relationship that existed between Persia and the Caucasus. A very similar rug, formerly in the Demotte collection, is in the Textile Museum, Washington.[14]

FLORAL RUGS OF KUBA (SEVENTEENTH CENTURY THROUGH NINETEENTH)

Besides dragon and animal rugs the peasant weavers of Kuba manufactured several types of floral rug with a bold palmette decoration, often with serrate leaves. Some of these rugs are related to the dragon rugs and to Persian floral rugs, including the vase rugs. The Kurdish and Caucasian weavers adopted many floral motifs from the vase rugs, such as large palmettes and the lyre-shaped lily or palmette. The latter motif, further stylized and simplified, occurs in eighteenth-century Kuba rugs as part of an allover floral pattern. A fine example of this type, its floral design, large palmettes, and half-palmettes arranged in rows, is in the Austrian Museum of Applied Art, Vienna.[15] In some of the rugs the lyrelike motif is transformed into a shieldlike device or escutcheon decorated with stylized elongated leaves. The escutcheons are arranged in rows, each motif flanked by stylized cypress trees (figure 230). Similar rugs were formerly in the Theodore M. Davis collection, the E. Beghian collection (now in the Textile Museum, Washington), and the Hollitscher collection, Berlin.[16] The Kurdish rugs with similar escutcheon patterns (page 88) are so close in design to the Kuba rugs that several authorities, among them Kurt Erdmann, have hesitated to attribute them to one or the other region, labeling them instead "Caucasus-northwest Persian." The Caucasian rugs, however, have design features and bright color schemes not found in the Kurdish rugs.

Several Kuba floral rugs have lozenge diaper patterns. One of the earliest and finest examples came originally from the mosque of Nigde in Asia Minor and can be dated to the first half of the seventeenth century (figure 231, page 162). Its bold pattern consists of a lozenge diaper in various colors enclosing palmette devices, large stylized composite blossoms, and cloud bands. The diaper and the rich polychromy are reminiscent not only of the dragon rugs but of some Persian vase rugs.

Other Kuba floral rugs recall Persian floral rugs, chiefly those of Kurdistan. One of the finest rugs of this type has an allover pattern of large palmettes combined with large lanceolate leaves and half-palmettes (figure 232). Two other rugs of this type, one whose present whereabouts is unknown and another, a fragment, in the Staatliche Museen, Berlin,[17] have similar lanceolate leaf patterns. The designs of such rugs, the work of peasant weavers, are often crude.

The manufacture of floral rugs continued in the Kuba district into the nineteenth century. In many of the late eighteenth- and early nineteenth-century rugs the palmettes are of enormous size and the lanceolate leaves are transformed into geometrical bands (figure 233). An early nineteenth-century example, now in the collection of Colonial Williamsburg, has a bold design derived from the dragon rugs, and colors on a yellow ground[18] similar to those of certain nineteenth-century Kuba silk embroideries. In other late eighteenth-century rugs cross-shaped medallions appear; these appear likewise in nineteenth-century Kazak rugs, discussed further on.

FIGURE 232 Floral rug, Kuba, XVIII century. Catalogue no. 165

FIGURE 233 Floral rug, Kuba, XIX century. Catalogue no. 166

FIGURE 234 Floral rug, Shirvan, early XIX century. Catalogue no. 168

FIGURE 235 Floral rug, Shirvan, first half of XIX century. Catalogue no. 169

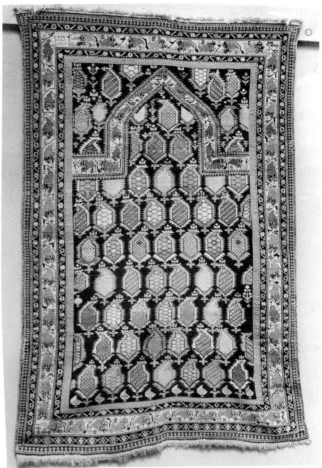

FIGURE 236 Arabesque rug, Shirvan, first half of XIX century. Catalogue no. 170

FIGURE 237 Prayer rug, Shirvan, dated 1223 H. (1808/09). Catalogue no. 171

RUGS OF THE SHIRVAN DISTRICT
(NINETEENTH CENTURY)

The most prolific production of rugs in the Caucasus in the nineteenth century was in the southeastern province of Shirvan. Many varieties of Shirvan rugs are known,[19] some of which are called in the trade Bakus, others Kabistans (a name derived from Kubistan, the province). All have a soft pile and harmonious color scheme. In general the rugs show either stylized floral designs or geometrical patterns. In some, the palmettes, rosettes, and arabesques are connected by stems (figure 234); in others the stems disappear and the floral motifs are arranged in rows (figure 235). Both types are related in design and color scheme to the Kuba floral rugs (and so are often called Kubas), as well as to Persian rugs of Kurdistan. An interesting feature in some of these rugs—that of figure 234, for example—is their use

of stylized half-palmettes reduced to simplest form. This motif derives from the borders of some of the dragon rugs and from the fields and borders of some of the floral rugs of Kuba. Many of the Shirvan rugs, including those of figures 234 and 235, have border designs of simulated Kufic, a decoration derived from certain rugs of Asia Minor (page 184). A Shirvan rug with a Kufic border (figure 236) has an allover design of arabesques that is based on Anatolian prototypes. A similar rug is known, dated 1831.[20] Small, geometrically stylized animals, birds, and human figures are often added to the decoration of the Shirvan rugs, as well as to the Kuba rugs.

A number of dated Shirvan prayer rugs are known. One dated 1808/09 (1223 H.) has a distinctive repeat pattern of stylized cone-shaped palmettes derived from Persia (figure 237). Rugs of this type have in the past been attributed to the looms of Baku, in the

272

ORIENTAL RUGS

FIGURE 238   Medallion rug, Chila, Baku, early XIX century. Catalogue no. 172

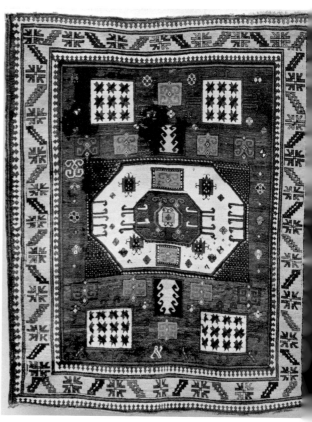

FIGURE 239   Geometrical rug, Kazak, XIX century. Catalogue no. 176

FIGURE 240   Geometrical rug, Kazak, XIX century. Catalogue no. 177

province of Azerbaijan, but recently they have been sometimes assigned to Marasali, in the Shirvan district. Several small Shirvan prayer rugs bear dates; for example, 1861[21] and 1867 (unpublished). Their borders usually have a "crab" motif consisting of a serrate rosette from which extend four arms bearing stylized leaves.

OTHER VARIETIES OF PILE RUGS (NINETEENTH CENTURY)

North of the Kuba district lies the province of Daghestan, with its capital of Derbent, known for its fine-textured rugs with strongly stylized floral patterns. Beautiful prayer rugs with floral motifs within a lozenge diaper were produced here during the nineteenth century. Some are dated as late as 1867.

To the southeast of Kuba lies the village of Chichi. Here was made a special variety of geometrical rug with a pattern of small polygons on a dark blue ground. In the borders of these rugs is a characteristic motif of diagonal bars alternating with rosettes.

In the town of Chila, in the Baku district, colorful rugs of various sizes were made, known as Boteh-

Chila, some of them having floral patterns of cone-shaped palmettes formed by numerous small flowers (figure 238).

Distinctive rugs known as Kazaks were woven in the nineteenth century by the Tartar and other nomadic tribes of the western Caucasus. The Kazaks are of several types, all having bold designs and high, lustrous piles. Some, deriving from the dragon group and Kuba rugs, are decorated with large palmette devices. Others, known as eagle Kazaks, have cross-shaped medallions with many arms, suggesting birds. Another type has a bold geometrical pattern of octagons and hooks (figure 239) or star shapes and hooks (figure 240), partly derived from the geometrical rugs of Anatolia. The crab motif found in the borders of the small Shirvans appears in a number of the Kazak borders.

South of the Kazak region lies the district of Karabagh, with its center of Shusha. Here designs of European origin, mainly French, in particular a rose pattern, were copied for the Western market in the nineteenth century. Similar rugs were woven for export in Sejshur, north of Kuba.

Other varieties of Caucasian pile rugs, many of which have distinctive patterns, are known as Mogans, Lesghians, and Ghengis, among others.

KILIMS AND OTHER FLAT-WOVEN RUGS (NINETEENTH CENTURY)

Besides knotted-pile rugs, the weavers of the Caucasus produced several types of flat-woven rugs. Kilims, or tapestry-woven rugs, were made in most of the districts in the nineteenth century. Their designs, markedly angular, are rendered in vivid

FIGURE 241 Palmette rug, Kuba, XIX century. Catalogue no. 179

FIGURE 242 Dragon rug, Kuba, early XIX century. Catalogue no. 180

colors. The kilims of Kuba and Shirvan have patterns of octagons, lozenges, and triangles, arranged in horizontal bands of various widths and filled with hook motifs of various sizes. In addition some of the Kuba kilims have floral patterns with strongly stylized palmettes (figure 241).

Other flat-woven rugs of the nineteenth century, known as Sumaks and made in the technique described on page 3, were produced in various districts of the Caucasus. Several show a survival of the lozenge diapers of the dragon rugs (figure 242). In addition some show, in extreme stylization, the dragon motifs themselves. Another type of Sumak has a geometrical pattern of large and small medallions, rosettes, and star shapes (figure 243). Some of the finest Sumaks, with patterns in vivid colors on a red ground, were made in the districts of Kuba and Derbent. In the town of Sejshur, Sumaks were made for the Western market with the same rose pattern used in the pile rugs mentioned above. The borders of these rose-pattern rugs have a characteristic running-wave ornament combined with stylized tulips.

FIGURE 243   Geometrical rug, probably Kuba, first half of XIX century. Catalogue no. 181

Rugs woven in the Sumak technique and known as Silés were made chiefly in the southeastern Caucasus. Their decoration consists of large, angular S-motifs with double bird heads attached, in yellow, blue, and red (figure 244). These S-motifs may well represent a survival of the principal motif of the earlier Kuba dragon rugs. A flat-woven rug now in the Metropolitan has simplified, strongly stylized dragon forms arranged in rows, in alternating white and dark blue on a red ground (figure 245). A de-scendant of the dragon rugs, this piece can be attributed to the looms of Kuba.

Still another type of flat-woven rug, often attributed to Shusha, in the Karabagh district in the southern Caucasus, is the so-called Verné. This is usually decorated with angularly stylized animals or birds in square compartments, or else with allover geometrical patterns.[22] The colors are cream white, yellow, red, and purple on a dark blue or dark red ground.

FIGURE 244 Bird rug (Silé), probably Shirvan, early XIX century. Catalogue no. 182

FIGURE 245 Dragon rug, Kuba, early XIX century. The Metropolitan Museum of Art, Gift of Joseph V. McMullan, 1971.263.5

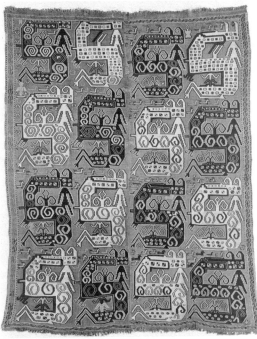

Notes to Chapter Nine

1 A. S. Bashkiroff, *The Art of Daghestan: Carved Stones* (Moscow, 1931).

2 Maurice S. Dimand, *A Handbook of Muhammadan Art*, fig. 57.

3 Ibid., fig. 135.

4 Tamara Talbot Rice, *The Scythians* (New York, 1957).

5 F. R. Martin, *A History of Oriental Carpets before 1800*, pp. 116, 118.

6 Washington, D. C., The Textile Museum, *Dragon Rugs: A Loan Exhibition from American Public and Private Collections* (Washington, D.C., 1948).

7 A. F. Kendrick and C. E. C. Tattersall, *Hand-Woven Carpets*, II, pl. 8; Friedrich Sarre and Hermann Trenkwald, *Old Oriental Carpets*, II, pl. 3.

8 Martin, pl. xxviii; Washington, 1948, no. 4; Wilhelm R. Valentiner, *Catalogue of a Loan Exhibition of Early Oriental Rugs*, nos. 2, 3.

9 Joseph V. McMullan, *Islamic Carpets*, no. 39; Arthur Upham Pope, *Catalogue of a Loan Exhibition of Early Oriental Carpets*, no. 31; Kendrick-Tattersall, II, pl. 7; Wilhelm von Bode and Ernst Kühnel, *Antique Rugs from the Near East*, fig. 40.

10 Washington, 1948, no. 15; Bode-Kühnel, fig. 42.

11 Kurt Erdmann, *Oriental Carpets*, fig. 99; Maurice S. Dimand, *The Ballard Collection of Oriental Rugs in the City Art Museum of St. Louis*, pl. LX.

12 Heinrich Jacoby, *Eine Sammlung orientalischer Teppiche*, pp. 39–48; Arthur Upham Pope, *Jahrbuch der asiatischen Kunst*, II, pp. 147–58.

13 Arménag Bey Sakisian, *Syria*, IX, pp. 238–56.

14 Pope, *Early Oriental Carpets*, no. 33.

15 Sarre-Trenkwald, I, pl. 40.

16 Valentiner, no. 19; Pope, *Early Oriental Carpets*, no. 36; Erdmann, fig. 116.

17 Pope, *Early Oriental Carpets*, no. 34; Bode-Kühnel, fig. 43.

18 Maurice S. Dimand, *Peasant and Nomad Rugs of Asia*, no. 15.

19 Ulrich Schürmann, *Kaukasische Teppiche*, nos. 97–112, 115.

20 Werner Grote-Hasenbalg, *Der Orientteppich*, II, pl. 34.

21 Dimand, *Peasant and Nomad Rugs*, no. 20.

22 Kendrick-Tattersall, II, pls. 143, 144.

CATALOGUE

158   FIGURE 227

Dragon rug, probably Kuba, early XVII century

12′ 7″ × 7′ 6″

WARP: Cotton

WEFT: Wool; 2 shoots after each row of knots

KNOTTING: Wool. Ghiordes knot, about 90 knots per square inch

COLORS: 6. *Ground*: red (field), ivory white (border). *Pattern*: ivory white, light yellow, red, purple, light blue, dark blue.

DECORATION: *Field*: A lozenge diaper formed by long serrate leaves overlaid with floral scrolls bearing leaves, rosettes, and palmettes. The lozenges are filled with a pattern of stylized horned dragons, alternating in transverse rows with large composite palmettes. The dragons are separated by large composite palmettes. *Border*: A wavy scroll with palmettes alternating with composite rosettes; simplified calyx-shaped arabesques issue from the palmettes and rosettes.

PUBLISHED: Breck-Morris, no. 16; Dimand, *Handbook*, fig. 212.

Gift of James F. Ballard, the James F. Ballard Collection

22. 100. 122

---

159   FIGURE 228

Dragon rug, probably Kuba, middle of XVII century

15′ 2″ × 7′ 2″

WARP: Wool

WEFT: Wool; 2 shoots after each row of knots

KNOTTING: Wool. Ghiordes knot, about 88 knots per square inch

COLORS: 11. *Ground*: deep blue (field), yellow (border), reciprocal deep blue and red (guard bands). *Pattern*: cream white, yellow tan, red, dull purple, light blue, deep blue, light green, blue green, brown, black.

DECORATION: *Field*: A lozenge diaper formed by long serrate leaves overlaid with floral scrolls. In the long axis the leaves are separated at intervals by large composite palmettes or rosettes. The lozenges are filled with a pattern of stylized dragons and large composite palmettes. *Border*: An angular wavy scroll of S-motifs and palmettes. *Guard bands*: Reciprocal trefoils.

PUBLISHED: Breck-Morris, no. 17.

Gift of James F. Ballard, the James F. Ballard Collection

22. 100. 119

---

160   FIGURE 229

Floral lozenge rug, probably Kuba, late XVII century

13′ 1″ × 6′

WARP: Wool

WEFT: Wool; 2 shoots after each row of knots

KNOTTING: Wool. Ghiordes knot, about 90 knots per square inch

COLORS: 10. *Ground*: cream white (central lozenge, corner areas of field), salmon (narrow band around central lozenge), light blue green (second lozenge), red (third, fifth, and seventh lozenges), dull purple (fourth lozenge), yellow (sixth lozenge, border). *Pattern*: cream white, yellow, salmon, pink, red, dull purple, blue, light blue green, light green, black.

DECORATION: *Field*: In the center, a lozenge with serrate outline filled with four leafy palmettes forming a cross. The central lozenge is surrounded by six concentric lozenges with stepped outlines. Each is filled with angular floral scrolls bearing leaves, buds, palmettes, and stylized birds. In the corners of the field are trees, floral scrolls, and stylized birds and animals, including antelopes and spotted deer. *Border*: A wavy scroll with stylized palmettes.

PUBLISHED: Hawley, pl. 19; Valentiner, no. 5.

Rogers Fund

08. 234. 2

---

161   NEXT PAGE, LEFT

Medallion rug, end of XVII or early XVIII century

17′ 5″ × 8′ 7″

WARP: Wool

WEFT: Wool; 3 shoots after each row of knots

KNOTTING: Wool. Ghiordes knot, about 121 knots per square inch.

COLORS: 9. *Ground*: dark brown (field), red (principal center medallion, pendants, border), light blue (inner center medallion), blue green (cartouches, inner guard band), light tan (outer guard band). *Pattern*: white, light tan, yellow, red, light blue, dark blue, blue green, green.

DECORATION: *Field*: A central lobed medallion containing a smaller lobed medallion with a cross-shaped central panel; at either end of the large medallion in the long axis, a cartouche and a pendant. The medallions are filled with floral scrolls bearing stylized palmettes, leaves, and buds. Similar decorations fill the pendants and cartouches, with a geometrical device added in the cartouches. The rest of the field contains an allover pattern of floral scrolls and arabesques forming various eight-pointed star devices, connected by rosettes, stars, and palmettes. *Border*: Two angular arabesque bands enclosing larged lobed compartments containing composite palmettes; alternating with the large compartments are small ones containing a star or a rosette. *Inner guard band*: A pattern of two arabesques. *Outer guard band*: An arabesque scroll interlaced with a floral scroll.

PUBLISHED: Breck-Morris, no. 3.
Gift of James F. Ballard, the James F. Ballard Collection 22. 100. 74

162   BELOW

Floral rug, probably Kuba, XVIII century

10′ 2″ × 5′ 5″

WARP: Wool

WEFT: Wool; 2 shoots after each row of knots

KNOTTING: Wool. Ghiordes knot, about 110 knots per square inch

COLORS: 8. *Ground*: dark blue (field), red (border), white (inner guard band), yellow (outer guard band). *Pattern*: white, yellow, red, light blue, blue green, green, brown.

DECORATION: *Field*: Lengthwise rows of floral motifs: oval shieldlike motifs and stylized open palmettes alternating on a stalk, the adjacent stalk having a series of double leaves. In the intervening spaces, tuliplike motifs. *Border*: A wavy scroll bearing angularly stylized leaves and palmettes in alternation. *Inner guard band*: S–motifs alternating with small geometrical devices.

Outer guard band: A wavy scroll bearing stylized leaves and blossoms.
PUBLISHED: Dilley, pl. XLI; Valentiner, no. 14.
Theodore M. Davis Collection, Bequest of Theodore M. Davis, 1915
30. 95. 146

PUBLISHED: Dimand, *Oriental Rugs and Textiles*, fig. 11; Dimand, *Handbook*, fig. 250; McMullan, no. 41; Martin, fig. 297.
EX COLL. William T. Dewart
Gift of Joseph V. McMullan
56. 217

163   FIGURE 230

Floral rug, Kuba, middle of XVIII century

14′ 2″ × 6′ 5″
WARP: Wool
WEFT: Wool; 2 shoots after each row of knots
KNOTTING: Wool. Ghiordes knot, about 121 knots per square inch
COLORS: 7. *Ground*: dark blue (field), white (border), yellow (guard bands). *Pattern*: white, yellow, red, violet, light blue, dark blue, dark brown.
DECORATION: *Field*: Ten transverse rows of a shieldlike device containing a candelabra arrangement of elongated stylized leaves. Between the rows, stylized cypress trees. *Border*: Interlaced geometrical scrolls enclosing heart-shaped leaves and rosettes. *Guard bands*: S–motifs.
PUBLISHED: Breck-Morris, no. 88.
Gift of James F. Ballard, the James F. Ballard Collection
22. 100. 118

164   FIGURE 231, PAGE 162

Floral compartment rug, probably Kuba, first half of XVII century

24′ 8″ × 10′
WARP: Cotton
WEFT: Cotton; 2 shoots after each row of knots.
KNOTTING: Wool. Ghiordes knot, about 99 knots per square inch
COLORS: 13. *Ground*: white (lozenges, border), yellow, orange, red, light blue, dark blue, green (lozenges). *Pattern*: white, ochre, yellow, orange, pink, red, lilac, purple, light blue, blue, dark blue, green, black.
DECORATION: *Field*: Large lozenge compartments formed by bands containing floral stems; these are overlaid at intervals and at their junctions with large composite rosette blossoms. Two designs alternate in the transverse rows of the lozenge compartments: a pair of wavy cloud bands in a symmetrical arrangement of floral scrolls with palmettes, leaves, and rosettes, and a cross-shaped medallion filled with four lotus palmettes whose stems form a lozenge and enclose a star motif. Curly leaves and blossoms project from the medallion, and at each end in the long axis there is a pendant. *Border*: A small six-sided medallion alternating with a rosette.
PROVENANCE: The mosque in Nigde, Asia Minor.

165   FIGURE 232

Floral rug, Kuba, XVIII century

9′ 3″ × 6′ 1″
WARP: Cotton
WEFT: Cotton; 2 shoots after each row of knots
KNOTTING: Wool. Ghiordes knot, about 100 knots per square inch
COLORS: 9. *Ground*: red (field), white (border). *Pattern*: white, yellow, red, purple, light blue, dark blue, blue green, light green, brown black.
DECORATION: *Field*: An allover floral pattern of four units in four transverse rows, each unit consisting of curling lanceolate leaves enclosing a highly stylized palmette. Superimposed on the leaves are floral stems bearing rosettes, buds, and leaves. In the spaces between the units are palmettes, rosettes, and hook motifs. *Border*: A chain of small rectangles.
PUBLISHED: Valentiner, no. 6.
Theodore M. Davis Collection, Bequest of Theodore M. Davis, 1915
30. 95. 144

166   FIGURE 233

Floral rug, Kuba, XIX century

10′ 7″ × 5′ 5″
WARP: Wool
WEFT: Wool; 2 shoots after each row of knots
KNOTTING: Wool. Ghiordes knot, about 88 knots per square inch
COLORS: 6. *Ground*: brown black (field), white (border). *Pattern*: white, yellow, red, dark blue, light brown.
DECORATION: *Field*: A symmetrical floral pattern, geometrically stylized, featuring three large composite palmettes, each within a medallion, the central one with serrate outline, accompanied by lanceolate leaves, smaller palmettes, and rosettes. *Border*: A wavy scroll with cross-shaped motifs from which issue simplified arabesques.
PUBLISHED: Valentiner, no. 15.
Theodore M. Davis Collection, Bequest of Theodore M. Davis, 1915
30. 95. 149

167   BELOW

Floral rug, probably Shirvan, first half of XIX
century

9′ 1″ × 3′ 3″
WARP: Wool

WEFT: Wool; 2 shoots after each row of knots
KNOTTING: Wool. Ghiordes knot, about 72 knots per
square inch
COLORS: 9. *Ground*: deep blue (field), white (border),
black (guard bands). *Pattern*: white, tan, light
yellow, rose, red, blue, deep blue, green, black.
DECORATION: *Field*: A lengthwise row of large, angularly
stylized palmettes; in the intervening spaces, hook
motifs, rosettes, stars, and two small birds. The field is
edged with buds on angular stems. *Border*: Large
rosettes containing a cross motif and giving off four
bent stems ending in stylized leaves, the unit com-
prising the so-called crab motif. *Guard bands*: Carnations on stems. *Edgings*: Angular S–motifs.
PUBLISHED: Breck-Morris, no. 101.
Gift of James F. Ballard, the James F. Ballard Collection
22. 100. 1

168   FIGURE 234

Floral rug, Shirvan, early XIX century

12′ 11″ × 5′ 5″
WARP: Wool
WEFT: Wool; 2 shoots after each row of knots
KNOTTING: Wool. Ghiordes knot, about 80 knots per
square inch
COLORS: 8. *Ground*: dark blue (field), red (border), light
tan (inner guard band), black (outer guard band).
Pattern: white, light tan, red, light blue, dark blue,
green, brown, black.
DECORATION: *Field*: An allover floral pattern with scrolls
forming lozenges along the lengthwise axis, the scrolls
bearing leaves, buds and palmettes. At the corners of
the lozenges are large composite palmettes; within the
lozenges are large rosettes or cross-shaped floral
devices. Large rosettes at the sides of the field send off
two or three arabesque scrolls with half-palmettes.
Border: Simulated Kufic writing alternating with a
geometrical medallion with curling outlines. *Guard
bands*: A wavy scroll with blossoms and leaves.
PUBLISHED: Dimand, *Peasant and Nomad Rugs*, no. 17.
Theodore M. Davis Collection, Bequest of Theodore M.
Davis, 1915
30. 95. 145

169   FIGURE 235

Floral rug, Shirvan, first half of XIX century

8′ 8″ × 3′ 6″
WARP: Wool
WEFT: Wool; 2 shoots after each row of knots
KNOTTING: Wool. Ghiordes knot, about 80 knots per
square inch

COLORS: 8. *Ground*: light blue (field), dark blue (border), light yellow (guard bands). *Pattern*: white, light yellow, yellow, pink, red, light blue, dark brown.

DECORATION: *Field*: An allover floral pattern of stylized, lozenge-shaped palmettes with serrate outlines arranged in staggered rows. Each palmette contains a star motif within a lozenge. *Border*: Simulated Kufic writing alternating with a geometrical medallion with curling outlines. *Guard bands*: Rosettes.

PUBLISHED: Hawley, pl. 41.

Rogers Fund

08.173.11

170   FIGURE 236

Arabesque rug, Shirvan, first half of XIX century

4′ 9″ × 3′ 6″

WARP: Wool

WEFT: Wool; 2 shoots after each row of knots

KNOTTING: Wool. Ghiordes knot, about 153 knots per square inch

COLORS: 9. *Ground*: black (field, frame of field), green (border), reciprocal blue and black (guard bands). *Pattern*: white, tan, yellow, orange, red, violet, blue, green, black.

DECORATION: *Field*: An allover pattern of angular arabesque scrolls bearing geometrically stylized palmettes and half-palmettes. The intervening spaces are filled with small stars and stylized flowers. The field is framed by a row of lozenges containing a rosette or a star. *Border*: Simulated Kufic writing alternating with a geometrical medallion with curling outlines. *Guard bands*: Reciprocal trefoils.

PUBLISHED: Breck-Morris, no. 94.

Gift of James F. Ballard, the James F. Ballard Collection

22.100.6

171   FIGURE 237

Prayer rug, Shirvan, dated (in border at top) 1223 H. (1808/09)

4′ 8″ × 3′ 2″

WARP: Wool

WEFT: Wool; 2 shoots after each row of knots

KNOTTING: Wool. Ghiordes knot, about 210 knots per square inch

COLORS: 12. *Ground*: dark blue (field, guard bands), white (border, band defining niche), reciprocal light blue and brown (edging of rug), reciprocal light blue and red (frame of field). *Pattern*: white, tan, yellow, pink, red, dark red, purple, light blue, dark blue, green, black.

DECORATION: *Field*: An arched niche filled with transverse rows of cone-shaped palmettes, some decorated with zigzag lines, others with diagonal stripes, lozenges, or a honeycomb pattern. Similar palmettes fill the spandrels. The band defining the niche contains a wavy scroll bearing cone-shaped palmettes. The field is framed by reciprocal trefoils. *Border*: A wavy scroll bearing cone-shaped palmettes. *Guard bands*: A wavy scroll with rosettes, with the exception of one end of the outer guard band which contains two types of alternating crosses. *Edging*: Reciprocal trefoils.

PUBLISHED: Breck-Morris, no. 95; Dimand, *Peasant and Nomad Rugs*, no. 16.

Gift of James F. Ballard, the James F. Ballard Collection

22.100.3

172   FIGURE 238

Medallion rug, Chila, Baku, early XIX century

6′ 1″ × 4′ 3″

WARP: Wool

WEFT: Wool; 2 shoots after each row of knots

KNOTTING: Wool. Ghiordes knot, about 90 knots per square inch

COLORS: 6. *Ground*: dark blue (field), white (central polygon, corners of field), light blue (border), red (guard bands), brown black (edging of rug). *Pattern*: white, tan, red, light blue, dark blue, brown black.

DECORATION: *Field*: In the center, a polygon containing stylized rosettes and carnations. In the corners of the field, triangular panels containing geometrical motifs. The rest of the field is patterned with cone-shaped palmettes in staggered rows, the palmettes formed by small blossoms. *Border*: Stylized carnations alternating with pairs of stylized leaves. *Guard bands*: Geometrical S–motifs. *Edging*: Geometrical rosettes.

PUBLISHED: Breck-Morris, no. 96.

Gift of James F. Ballard, the James F. Ballard Collection

22.100.2

173   NEXT PAGE, LEFT

Floral rug, Shirvan, middle of XIX century

4′ 4″ × 2′ 9″

WARP: Wool

WEFT: Wool; 2 shoots after each row of knots

KNOTTING: Wool. Ghiordes knot, about 126 knots per square inch

COLORS: 6. *Ground*: white (field), dark red (border), dark blue (guard band). *Pattern*: white, light red, dark red, light blue, dark blue, green.

DECORATION: *Field*: An allover pattern of stylized roses in
staggered transverse rows. The field is edged with
trefoils. *Border*: A rosette with two arabesque stems.
Guard band: A geometrical scroll.
PUBLISHED: Breck-Morris, no. 92.
Gift of James F. Ballard, the James F. Ballard Collection
22.100.5

174   ABOVE RIGHT

Geometrical rug, Shirvan, first half of XIX
century

7′ 8″ × 4′ 4″
WARP: Wool
WEFT: Wool; 2 shoots after each row of knots
KNOTTING: Wool. Ghiordes knot, about 96 knots per
square inch
COLORS: 15. *Ground*: blue (field, guard bands), yellow tan
(border). *Pattern*: white, yellow tan, tan, beige, wine
red, red, violet, light blue, dark blue, blue green, olive
green, light green, green, light brown.
DECORATION: *Field*: On the lengthwise axis, three
lozenge medallions and two large palmettes, the
medallions filled with geometrical motifs and rosettes,

the palmettes with a small lozenge medallion and leaves.
The rest of the field is patterned with a variety of
rosettes, star motifs, lozenges, and small, geometrically
stylized animals. *Border*: A geometrical S–motif
alternating with a geometrical leaf giving off two
stems. *Guard bands*: A wavy scroll.
PUBLISHED: Breck-Morris, no. 93.
Gift of James F. Ballard, the James F. Ballard Collection
22.100.4

175   FACING PAGE

Geometrical rug, Shirvan, middle of XIX century

9′ 3″ × 5′ 3½″
WARP: Wool
WEFT: Wool; 2 shoots after each row of knots
KNOTTING: Wool. Ghiordes knot, about 72 knots per
square inch
COLORS: 8. *Ground*: sand, orange, brick red, red, blue,

KNOTTING: Wool. Ghiordes knot, about 64 knots per square inch

COLORS: 9. *Ground*: blue green (field), tan (border), reciprocal red and white (guard bands). *Pattern*: white, pink, red, violet, blue, dark blue, blue green, dark brown.

DECORATION: *Field*: A large central octagon encloses a smaller one containing a central square. The smaller octagon is partly filled with latch-hooks. The large octagon is filled with latch-hooks, hook-adorned squares, and rosettes. Four triangles filled with checkering are appended to the large octagon, forming a rectangle. Each corner of the field contains a large square adorned with latch-hooks and filled with geometrical rosettes. The rest of the field is patterned with squares containing hook motifs and rosettes. *Border*: A geometrical rosette alternating with a stylized leaf, forming a scroll. *Guard bands*: Reciprocal trefoils.

PUBLISHED: Breck-Morris, no. 99.

Gift of James F. Ballard, the James F. Ballard Collection 22.100.16

177   FIGURE 240

Geometrical rug, Kazak, XIX century

6′ 2″ × 5′ 4″

WARP: Wool

WEFT: Wool; 3 shoots after each row of knots

KNOTTING: Wool. Ghiordes knot, about 72 knots per square inch

COLORS: 8. *Ground*: white (field), tan (border), reciprocal red and light blue (guard bands). *Pattern*: white, tan, red, violet, brown, light blue, blue, dark blue.

DECORATION: *Field*: An allover pattern of star-shaped polygons and compartments of irregular shape adorned with latch-hooks. Most of these figures contain small squares enclosing a rosette; some contain arabesque motifs. *Border*: A lozenge bearing four hooks, the so-called crab motif. *Guard bands*: Reciprocal triangles.

PUBLISHED: Breck-Morris, no. 97.

Gift of James F. Ballard, the James F. Ballard Collection 22.100.17

dark blue, brown green, green (polygons), white (octagons, guard bands). *Pattern*: white, orange, red, light blue, dark blue, green, light brown, dark brown.

DECORATION: *Field*: Sixteen transverse rows of four rectangular compartments, each containing a polygon adorned with hooks within an octagon; within the polygon, a star motif. *Border*: Small rectangles, most of them enclosing an ornamented lozenge, the type varying randomly. *Guard bands*: A zigzag band.

Gift of Arthur L. Gale, in memory of Colonel Roy Winton

49.79

176   FIGURE 239

Geometrical rug, Kazak, XIX century

6′ 10″ × 5′ 6″

WARP: Wool

WEFT: Wool; 3 shoots after each row of knots

178   NEXT PAGE

Geometrical rug, Kazak, XIX century

8′ 7″ × 5′ 10″

WARP: Wool

WEFT: Wool; 3 shoots after each row of knots

KNOTTING: Wool. Ghiordes knot, about 49 knots per square inch

COLORS: 7. *Ground*: red (field), white (border), yellow (guard bands). *Pattern*: white, yellow, red, violet, light blue, dark blue, green, dark brown.

DECORATION: *Field*: A lozenge diaper formed by oblong panels adorned with hook motifs; a rosette at each corner of the lozenge. Each compartment is filled with an irregular polygon adorned with angular hook motifs and containing a rosette. Across one end of the field, a row of small hooked devices. *Border*: A lozenge alternating with a version of the crab motif. *Guard bands*: A broad zigzag band.

PUBLISHED: Breck-Morris, no. 98.

Gift of James F. Ballard, the James F. Ballard Collection

22.100.18

179   FIGURE 241

Palmette rug, Kuba, XIX century

8′ × 4′ 9″

WARP: Wool

WEFT: Wool

TECHNIQUE: Tapestry, 20 warp threads per inch

COLORS: 9. *Ground*: red (field), dark brown (border). *Pattern*: white, yellow, red, light blue, blue, dark blue, yellow green, red brown, dark brown.

DECORATION: *Field*: Six staggered transverse rows of angularly stylized palmettes, each containing a lozenge filled with checkering. *Border*: A wavy scroll with stylized buds.

Rogers Fund

44.156

180   FIGURE 242

Dragon rug, Kuba, early XIX century

10′ × 6′ 2″

WARP: Wool

WEFT: Wool

TECHNIQUE: Sumak, 10 threads per inch

COLORS: 10. *Ground*: red (field), dark brown (border), white (guard bands). *Pattern*: white, tan, yellow, orange red, light blue, dark blue, yellow green, light green.

DECORATION: *Field*: An incomplete lozenge diaper derived from earlier Caucasian dragon rugs. The large serrate leaves of the original design are here transformed into irregular geometrical compartments filled with latch-hooks, rosettes, and a few geometrically stylized human figures and animals. The large palmettes seen within the lozenges of the original design are here transformed into geometrical forms. In the intervening spaces, placed at random, are hook motifs, rosettes, human figures, and animals. *Border*: Latch-hooks, S–motifs, and geometrical rosettes. *Guard bands*: Rosettes.

PUBLISHED: Breck-Morris, no. 89; Dimand, *Peasant and Nomad Rugs*, no. 21.

Gift of James F. Ballard, the James F. Ballard Collection

22.100.21

181   FIGURE 243

Geometrical rug, probably Kuba, first half of XIX century

9′ 8″ × 7′ 9″

WARP: Wool

WEFT: Wool

TECHNIQUE: Sumak, 15 threads per inch

COLORS: 7. *Ground*: red (field, edging), dark brown (border), white (guard bands). *Pattern*: white, yellow, light blue, dark blue, green, dark brown.

DECORATION: *Field*: In the lengthwise axis, four lobed medallions, each containing an octagon enclosing a cross motif surrounded by eight rosettes. The rest of the field is patterned with large and small octagons, panels of various shape, rosettes, star-shaped motifs, and geometrical devices. Some of these are edged with leaves, hooks, or trefoils; the field is edged with trefoils. *Border*: A zigzag band, its angles filled with

stepped triangles. *Guard bands*: Rosettes. *Edging*: Hooks.
PUBLISHED: Breck-Morris, no. 90.
Gift of James F. Ballard, the James F. Ballard Collection
22. 100. 20

182 FIGURE 244

Bird rug (Silé), probably Shirvan, early XIX century

9′ 11″ × 7′ 3″
WARP: Wool
WEFT: Wool
TECHNIQUE: Sumak, 18 threads per inch

COLORS: 15. *Ground*: orange red (field), reciprocal black and blue (border). *Pattern*: white, tan, yellow, light salmon, orange, orange red, red, light blue, blue, dark blue, blue green, light green, dark green, black brown.
DECORATION: *Field*: Sixteen large, angular S-motifs in four transverse rows, each with two bird heads at the top; the units, which probably represent stylized dragons, are filled with small S-motifs. In the spaces of the large S-motifs, two rows of geometrically stylized palmettes with hook motifs, and checkered lozenges. *Border*: Reciprocal trefoils.
PUBLISHED: Breck-Morris, no. 91; Dimand, *Peasant and Nomad Rugs*, no. 22.
Gift of James F. Ballard, the James F. Ballard Collection
22. 100. 19

Ten:

RUGS OF WESTERN TURKESTAN

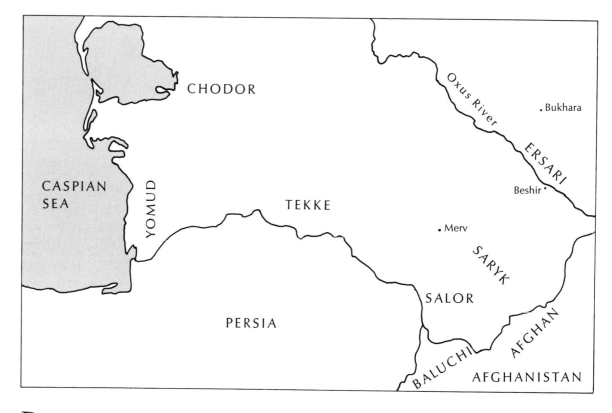

During the nineteenth century several wandering Turkoman tribes occupied the region stretching from the Caspian Sea eastward to Bukhara, northward to the Aral Sea, and southward to Persia, including Afghanistan and areas of Baluchistan. These tribes were skilled weavers of rugs, which served as floor coverings for their tents, or *kibitkas*, as hangings for the tent entrances, and as tent bags and saddlebags. The rugs were practically unknown in the Western world until the end of the nineteenth century, when Russia took control of most of the

Transcaspian region. The first man to collect and classify the rugs was General A. Bogolubov,[1] who, during the period 1900-1905, acquired a hundred and thirty examples and presented them to Czar Alexander III.

Although all the rugs have characteristics in common, each tribe developed its own distinctive motif in its tribal *gul* or flower.[2] To recognize the gul is to know the tribe that produced the rug. The names of the tribes are used to designate the different types of rug: Tekke, Salor, Saryk, Yomud, Ersari, and

Afghan. The patterns, entirely geometrical, go back to old Turkish and Central Asian traditions. The predominant color ranges from a reddish brown to a dark brown; the additional colors, usually few in number, are mainly shades of blue, green, orange, and yellow. Often tightly knotted, the rugs are tied either with the Ghiordes or Senna knot. None of the known rugs predates the nineteenth century.

The Turkoman rugs best known in the West are those made by the Tekke tribe. Often called "Bukharas" in the trade, they have allover field patterns of octagonal guls divided into quarters and contain-

ing a leaf design. These main guls are arranged in rows, separated by secondary cross-shaped guls (figure 246).

Related in design to the Tekke rugs are those of the Salor and Saryk tribes. According to Bogolubov, these two tribes occupied the region of Merv until 1856. The Salor were the parent stock of many of the other tribes. The Salor rugs may be recognized by their deep, lustrous colors and the turreted outline of the gul.[3] The rugs of the Saryks have a gul consisting of a flattened octagon with a central cross motif. Of great beauty are the Saryk door rugs, some-

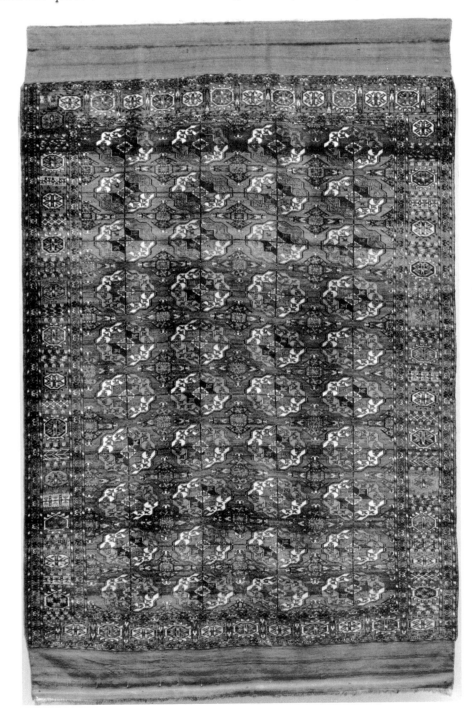

FIGURE 246
Geometrical rug,
Tekke, middle of XIX
century. Catalogue
no. 183

times regarded as prayer rugs, made in the oasis of Pindé. They have a mosaiclike pattern and a variety of geometrical motifs, some of which end in stylized bird heads (figure 247).

The Yomud and several related tribes occupied the region along the eastern shore of the Caspian. The Yomud gul is diamond-shaped, and the rugs show a great variety of pattern. A fine example with a repeat pattern of octagons is in the McMullan collection (figure 248). The Yomuds were particularly fond of the latchhook design in diagonal color bands. In one of their rugs the guls are arranged in staggered rows in an allover pattern (figure 249). In another, representing the finest and most colorful type of Yomud, the gul, with seven vertical panels attached to it,

appears in diagonal rows of different colors (figure 250). Richness of color is apparent in the endpieces of this and other Yomud rugs, which usually have star-shaped rosettes in varying colors. The Chodor, one of the related tribes, produced rugs with lozenge diapers in three shades of red.[4]

The clans of the Ersari tribe, occupying the territory on both sides of the Oxus River northward from Afghanistan to the city of Bukhara, produced several types of rugs. Some are known in the trade as "Beshirs." The Ersari of the southern region, the Kizil-Ayak clan, often used the motifs of their neighbors—for instance, the flattened octagonal gul of the Saryk, filling it with stylized sheep dogs (figure 251). Further north, in the Bukhara region,

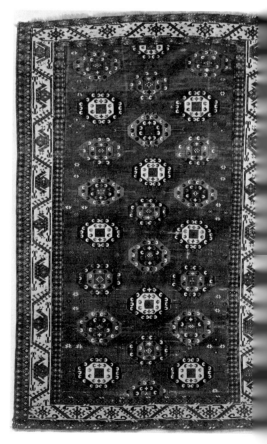

FIGURE 247   Door rug, Saryk (Pindé), first half of XIX century. Catalogue no. 186

FIGURE 248   Geometrical rug, Yomud, first half of XIX century. Collection of Joseph V. McMullan, New York

FIGURE 249 Geometrical
rug, Yomud, first half of
XIX century. Catalogue
no. 187

the Ersari weavers were influenced by the designs of Persian and Caucasian rugs.

A distinctive group of Turkoman rugs are the Afghans, made by tribes that roamed the Turkestan-Afghanistan border area. The large octagonal guls of these rugs consist of a design of three-leaf clovers and stars. Arranged in rows, the guls are separated by star-shaped devices.[5]

Further south, in various parts of southern Afghanistan and adjoining areas of Persia, several types of rugs were made, known as Baluchis or Baluchistans.[6] Some of them, assigned to the valley of Adraskand, have a palmette design derived from the Herat patterns of Persia.[7]

FIGURE 250   Geometrical rug, Yomud, first half of XIX century. Catalogue no. 188

FIGURE 251   Geometrical rug, Ersari, first half of XIX century. Catalogue no. 192

Notes to Chapter Ten

1 A. Bogolubov, *Tapis de l' Asie Centrale.*

2 Amos Bateman Thacher, *Turkoman Rugs*, pl. 4.

3 Ibid., pl. 5.

4 Ibid., pls. 30–32.

5 Ibid., pl. 33.

6 Ibid., pl. 50.

7 Ibid., pl. 49.

183   FIGURE 246

Geometrical rug, Tekke, middle of XIX century

9′ × 6′

WARP: Goat hair

WEFT: Wool; 2 shoots after each row of knots

KNOTTING: Wool. Senna knot, about 145 knots per square
inch

COLORS: 5. *Ground*: red brown. *Pattern*: white, orange,
light blue, dark blue, red brown.

DECORATION: *Field*: An allover pattern, in rows, of the
Tekke gul: a lobed octagonal medallion containing a
star bordered with and containing trefoils. Between
the guls are cross-shaped secondary guls. Slender
lines intersecting at right angles on the large guls
divide the field into rectangular panels. *Border*: Octagons
containing a cross device with hooks, the frames of the
octagons adorned with stylized leaves; between the
octagons are bands containing various geometrical
devices. *Guard bands*: Geometrical trefoils.

PUBLISHED: Breck-Morris, no. 103; Dimand, *Peasant and
Nomad Rugs*, no. 25.

Gift of James F. Ballard, the James F. Ballard Collection
22. 100. 45

184   BELOW

Saddle bag, Tekke, middle of XIX century

4′ 11″ × 4′ 6″

WARP: Goat hair

WEFT: Goat hair and cotton; 2 shoots after each row of
knots

KNOTTING: Wool and goat hair. Senna knot, about
108 knots per square inch

COLORS: 6. *Ground*: red brown. *Pattern*: white, orange,
dark blue, green, red brown, brown.

DECORATION: *Field*: An allover pattern of the Tekke gul;
a lobed octagonal medallion containing a star bordered
with trefoils. Between the guls are secondary guls
consisting of a cross-shaped device containing a central
octagon filled with a star. *Border*: Lozenges alternating
with pairs of hook devices, the lozenges containing a
hooked cross. *Guard bands* (two sides only): T-shaped
hooks.

NOTE: Two pieces are sewn together.

PUBLISHED: Breck-Morris, no. 104.

Gift of James F. Ballard, the James F. Ballard Collection
22. 100. 40

185   BELOW

Tent bag, Tekke, first half of XIX century

3′ 10½″ × 2′ 4½″

WARP: Goat hair

WEFT: Wool; 1 shoot after each row of knots

KNOTTING: Wool and silk. Senna knot, about 276 knots
per square inch

COLORS: 7. *Ground*: brown. *Pattern*: white, red, violet,
dark blue, green blue, brown, dark brown.

DECORATION: *Field*: Horizontal and vertical bands filled
with lozenges with stepped outlines divide the field
into rectangular panels; each panel contains a lozenge
divided into triangles and surrounded by stylized leaves.
Border: Geometrical rosettes. *Endpiece*: A row of stylized trees with blossoms.

PUBLISHED: Breck-Morris, no. 105.

Gift of James F. Ballard, the James F. Ballard Collection
22. 100. 39

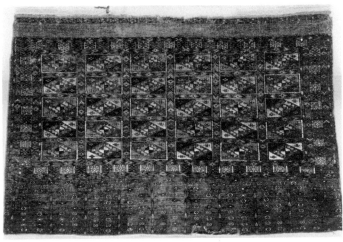

186   FIGURE 247

Door rug, Saryk (Pindé), first half of XIX century

6′ 2″ × 4′ 6″
WARP: Goat hair
WEFT: Goat hair; 2 shoots after each row of knots
KNOTTING: Wool and cotton. Senna knot, about 117 knots per square inch
COLORS: 5. *Ground*: purple brown (field, upper panel, smaller lower panel), green brown (side and top border, larger lower panel). *Pattern*: white, orange, dark blue, purple brown.
DECORATION: *Field*: In the center, a rectangular vertical panel bordered at sides and top with scrolls and divided transversely by a smaller panel containing rows of trefoils on stems. The two halves of the vertical panel each contain a stylized tree bearing palmettes; the tree is flanked by bands containing S-motifs, and bands filled with pairs of an angular motif ending in stylized bird heads, the motif recalling Kufic writing. The field at the sides of and above the vertical panel is filled with a geometrical scroll whose projections end in stylized bird heads. Crossing the foot of the field are two rectangular panels, the larger one filled with stylized trees, the smaller one with groups of stylized birds alternating with groups of hook motifs. Crossing the top of the field is a panel filled with angular arches and groups of lozenges. *Border*: Pairs of angular hooks (sides and top), and a pattern of triangles (bottom). *Guard bands*: A pattern of triangles, point to point. *Edging* (at sides): Checkering.
PUBLISHED: Breck-Morris, no. 106.
Gift of James F. Ballard, the James F. Ballard Collection
22.100.42

187   FIGURE 249

Geometrical rug, Yomud, first half of XIX century

10′ 7″ × 5′ 5″
WARP: Goat hair
WEFT: Goat hair; 2 shoots after each row of knots
KNOTTING: Wool and goat hair. Ghiordes knot, about 91 knots per square inch
COLORS: 6. *Ground*: violet red (field, guard bands, end-pieces), white (border). *Pattern*: white, deep orange, violet red, light blue, dark blue, blue green.
DECORATION: *Field*: A repeat pattern in staggered rows of the Yomud gul: an octagon containing zigzag motifs, the octagon centered in a group of five panels containing geometrical trefoils. *Border*: A star-shaped motif bracketed by stylized leaves, the unit alternating with a diagonal geometrical leaf. *Guard bands*: Triangular motifs. *Endpieces*: Stylized tree motifs.

PUBLISHED: Breck-Morris, no. 108.
Gift of James F. Ballard, the James F. Ballard Collection
22.100.47

188   FIGURE 250

Geometrical rug, Yomud, first half of XIX century

9′ 2″ × 5′ 6″
WARP: Goat hair
WEFT: Goat hair; 2 shoots after each row of knots
KNOTTING: Wool. Ghiordes knot, about 135 knots per square inch
COLORS: 11. *Ground*: red brown (field), white (border), red (guard bands), brown violet (endpieces). *Pattern*: white, yellow, salmon pink, red, brown violet, light blue, blue, dark blue, green, red brown, black.
DECORATION: *Field*: A repeat pattern of the Yomud gul: a hexagon containing latch-hook motifs, centered in a group of seven panels containing geometrical trefoils. The guls are in staggered rows, with the color scheme so arranged that they form diagonal bands across the field. *Border*: Hexagons enclosing a stylized lily palmette. *Guard bands*: A cross-shaped motif. *Endpieces*: Floral rosettes in staggered rows.
PUBLISHED: Dimand, *Peasant and Nomad Rugs*, no. 26; Thacher, pl. 20.
Gift of Dr. and Mrs. F. M. Al Akl
61.226

189   BELOW

Tent bag, probably Yomud, middle of XIX century

3′ 10″ × 2′ 8″
WARP: Goat hair
WEFT: Goat hair; 2 shoots after each row of knots

KNOTTING: Wool. Senna knot, about 560 knots per square inch

COLORS: 4. *Ground*: rose red (field), white (band at bottom) *Pattern*: white, red, dark blue.

DECORATION: *Field*: Transverse bands filled with stars in octagons, hook motifs, or small lozenges. *Band at bottom*: Stylized trees and hook motifs.

PUBLISHED: Breck-Morris, no. 112.

Gift of James F. Ballard, the James F. Ballard Collection 22. 100. 43

190   BELOW

Tent door hanging, Yomud, first half of XIX century

4′ 5″ × 4′ 3″

WARP: Goat hair

WEFT: Goat hair; 2 shoots after each row of knots

KNOTTING: Wool. Senna knot, about 143 knots per square inch

COLORS: 3. *Ground*: white (field), red (guard bands). *Pattern*: white, red, dark blue.

DECORATION: *Top band*: Geometrical scrolls with serrate outlines, ending in hook motifs; in the compartments, polygons with book motifs. *Borders*: A geometrical cross device. *Side bands*: Angular geometrical scrolls adorned with small hooks; in the compartments, polygons with hook motifs. *Guard bands*: Stars and zigzags.

PUBLISHED: Breck-Morris, no. 110.

Gift of James F. Ballard, the James F. Ballard Collection 22. 100. 37

191   ABOVE

Tent decoration, Yomud, middle of XIX century

40′ 3″ × 1′ 2″

WARP: Wool

WEFT: Wool; 1 shoot after each row of knots

KNOTTING: Wool. Ghiordes knot, about 180 knots per square inch

COLORS: 5. *Ground*: white. *Pattern*: white, yellow, dark green, red brown, black.

DECORATION: *Field*: Repeats of a group of three lozenges adorned with hooks. The lozenges are connected by a central lengthwise band and crossed by a band that repeats between them. Between the groups of lozenges, a transverse band containing trefoils. *Border*: A zigzag. *Endpieces*: Stylized trees and bands of geometrical motifs.

PUBLISHED: Breck-Morris, no. 111.

Gift of James F. Ballard, the James F. Ballard Collection 22. 100. 38

192   FIGURE 251

Geometrical rug, Ersari, first half of XIX century

8′ 1″ × 4′ 9″

WARP: Goat hair

WEFT: Goat hair; 2 shoots after each row of knots

KNOTTING: Wool. Senna knot, about 72 knots per square inch

COLORS: 4. *Ground*: purple brown (field), pale yellow (border), light brown (guard bands). *Pattern*: pale yellow, dark blue, light brown, purple brown.

DECORATION: *Field*: Three lengthwise rows of the Ersari gul: an octagon enclosing a central star surrounded by eight stylized sheep dogs. Between the octagons, small medallions. *Border*: A geometrical leaf pattern (sides) and a star motif (ends).

PUBLISHED: Breck-Morris, no. 107; Thacher, pl. 39.
Gift of James F. Ballard, the James F. Ballard Collection
22. 100. 46

193   LEFT

Floral rug, Ersari (Beshir), XIX century

$8' 9'' \times 5' 1\frac{1}{2}''$

WARP: Goat hair

WEFT: Goat hair; 2 shoots after each row of knots

KNOTTING: Wool. Senna knot, about 104 knots per square inch

COLORS: 7. *Ground*: red (field, outer guard band), blue, green (border). *Pattern*: white, yellow, red, light blue, blue, green, brown.

DECORATION: *Field*: Lengthwise narrow bands decorated alternately with a wavy floral scroll bearing leaves and cone-shaped palmettes bordered with small blossoms. *Border*: A checkered lozenge alternating with a square panel, the intervening spaces filled with small blossoms. *Inner guard band*: Diagonal panels. *Outer guard band*: A repeat pattern of small stepped triangles.

PUBLISHED: Breck-Morris, no. 113.
Gift of James F. Ballard, the James F. Ballard Collection
22. 100. 50

194   FACING PAGE

Tent bag, Baluchistan, middle of XIX century

$5' 8'' \times 3' 1''$

WARP: Goat hair

WEFT: Goat hair; 2 shoots after each row of knots

KNOTTING: Wool. Senna knot, about 117 knots per square inch

COLORS: 9. *Ground*: red (field), dark blue (border). *Pattern*: white, yellow, orange, deep pink, red, blue, dark blue, dark green, brown.

DECORATION: *Field*: A lozenge diaper made of two intertwined floral scrolls, overlaid at intervals with small blossoms. At the intersections of the lozenges, either a floral rosette or a star-shaped rosette. *Border*: A floral and a geometrical rosette alternating, with a hooked band between them, the intervening spaces filled with checkering. Beneath the lower border, a row of small stylized trees.

PUBLISHED: Breck-Morris, no. 114.
Gift of James F. Ballard, the James F. Ballard Collection
22. 100. 41

Eleven:

RUGS OF CHINA AND CHINESE TURKESTAN

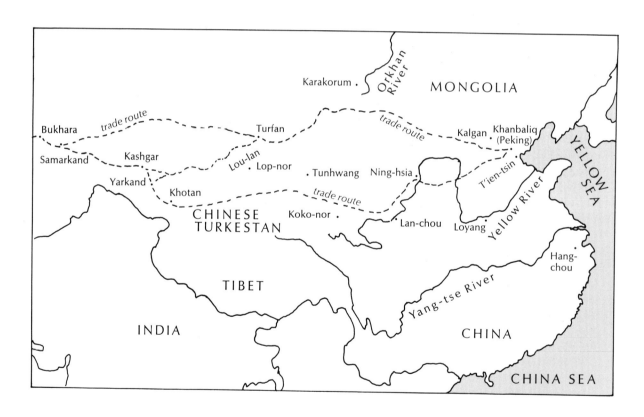

Map labels:

Karakorum · | Orkhan River | MONGOLIA

Bukhara — trade route — Turfan — trade route — Kalgan · Khanbaliq (Peking)

Samarkand — Kashgar — Lou-lan · Lop-nor — · Tunhwang — Ning-hsia — T'ien-tsin — YELLOW SEA

Yarkand · — Khotan — Koko-nor · — · Lan-chou — Loyang — Yellow River

CHINESE TURKESTAN — trade route

TIBET

Hang-chou

Yang-tse River

INDIA — CHINA

CHINA SEA

FIGURE 252   Warp-patterned silk border, Chinese, on nomad woolen rug, from Noin-ula, Mongolia, before
2 B.C. State Hermitage Museum, Leningrad

From the earliest days of Chinese history, the Chinese genius for weaving has expressed itself in silk fabrics. Both the miraculous fiber and an ingenious loom technique for weaving warp-patterned fabrics of silk were first developed, as far as we know from present evidence, in the Shang period (1600–1030 B.C.). The elaborately patterned early silks, with their constellationlike arrangements of mysterious geometrical motifs, or their mythical creatures stalking and running through cloud-mountains, recall bronze and lacquer pieces of the Chou period (1050–249 B.C.) and the Han period (206 B.C.–A.D. 220), both in complexity of design and mastery of material.

Pile rugs, however, represent a taste alien to the subtle and highly refined culture that had developed in China before the thirteenth century A.D. In 1279 the Mongols, the most powerful of the many "barbarian" tribes of Central Asia and Mongolia in contact with the Chinese since the days of the feudal kingdoms (Late Eastern Chou period, 770–249 B.C.), overthrew both the Northern and the Southern Sung dynasties, an early step in the building of an empire that eventually extended from Korea to the Danube. Various sources suggest that these horse-riders from

the northwest brought with them a characteristic northern nomad taste for woolen saddle covers, tent door curtains, tent floor coverings, hangings, banners, and pillows—all with bold geometrical designs, many woven in pile.

Pile rugs had their precursors in a number of different materials in early China. Mats, some of them patterned or bordered, seem to have been variously and widely used. The Chinese Classics refer to them explicitly and frequently. The *Shih Ching* (*Book of Songs*), containing passages from the days of the Warring States (Late Eastern Chou), tells of a small war chariot with a patterned mat.[1] The same book describes the sleeping arrangements in a palace:

Below, the rush-mats; over them the bamboo-mats
Comfortably he sleeps,[2]

and a banquet:

The guests are taking their seats [mats];
To left, to right they range themselves.
The food-baskets and dishes are in their rows.[3]

The *Ch'u Tzu* (*Songs of the South*), from the feudal kingdom of Ch'u, mentions a god's "jewelled mat" with jade weights.[4] And the importance of mats in a royal funeral ceremony is suggested in this

FIGURE 253   A Noble Scholar under a Willow,
anonymous, ink and colors on silk, perhaps XI
century. Collection of the National Palace Museum,
Taipei, Taiwan

passage from the *Shu Ching* (*Book of History*), compiled
in the Han period:

> Between the window (and the door), facing the
> south, they place the (three)fold mat of fine bam-
> boo splints, with its striped border of white and
> black silk, and the usual bench adorned with
> different-coloured gems. In the side-space on the
> west, which faced the east, they placed the three-
> fold rush mat, with its variegated border, and the
> usual bench adorned with beautiful shells. In the
> side-space on the east, which faced the west, they
> placed the threefold mat of fine grass, with its
> border of painted silk, and the usual bench carved,
> and adorned with gems. Before the western side-
> chamber, and facing the south, they placed the

threefold mat of fine bamboo, with its dark mixed
border, and the usual lacquered bench.[5]

A Chinese patterned silk border on a nomad woolen
rug survives from this period (figure 252); it comes
from the tomb of a Hunnic chieftain at Noin-ula,
northwest of China, dated 2 B.C.

A fur rug of extraordinary powers is mentioned
among the fanciful decorations of a royal hall in the
Hsi-ching Tsa-chi (*Miscellaneous Records of the Western
Capital*) of the Han period:

> ... a green bear rug. The hair of the rug was more
> than two feet long; if a person sleeping on it
> stroked the fur, he would hide himself and could
> no longer be seen. When anyone sat on it, the hair
> would cover his knees. It was permeated with
> various perfumes. Once a person sat on it, he
> would be fragrant until a hundred days had
> elapsed.[6]

Undoubtedly fur rugs were early in use, especially in
the northern provinces; Chinese travelers on the
northern border noted them in Sung times (950–
1279), and they appear in paintings as well (figure
253).

Felt, a fabric of matted, not woven, fibers of wool,
was adopted by the Chinese for mats as early as the
Han period from the nomads, who had been using it
for many purposes. According to T'ang tribute lists,
it was produced by that time in China in provinces
where wool was available. Felt is the material of the
earliest Chinese, or presumably Chinese, rugs that
have been preserved. Thirty-one patterned and fourteen unpatterned rugs were included in the household
effects of the Emperor Shomu of Japan given as a
memorial by his widow to the Todai-ji in Nara in
A.D. 756. The patterned rugs in the original inventory
apparently were withdrawn from the gift in 759, and
there is no record of their return. Accordingly, the
thirty-one patterned rugs at present in the temple's
storehouse, the Shoso-in, though they have the
Todai-ji seal stamped on them, cannot be linked with
the original gift with absolute certainty. However,
they are very much in the style of the T'ang period,
with patterns in shades of brown and indigo on
white, pale blue, or gray grounds. Some of the rugs
have the large floral rosettes so popular in all T'ang
decoration, in serpentines, interlaces, repeats, or
lattices of various bold floral forms. One of the rugs
(figure 254) suggests T'ang landscape details, as seen
in some of the earlier Tunhwang frescoes, with its
central roundels of two circling birds, a small mound

centered at each end with a flowering plant rising from it, a small mound centered on each side with three flowering plants, similar mounds with plants and various cloud forms in a free but balanced arrangement over the field, and flowers rising into the field from the side borders. All of these decorative treatments, here interpreted in thick felt, appear repeatedly in Chinese pile rugs of much later periods. Japanese scholars call the Shoso-in felt carpet designs "inlaid," and suggest that they were probably executed "by setting into position coloured felts cut in shapes to fit a pattern previously outlined on the ground felt, after which the rug was subjected to sufficient pressure

to make the applied pattern sink into to the ground"[7] (figure 255).

Mats identified as of bullrush, dragon-beard bush, phoenix quill, rattan, reed, Su's basil, water onion, and white horn (figure 256) are listed on local tribute records of the T'ang dynasty (618–906). Fragments of such mats have been found in many of the sites of early burials and settlements in China proper and Turkestan. Reliefs, frescoes, and other products of the Han and T'ang periods show mats beneath figures kneeling in worship of a deity (figure 257) or in respectful salutation of a dignitary, and beneath groups of musicians, dancers, jugglers, and acrobats

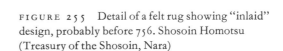

FIGURE 254 Felt rug, probably before 756. Shosoin Homotsu (Treasury of the Shosoin, Nara)

FIGURE 255 Detail of a felt rug showing "inlaid" design, probably before 756. Shosoin Homotsu (Treasury of the Shosoin, Nara)

at a banquet or celebration,[8] or beneath personages of religious or civil importance. A famous fragmentary hand scroll dating between Han and T'ang, The Admonitions of the Instructress, shows a noble lady kneeling on a bordered mat in front of her toilet table while her maid stands behind her, combing her hair.[9]

The importance of patterned rugs, whatever their materials, to the ceremonies of the dominant religion of the T'ang period, Buddhism, is made quite clear in frescoes, paintings, manuscripts, and other material from the great religious centers of Chinese Turkestan (also known as Eastern Turkestan). These

FIGURE 256   Scholar Fu Sheng, anonymous handscroll, ink and colors on silk, perhaps IX century. Osaka Municipal Museum

FIGURE 257   Silk embroidered panel from Tunhwang, showing Buddha, bodhisattvas, and attendants, T'ang period (618–906). Courtesy of the Trustees of the British Museum

show, as enhancements for the central holy figures and their attendants, richly flowered rugs and hangings, closely related to the Shoso-in felt carpets in design (figure 258). In frescoes from Tunhwang,[10] the donors or worshipers have small rectangular mats with occasional sketchy floral patterns, and sometimes the suggestion of a fringe, often in a combination of cream and brick red—the favored colors in many of these frescoes. Far-flung Buddhist shrines, festivals, and even secular ceremonies where rugs had an important place have been recorded by Buddhist pilgrims who traveled west through Turkestan to India from the sixth century on, and from Japan to China in the late T'ang period, in search of the True Word. In Chü-chou, between the Yangtse and Yellow Rivers in eastern China, a pilgrim from Japan, Ennin (793–864), observed that at ceremonies for new nuns in a Buddhist convent "banners had been hung in the hall and seating mats spread around."[11] And of another cloister, near Mount Wu T'ai in eastern Shantung, he said: "on the platform is spread a silk carpet of five colors, also octagonal and made to fit the plat-

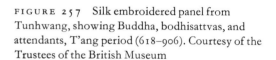

FIGURE 258   Thousand-armed Kuanyin, colors on silk, from Tunhwang, 981. Musée Guimet, Paris

form exactly."[12] Also in the neighborhood of the holy mountain, Ennin noted that in a ceremony in honor of saints and sages, "valuable banners and jewels in all the beautiful colors of the world were spread out and displayed, and carpets of varied colors covered the whole floor."[13] And a yearly ceremony for the image of the bodhisattva Wên Shu Shih Li on Mount Wu T'ai, he says, caused the Imperial Commissioner to send, among many colorful contributions, "flow-ered carpets."[14] In Têng-chou, a provincial city on the northeast coast of China, Ennin describes the ceremonial reception of an Imperial Rescript: "Two carpets were spread in the court in front of the gate. . . . The Magistrate stood on one of the carpets and an Administrative Officer stood on the other. . . . Then the Commissioner who had brought the Imperial Rescript walked up in front of the Magistrate and bowed again, whereupon the Magistrate stepped off his carpet and stopped him with his sleeve."[15] And in

FIGURE 259 Serindian Musicians on a Carpet, mural detail from Tunhwang, T'ang period (618–906). Courtesy of Irene Vincent

the land of the Ye-tha (White Huns or Ephthalites), Sung-Yun and Hwei Săng, who traveled west from China in 518, tell us that a large rug about forty paces square was spread out, surrounded by "a sort of rug hung up as a screen."[16]

A more homely setting of the T'ang period is described by Li Chao in a contemporary historical work, the *T'ang Kuo Shi Pu*:

Wei Chi was ill. Marshall Fang sent his younger son to make enquiries. On being invited to enter the bedroom and to walk across a carpet (*yin t'an*) which covered the whole of the floor, Fang's younger son removed his footwear before treading on the carpet. All the slave girls in attendance broke into laughter.[17]

Most frequently we have no idea whether any of these rugs, usually referred to by the character still used in China for "rug"—*t'an* (毯)—were of inlaid or printed felt, of plant or animal fiber, of skin or fur, or of couched, applied, or embroidered silk. One entry in the pilgrim Ennin's diary offers explicit in-formation. He had mats for sitting and sleeping made for his two disciples in Yang-chow, an important trade center at the confluence of the Yangtse River and the Grand Canal in eastern China. Costing 250 pieces of cash each, the mats were of coarse silk—eight feet four inches each for the top and bottom surfaces, four feet two inches for the border.[18]

The use of wool and woolen materials other than felt for rugs, mats, and saddle covers must have been known to the Chinese from their early contacts with the "barbarians" on their northern and western borders. These inhabitants of the great wool belt of Asia were in turn in close contact with the wool-raising and wool-using peoples of Central Asia and the Near East. Many exchanged diplomatic gifts— "tribute" in Chinese eyes—with the Chinese. A "Roman embroidered carpet" is recorded as being sent by the king of Bukhara to a T'ang emperor in 726, recalling the fragments of woven wool rugs with figures and embellishments in classical style, em-broidered in wool, found with nomad felts and Chinese patterned silks and lacquers in the graves of Hunnic chieftains buried in Noin-ula before 2 B.C. "Carpets" were sent by the Persians to the Chinese court from the fifth century on, and "dance mats" with living dancers or musicians included were understandably popular gifts from the kingdoms of Central Asia (figure 259). These Persian and Central Asian products, sometimes characterized as "great hair" or "long hair,"[19] are mentioned in T'ang records with various enigmatic characters, occasion-

Chinese colonial sites outside of China proper, where Chinese, nomad, and Near Eastern material was deposited together. With the exception of the great Pazyryk rug (figure 8), these are so small as to make reading of their pattern and conjecture about their possible use a puzzle. The earliest is a wool fragment from Bashadar in the Altai Mountains, in Senna knotting.[21]

The fragments of wool pile-weaving among Sir Aurel Stein's finds from civilizations of the Near and Far East along the trade routes of Chinese Turkestan were thought by Stein to be remains of rugs probably made in the Tarim Basin, where wool was produced in great quantity.[22] Some of these fragments are patterned with lozenges, bands of pothooks, and suggestions of stylized floral and geometrical elements, but all of these motifs were widely used and cannot be attributed to a specific locality. Their mellow pinks, blues, and greens suggest the late Roman taste of the Near East (as well as that seen in frescoes of T'ang China), as does their technique, in

FIGURE 261 Knotted-pile fragment, II–III century A.D., found by Stein in Lou-lan, Chinese Turkestan. Courtesy of the Trustees of the British Museum

ally *t'an*. A single entry in the long lists of local tribute for northern Kansu, on the northwestern border of China, indicates production in China itself of some kind of rug with this designation.[20] Can this refer to pile-weaving, as has been suggested? If so, Chinese taste at this time apparently did not create much of a demand for this type of product. The Chinese, to some extent in every age, looked down on wool as associated with "barbarians" and milk-drinkers.

Bold smooth patterns and shaggy textures, both patterned and unpatterned, are seen frequently on the earthernware tomb figures and other arts of the T'ang period, decorating the saddle covers of horses, camels and elephants (figure 260). Judging from surviving textile material of this period, one might surmise that these could represent inlaid felt, patterned silk, sheepskin, fur mosaic, or simply fur.

Fragments of actual early knotted pile pieces dating from the fifth century B.C. through the T'ang period have been found in tombs, on trade routes, and at

some cases identified as single warp knots of various kinds.[23] In certain examples, the pile might also be the cut and uncut weft loops common in the late classical and Coptic fabrics found in Egyptian tombs. The single piece of knotted pile from Stein's finds, now in the British Museum (figure 261), is described thus:

> The colours are black, dull white, red, pink, buff, yellow and bright blue. A pale green appears but this was probably caused by damp affecting the blue. The ground colours are red and pink. The warp is a thin, brown string; the weft, four picks of loosely twisted yarn; the pile a woollen yarn about one inch long, turned twice around each thread of the warp forming a very firm knot. The length of the pile is sometimes more than half an inch.[24]

The technique of similar fragments from Lop-nor and Lou-lan has been described as "non-Chinese."[25]

There is a gap of several hundred years between these trade route fragments and actual representations of what appear to be knotted pile rugs in Chinese paintings of the Sung period (960–1279), reflecting China's increasing preoccupation with the Mongols on her northern border. Surviving paintings, discussed in chapter four, picture the Mongols using saddle covers, ceremonial mats, tent rugs, and hangings of what appear to be pile and tapestry. The bold geometrical ornament of these pieces further dis-

tinguishes them from the smooth, patterned fabrics represented in the costumes and saddle covers of the Chinese in the same paintings.

The Mongol period in China (Yüan dynasty, 1206–1368), had Kublai Khan as one of its great emperors. He renamed Peking Khanbaliq—City of Khans—and ruled the vast Mongol empire from there. To this city Marco Polo came as a trade emissary from Venice, remaining for many years as an official of Kublai's empire. His voluminous travel notes describe palaces, gardens, and banquets in the imperial court, but offer only occasional information pertinent to our study. "The greater part of knights and barons eat in the hall on carpets, because they have not tables," he writes.[26] More exact information on rugs appears in a series of technological and historical notes from the end of the Yüan period (1366), by Tao Tsung-i, a scholar and farmer. Delightfully entitled *Nan-Ts'un Cho-Kêng Lu* (*Talks at the South Village While the Plow is Resting*), the notes mention manufactories of rugs for the imperial court in the northern suburb of Peking. The author uses the character *t'an* for these rugs.[27]

A discussion of the manufacture of carpets, in a mixture of Chinese and Mongol, is also contained in one of two chapters from the lost Yüan dynastic history that are incorporated in Wang-kuo Wei's encyclopedia *Kuang-Ts'ang Hsüeh-Chun Ts'ung-Shu.* Here the characters for felt and mat or carpet seem to be

FIGURE 262   Mahaprajapati Nursing the Infant Buddha, handscroll by Wang Chen-p'eng, active early XIV century, ink and colors on silk. Courtesy, Museum of Fine Arts, Boston

often used interchangeably as far as function, material, and acting verb—weave or make—are concerned. Hair carpeting for imperial use is described with a long list of ingredients: sheep wool, madder, shallow water, white alum, yellow reeds, lime, acorns, black alum, vinegar, bramble leaves, ox plums, and hard wood for fire. Floor carpets of patterned matting for imperial mausoleums have cut velvety pile. Also mentioned are large carpets for the main hall and four carpets for the front hall, various carpetings for halls and porches, including a white piece for a door or window curtain—many of similar ingredients to those in the list above. Felts specifically designated as such include yak-hair carpets, felts made with a medicinal plant, felts made with white alum, a white felt belt, and sheep- and camel-hair felt carpets of large dimension for the Mongol camp. Some of the colors mentioned are deep red, greenish gray, and poplar yellow. Artisans for carpets, lacquer, and felt are distinguished, and mentioned in terms of groups of 7,000 families, or 29,000 families. According to this evidence wool carpet manufacturing, including other forms than the traditional felt, was well established in China by the Yüan period.[28]

Another ambiguous rug reference of Yüan date is supplied by Wang Chen-p'eng (active early fourteenth century), a painter known for his extraordinarily detailed and precise rendering of religious and historical subjects, who left an interesting example of his speciality in the western Buddhist "boundary painting," Mahaprajapati Nursing the Infant Buddha (figure 262). A rug student would wish that the numerous overlaid rugs with their T'ang-style rosettes and floral patterns and fringed borders truly reflect a Yüan usage, but it is more likely that they reflect the painter's skillful recapitulation of T'ang Buddhist scenes—to meet a certain kind of Yüan taste.

Fragmentary and ambiguous as are these references and reflections from the Yüan period, they seem to support the idea that the Mongols in China ordered and used large numbers of both felt and pile products. The question is whether the Mongols brought the craft of knotting a wool pile with a woven ground, or merely a commanding taste for such materials, into China. Ethnologists agree on the traditional Mongolian lack of interest in weaving, as against other handicrafts—in fact, Mongolian admiration for skillfulness in any craft in others far outran their desire to attain that skill themselves. History repeatedly records the Mongols' practice of transporting skilled craftsmen from conquered cities to their own centers.

The cities of Central Asia and Persia were famous, long before the Mongol conquest, for their rugs and textiles. These cities were the next to fall to the Mongols after China. It may well be that some of their craftsmen were brought back to Khanbaliq to produce to the taste of the Mongol dynasty in China and to implant their skill there, to persist in later dynasties after the Mongols had left China to the Chinese.

It is also possible that the Uigurs, a people of Turkish linguistic stock who came from north and west of the Orkhan River in northern Mongolia and lived on the western Chinese border and in Chinese Turkestan from T'ang times on, had something to do with this. Ardent Buddhists and somewhat haughty friends of the Chinese, they are known to have advised the Mongols on many matters. The Muslim Uigur, Ahmad, succeeded the famous Liu Ping-chung as personal advisor to Kublai himself. Frescoes from the Uigur centers of Turfan frequently show patterned rugs of unknown material, possibly of felt, in both secular and religious scenes (page 310). And among Uigur "gifts" in Chinese tribute lists of the tenth century, pile or hair weavings are mentioned several times, although with no explanation of technique or use.[29]

Rugs after the Mongol Conquest

Chinese pile rugs of wool and of silk actually exist in number in the styles of Chinese periods succeeding the Mongol conquest—that is, the Ming (1368–1644) and Ch'ing (1644–1912) periods. Their sizes and shapes sometimes suggest that they were used as the nomads used them—as travel rugs, saddle covers, banners, and, to make tent life more comfortable, as circular floor coverings in several sections and wall hangings. Some, more in keeping with older Chinese custom, appear to have been used as temple rugs or hangings, altar frontals, pillar rugs, or kneeling mats. Others seem associated with home or palace use. Since furniture types by then were of fairly standard dimension, one can recognize, by their size, rugs as well as patterned silk mats intended for use on furniture. The movable couch and the postered bed were approximately the same size—6½ by 4½ feet, requiring a single rug or one divided into three squares for kneeling. The low stool for sitting with crossed legs measured from 2 feet 2 inches to 3 feet by 3 feet 4 inches, and would take a kneeling mat of ordinary size. So too would Ming chairs, with their seat dimensions of 20 by 40 inches, and Ch'ing audience chairs, measuring 34 inches from back to front and

306

44 inches wide, their shaped backs 21 inches high in the center. On the other hand, rugs for the *k'ang*, the heated platform built in at the end of the rooms in northern China, could be any size; frequently a combination of small rugs was used on these. Rugs for floor use in both the Ming and Ch'ing periods were usually large and square (for example, 13 by 13 feet) or with one dimension doubled (for example, 13 by 26 feet). Such rugs were sometimes used in combination, apparently in matched sets.[30] In paintings, we see groups of picnickers or musicians seated upon rugs or mats in gardens and woods, and children playing on them (figure 263). Rugs in homes were identified with wealth, and fur rugs were still sometimes used here, as we see in a description, from a Ming novel, of the reception hall of a cultivated mandarin:

> How lofty were the dimensions of this stately hall, how spacious were the great courtyards! At the entrance, like the hairs of a beard, hung the glittering strings of the green bead curtain, which displayed a design of frogs seated upon a tortoise. The floors were covered with lionskins and long-piled carpets.[31]

FIGURE 263   The Hundred Children, detail from anonymous painting, Ming period (1368–1644). Courtesy of the Trustees of the British Museum

Bamboo and grass mats, in contrast to the elegant rugs just described, continued to be widely used for eating and sleeping among less monied classes; these mats are known today in southern China, where wool rugs were apparently never made or used. And

FIGURE 264   One of a pair of rugs or hangings, western China, XIX century. Catalogue no. 195a

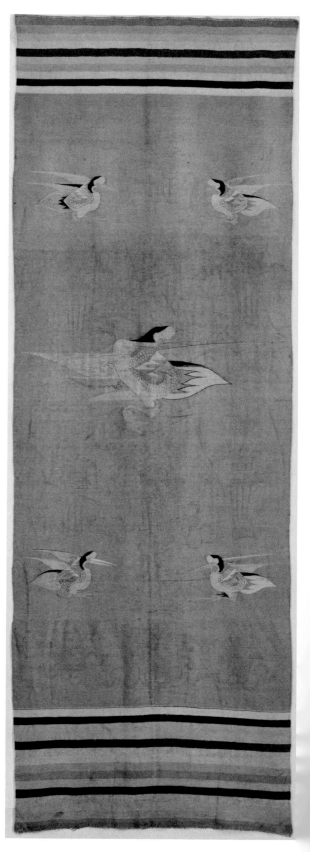

coarse tapestry-woven wool mats and blankets with crude but sometimes extraordinarily effective woven, stamped, and painted decorations in combination have long been associated with riverboats, especially in the Yangtse region (figure 264).

PILE RUGS

When Chinese rugs appeared in the American art market early in this century, cast adrift from homes, temples, and palaces by the Boxer rebellion, they had not hitherto been widely known in the West, unlike the rugs of the Near East, which had been treasured in Europe since the time of the Crusades. Chinese rugs, newcomers though they may be in the long reaches of Chinese history, generally reflect the decorative styles of the Ming and Ch'ing periods, styles already known to the West in the brilliant porcelains and patterned silks exported from China for hundreds of years. Some of the rugs retain stylistic influences and shapes from their original home in the north and west of China—the cool regions where wool pile rugs seem more likely to have been always at home. Another group may well be from the old city of Khotan on the southern silk trade route from China to the Near East, though made there long after that city's early days of glory. Still another group, produced in the late nineteenth and early twentieth centuries in Peking and T'ien-tsin, recapitulates traditional styles or presents a new stylization of landscape and still life characteristic of more modern times. Rugs from the western provinces, of the same date, have the appealing simplicity of folk art.

As a whole, these rugs show a wide range of sophistication and quality. Some obviously are the work of weavers in a great center or a palace workshop of the kind first mentioned in late Yüan records (page 305); some, with religious motifs predominating, may well have been made for temple use by a monastery workshop; some are clearly the products of village weavers or homemakers—peasants in the Yellow River Valley are mentioned in this connection; some more recent examples are from industrial schools or factories in such cities as Peking. A famous rug center for centuries was Ning-hsia, a border city on the loop of the Yellow River near some of the finest pasturage in China. In the thirteenth century Marco Polo noted the white camel-hair fabrics, called camlets, when he passed north of the great bend of the river on his way to Peking. Other rug centers referred to in more recent centuries were nearby Pao-t'ou, founded by Ning-hsia

weavers; Kalgan in Chih-li; Chi-nan-fu in Shantung; T'ai-yuan-fu in northern Shansi; and Peking and its port, T'ien-tsin, especially active in supplying the Western market in the early twentieth century. It is one thing to name the known centers, however, and quite another to say precisely where surviving rugs were produced. Except for rugs of recent date, such attributions are matters of surmise or rumor.

Chinese rugs are usually made with the Persian, or Senna, knot. The Chinese version usually has the loop to the right, with the Turkish, or Ghiordes, knot found occasionally scattered through the field or in the border. The Ghiordes knot has also been reported along the selvages,[32] where its function seems to be to keep the outermost warp from rising; since it functions here as a binder, rather than as a pile element, it is regarded by at least one authority as not a true Turkish knot.[33] The selvage is often formed of two cords—the outer consisting of two regular warps, the inner of one regular warp, both part of the plain-weave ground. The space on these cords formed by the spacing in the ground weave caused by each row of knots is filled by wrapping the upper adjacent ground weft once around the outer cord before it continues back across the fabric in regular weave below the row of knots. The warp and weft are most commonly of bunched plied cotton yarns, though they may be of plied silk when the pile is of silk, and occasionally of ramie. Two or four shoots of weft are usually inserted after each row of knots. The pile, usually not as finely knotted as in Persian rugs, and often having a marked lean, may be of wild or cultivated silk or a variety of wools, including sheep, goat, camel, or yak.

A technological encyclopedia of the first half of the seventeenth century, the *T'ien-kung K'ai-wu*, gives interesting information about sheep and their wool in China.[34] The coarse fleece of the woolly sheep flourishing north of Hsü-chou and the Huai River, and also raised in Hu-chou south of the Yangtse, was used from pre-Han times for felt or "downlike" fabric for hats, socks, and coarse fabrics for poor folk. Western Region sheep, called cashmere by Shensi people, were introduced into China either in the Han period or toward the end of the T'ang period by "barbarians." Weavers of these woolens, which were called *lan-chou* or *ku-lu*, were still members of this "barbarian" race of unknown name in the seventeenth century, at which time they were centered in Lan-chou in western China. No mention of rugs appears in connection with these wools until Matteo Ricci, a Jesuit missionary in the late sixteenth and

early seventeenth centuries, mentions "woolen cloth
of light weight for summer use which is much in
demand by the poorer classes for hats and for the
carpets which they use for sleeping mats."[35]

The pile rugs now known were made, according to
travelers' reports of the last hundred years, on vertical
frames. The design was inked on the stretched warps
or on a paper cartoon placed behind the warps. The
Persian or Turkish practice of having a boy call
directions to the weavers was sometimes used. The
weaver, or several weavers in a row, sat in front of
the loom on a plank, which was raised as the weaving
progressed upward (figure 265).

The colors of these rugs, deliberately streaked or
marbled in certain areas, can present a delightful
combination of soft yet brilliant hues, only suggested

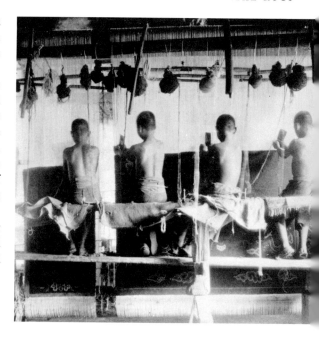

FIGURE 265   Boys knotting a carpet in Peking.
Courtesy of Dr. Gösta Montell

FIGURE 266   K'ang rug, XVII century style.
Catalogue no. 196

FIGURE 267   K'ang rug, K'ang-hsi period
(1662–1722). Catalogue no. 198

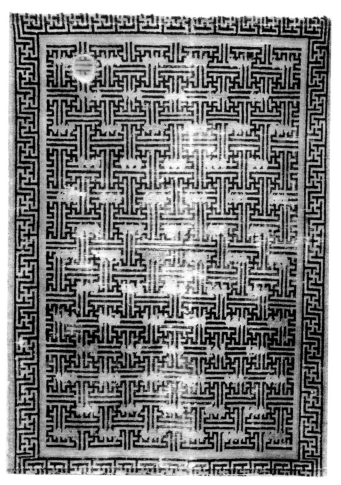

by some faded surviving versions. These are sometimes the natural colors of the fibers, but more usually the product of vegetable dyes. Especially frequent are blues, browns, and shades of tan and gold, but white and many tones of red, pink, orange, yellow, green, and a dark mordanted brown close to black also occur. When the coal-tar dyes of the West reached China toward the end of the nineteenth century, artificial rug-aging to mellow the harsher colors became a standard practice. Contouring of design edges by shearing after the weaving was completed is often seen in Chinese rugs of late date. This gives a relief effect to the pile and enhances the design. Many old rugs, not sheared, suggest this effect through the uneven wearing quality of differently dyed and mordanted sections of the pile.

PATTERNS

The use of diaper patterns of relatively small scale distinguishes Chinese rugs from almost all others—a predilection also richly apparent in silks, bronzes, lacquers, ceramics, and architectural detail. Fret diapers and borders are important parts of the decoration on Shang, Chou, and Han bronzes, and on molded pottery grave bricks of the Chou and Han periods. Most frequently used are the angular scroll and the swastika fret based on the symbol for "ten thousand" (卍), which is both an implied wish for longevity and the ancient symbol for thunder. In rugs, frets are used as a strongly marked diaper for the central field, sometimes set with decorative details, or as a subtler background, often in two shades of the same color. Frets are also used as a border, or as a corner or border detail.

A bold swastika-fret field diaper in deep blue on rosy tan, set with horizontal rows of small bats in turquoise and golden yellow, occurs frequently in rugs of the K'ang-hsi period (1662–1722), suggesting the taste of the earlier Ming period. One such rug, probably a k'ang piece (figure 266), has guard bands in several colors setting off the bold continuous swastika fret that forms the border. Smaller rugs of this design, perhaps stool or cushion covers, were made without borders. In another small k'ang rug, the swastika-fret diaper occurs as a more subordinate background (figure 267) laid obliquely behind symmetrically spaced repeats of a peony branch with a large profile flower and bud. A strong interlocking running T-fret set off by guard stripes forms the border. Such frets in obliquely set diapers are often used in rug borders between the lobed medallions containing flowers, birds, and similar motifs, recal-

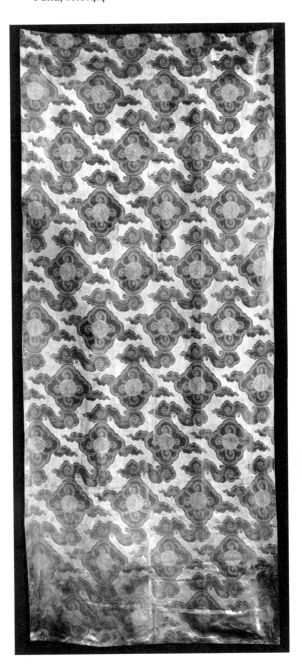

FIGURE 269 Cloud-patterned satin damask, probably from tombs of Kuo-chin Wang, early XVIII century. The Metropolitan Museum of Art, Seymour Fund, 60.104.4

ling the borders of Ch'ing porcelains and lacquer. Or these frets may form the background of a whole, wider border set with such objects as longevity symbols and variously decorated discs (figure 292).

Less purely geometrical diapers are also frequent. Tangent four-lobed cloud medallions, one row en-

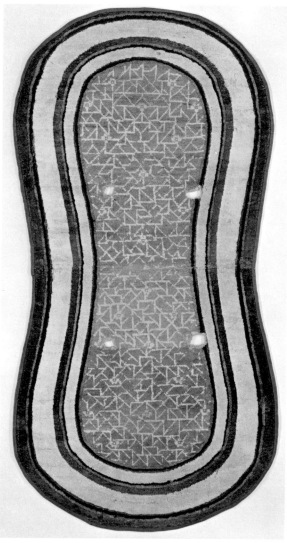

FIGURE 270 Cloud-patterned rug, probably XVII century. Textile Museum Collection, Washington, D.C.

FIGURE 271 Saddle cover, northern China, XVII–XVIII century. Collection of Joseph V. McMullan, New York

closing bats, the alternate row peach sprays, appear on the field of a large square rug (figure 268, page 164). The field is set off from a bold, running, swastika-fret border by grouped guard bands and stripes. Chinese paintings of the late Ming period show this type of diaper rug on shallow platforms, couches, or on the ground.

Another distinctly Chinese allover pattern of lobed clouds with curving tails, seen in the beautiful damasks worn in Ming ancestor portraits, and in an early eighteenth-century damask in the Metropolitan (figure 269), is also found in Ch'ing rugs and prob-

ably existed in grander scale in Ming rugs. An example with clouds and flying cranes with wings above and spread at right angles to their bodies, in late Ming or early Ch'ing style, is in the collection of Ernest Erickson (unpublished). A small rectangular rug in the Textile Museum, Washington (figure 270), with a central crane roundel and a lotus border, shows another use of the pattern. Interestingly enough, the slim, curly, "Chinese" cloud bands that appear as details in the richly decorated fields and borders of so many Persian and Turkish rugs are not seen in surviving Chinese rugs.

The well-known cracked ice and plum blossom diaper, associated most often with K'ang-hsi blue and white porcelains but occurring in other Chinese decoration, is also used occasionally on rugs—for instance, on a saddle cover, probably of the same date, in the collection of Joseph V. McMullan (figure 271).

Other diapers, originally from "barbarians," are incorporated in many Chinese rugs, a result of China's long history of relations with various tribes and cultures of Turkestan and the Near East. Some of these appear in other media long before the date of any surviving Chinese rugs, for instance in the representations of small fringed rugs beneath standing dignitaries, seated musicians, and kneeling adorers in the Uigur frescoes, as well as in miniatures from Chotcho, on the southern silk route to the Mediterranean world. These include dotted lozenges, allover imbrications, and scrolling or serpentine acanthus borders, originally from the classical world.[36] The octagon-and-square diaper is seen in a small Chinese k'ang rug of much later date (figure 282). Here octagons linked by four-partite squares form a field in which is centered a large lobed medallion enclosing lions. A similar diaper appears on a rug depicted in a Ming painting (figure 272) in the Metropolitan.

Other "barbarian" diapers, the trellis set with rosettes, and imbrications including the overlapping circles known in China as the "cash" motif, appear as field patterns in saddle covers and rugs of the Ming and Ch'ing periods. They perhaps came originally from the late classical world during the first

FIGURE 272 T'ang Emperor Instructing his Heir, handscroll in ink and colors on silk, Ming copy (1368–1644) after painting by Sung emperor Hui Tsung. The Metropolitan Museum of Art, Kennedy Fund, 13.220.89

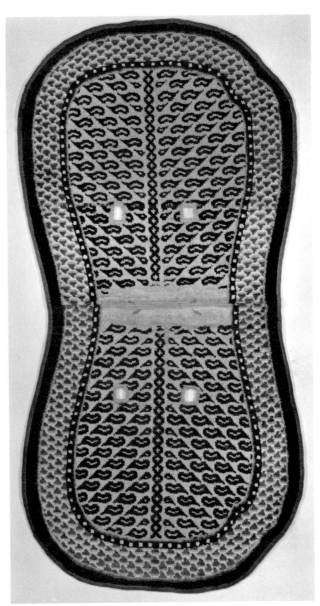

FIGURE 273 Saddle cover, northern China, XVII–XVIII century. Collection of Joseph V. McMullan, New York

centuries of the Christian era, where they were common at a much earlier date than they appear in China.

The tiger stripe was an early decorative treatment in China, doubtless because tigers were common there in ancient days. The tiger-stripe motif in shades of blue makes an entertaining field pattern on a saddle rug in the McMullan collection (figure 273), as does a treatment in browns suggesting a striped animal skin of unknown species on another McMullan

FIGURE 275 Felt rug, probably before 756.
Shosoin Homotsu (Treasury of the Shosoin, Nara)

FIGURE 274 Saddle cover, northern China,
XVIII century. Collection of Joseph V. McMullan,
New York

FIGURE 276 Felt rug, probably before 756.
Shosoin Homotsu (Treasury of the Shosoin, Nara)

saddle rug (figure 274). These are perhaps of the seventeenth century. Crude Chinese rugs from the northern and western provinces, last seen on the New York art market, include a large striped tiger skin almost filling an otherwise undecorated rectangular rug, and a skin-shaped rug with a gesticulating shamanlike figure covered with tiger stripes, perhaps representing the flayed skin of the son of the terrifying Lamaist deity, Palden Lhamo.[37]

Flowers, a universally beloved decorative motif, appear in many aspects in Chinese rugs. The T'ang taste for heavy many-petaled flowers in symmetrical arrangements, with emphatic stems and small leaves, shows in one of the felt rugs in the Shoso-in (figure 275). Others of these rugs have even more fully petaled flowers, probably peonies, or flowers artfully grouped in roundels or lozenges, often with small leafy sprigs in the intervening spaces. In other arrangements, a single large roundel, formed of a frontal lotus closely wreathed by many linked profile lotuses, has dense floral corner fillings (figure 276), or is flanked by smaller detached curving flower sprays and cloud bands (figure 277).

A great number of surviving pile rugs show elaborations of the flower theme in accord with Ming and Ch'ing tastes. One such rug (figure 278) has interlaced tree peony branches bearing flowers in a balanced arrangement, with small trilobed leaves spaced seemingly at random over the surface of a vertical rectangle without borders. The pattern seems more or less self-contained, and it may be that this k'ang cover never had a border or had only the narrow unpatterned band seen on many of the Shoso-in rugs. Its thick, firm, fine pile has a lightly

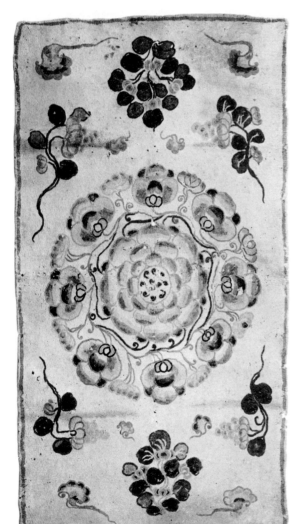

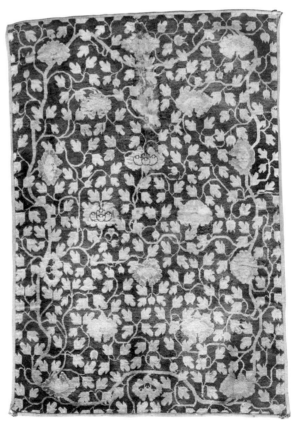

FIGURE 277   Felt rug, probably before 756. Shosoin Homotsu (Treasury of the Shosoin, Nara)

FIGURE 278   K'ang rug, second half of XVII century. Catalogue no. 200

FIGURE 279 Lotus
rug (detail), perhaps
K'ang-hsi period
(1602–1722). The
University Museum,
Philadelphia

FIGURE 280 Cushion cover for seat, XVII century
or earlier. Catalogue no. 201

contoured surface, and the flowering branches, their
colors mellowed by time, now appear in two shades
of gold on a deep blue ground. The treatment
suggests the flowering branches seen in Ming three-
color ceramic wares of the sixteenth and seventeenth
centuries, in which whole designs are outlined in
thread relief on a deeply colored ground, but this rug
and others in this style are usually dated a little later,
in the K'ang-hsi period (1662–1722).

The lotus and its more stylized relative, the
Precious Image Flower, were favored in China
because of their association with Buddhism, and
occur as popular motifs in the Shoso-in rugs. Both
appear in majestic scale on Ming rugs and, with
variations of stylization and size, on Ch'ing rugs as
well. Two handsome rugs about twenty feet square,
now in the University Museum, Philadelphia, and
probably originally used in Buddhist temples, show
an allover interlacing of this motif in the style of late
Ming and early Ch'ing periods. One[38] has a rich,
heavy design of stylized flowers and curling leaves on
rhythmically scrolling stems, in deep blue on a golden
tan ground, with dependent, smaller, three-petaled,
profile flowers associated with Turkish design, outlined in light blue, yellow, and cream. Two wide
angular scroll borders, in deep blue and variously

colored guard bands are surrounded by a dark brown
outer border about six inches wide, a typical propor-
tion for a rug of this size. The other rug (figure 279)
has an unusual allover pattern of linked flower sprays
with small profile lotuses, one to a spray, and long
elaborate clusters of small leaves curling, singly or in
pairs, from a contrastingly colored bud borne on

slim, angular stems. The colors are also unusual—a combination of browns, blue, pale yellow, and pearl gray on a soft yellow ground. The angular stylization, the elaborate multiple narrow borders, and the diagonals of color variations in the allover pattern suggest an influence from Chinese Turkestan, while the allover pattern of branches may have come, by some devious route in time and geography, from the great Safavid tree rugs of Persia.

A stool or cushion cover (figure 280) with short, lightly contoured wool pile shows the Precious Image Flower in many-petaled profile, with small leaves on stems from which a great number of double tendrils wander without repeat. The attenuated, slightly stiffened treatment in pale yellow on deep blue recalls a group of decorated porcelains of the early Ch'ing period, and this cushion cover may well be contemporary with them. A large stylized Precious Image Flower repeat of an entirely different sort forms the

allover pattern on a rug in the Metropolitan (figure 281). Each profile flower is framed on four sides by large, stylized, symmetrically curling leaves that form a rectangular unit, which, in soft blues and browns, covers the entire cream colored rug. This distinctive treatment of the flower is called the "western lotus," and may well have come from the strongly Buddhist territory of Chinese Turkestan, though it must postdate by many centuries the famous Buddhist frescoes in this area. The "western lotus" occurs frequently as a border repeat in Ch'ing blue and white porcelains, and its bold and simple use as a rug pattern may be of the K'ang-hsi period. A different version of the lotus, usually in profile with artfully arranged small leaves, is used as a cornerpiece or as a border repeat in many eighteenth- and nineteenth-century rugs (figure 287). Another use is seen in a seventeenth-century rug in the Metropolitan (figure 282), where a serpentining lotus spray forms one of the outer borders, in the

FIGURE 281   K'ang, Buddhist temple, or altar rug, XVIII century. Catalogue no. 202

FIGURE 282   K'ang rug, XVII century. Catalogue no. 203

form so often used in Persian rugs of the same date.

The large roundels and flower sprays of the felt rugs in the Shoso-in apparently continue in pile rugs of later periods—for instance, a large rug belonging to John Davis Hatch (unpublished) has an enormous lion roundel in the center of a diapered field, the imposing scale of the roundel suggesting an early date. An early Ch'ing version of the roundel and flower style is suggested in a series of small rectangular rugs. In one (figure 283), the central medallion is formed of a large rosette with two long-nosed archaic dragons confronted on either side, and decorated spires between, completing the circle; the whole has an attenuated, linear quality. Three angular tree-peony sprays in gracefully balanced positions at either end almost fill the remainder of the field. The symmetrical

corner fillings are elaborated swastika frets. The fairly wide border, set off by a pearled guard band and a slightly wider band with an endless knot repeat, is filled by a bold continuous swastika fret, emphasized at regular intervals by deepening color so that it has a shaded three-dimensional effect. With its delicate elaboration of archaic and contemporary designs and wide range of agreeable colors (now faded), this rug suggests the taste of the Yung-chêng period (1723–1736). Another floral rug in the Metropolitan (figure 284) is of about the same period.

Flowery roundels and sprays reached an enchanting efflorescence in the eighteenth century and became the characteristic rug design of the Ch'ien-lung period (1736–1795). The flowers have a charming decorative naturalism with a certain rococo

FIGURE 283   Rug, early XVIII century. Catalogue no. 204

FIGURE 284   Rug, early XVIII century. Catalogue no. 206

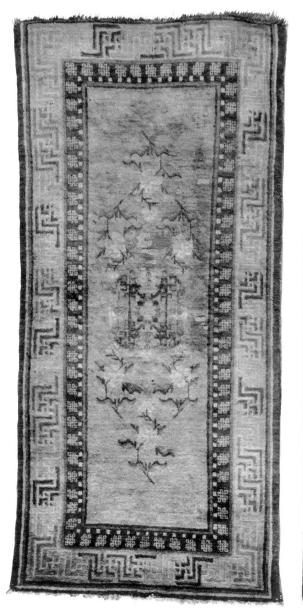

contains a decorated lantern or pendant suspended by a bat over a lotus.[40]

The Ch'ien-lung flower and roundel style has great charm in its numerous nineteenth-century interpretations, though it becomes somewhat hardened and coarsened. In one fine example, not far from the original style, a large central floral roundel is framed in a tight cloud circle; two smaller roundels are placed at either end of the field, one of each pair containing a spotted deer and a bird, the other containing lions (figure 287). Flowers and butterflies in the same vivid pastels as the roundels appear scattered on a pale golden yellow ground. Here, as often, the horizontally oriented flower sprays of the border are interspersed with Buddhist emblems of Happy Augury. Another rug of this type, dating

FIGURE 286   Cushion cover for chair, late XVIII century. Catalogue no. 209

FIGURE 287   Rug, XIX century, Ch'ien-lung style. Catalogue no. 212

quality. They are arranged in roundels, either skillfully intertwined or seeming to grow with perfect grace within the confines of a circle; as sprays or plants; or strewn with a light hand so that they fall into perfect, freely balanced arrangements in a spacious field of off-white, soft yellow, or some other pastel shade. The colors, like the designs, suggest a summer garden—soft blues, pinks, yellows, greens, and browns, with touches of vivid orange and black. A characteristic rug of this period has a pale yellow field scattered with butterflies and flowers of all seasons, with the lotus in central position at either end and eight flower-and-fruit roundels of subtly varied size, symmetrically arranged. The cornerpieces and border contain gracefully stylized flower sprays (figure 285, page 166).

Various elegant contemporary and later versions of this style occur, with the number of roundels varying from one, as on cushion covers (figure 286), to many, for instance a stylized symmetrical floral repeat, in blue shading to white, closely covering a deep blue ground.[39] One example of a rare variation of the style has five lobed medallions, the largest in the center, two slightly smaller ones at either end, on a lattice-diaper field, in soft blue and yellow on brown. The border is a strong version of the typical eighteenth-century lotus scroll set off by unpatterned guard bands, the center band pearled. Each medallion

FIGURE 288   Rug, XIX century. Catalogue no. 213

later in the nineteenth century, has a lion and cub in a landscape in the central medallion and a border of what appear to be "upright water" stripes (figure 288). Among the somewhat simplified flowers of the field, we see a small version of the profile peony spray with rising bud popular in both eighteenth- and nineteenth-century rugs (figure 267).

The roundel and flower style in the strong, fresh shades of blue and white popular in the second half of the nineteenth century appears in a saddle cover with stylized wave-and-mountain patterns in the Metropolitan (figure 289), and in another in the

FIGURE 290   Rug, late XIX or early XX century, Ch'ien-lung style. Catalogue no. 216

FIGURE 289   Saddle rug, XIX century. Catalogue no. 215

McMullan collection.[41] The pile of this piece slants downward, in the interest of comfort, on either side of the central seam. This seam, as on many saddle covers, bisects a highly stylized and compressed ancient Chinese symbol for the center of the world. The skillful recapitulation of Ch'ien-lung styles, popular much later in centers like Peking, is perhaps represented in a delightful small flowery rug with corner fillings of fret dragons twined with flowers (figure 290). Its almost over-sophisticated detail and the identical slant of all its flower sprays, contrary to the basic Chinese instinct for balance in this type of design, indicate its distance from the original style.

Many other objects from Chinese culture and

religion appear on Ming and Ch'ing rugs—sometimes in compositions obviously related to those of the Shoso-in rugs, sometimes in simpler layout. The Four Attributes of the Scholar, the Hundred Antiques, and the Symbols of the Eight Immortals of Taoism are often used in combination, either in horizontal rows from top to bottom or skillfully spaced from a central cross-axis toward either end of the rug, as on a finely knotted example (figure 291). Sometimes they are interspersed with smaller fruit and flower sprays. The Eight Buddhist Emblems tied with scalloped ribbons and arranged in two vertical rows decorate a small, pale, beautifully carved rug (figure 292). Its wide border is filled with a diagonal swastika-fret

FIGURE 291 Rug, XIX century, Ch'ien-lung style. Catalogue no. 217

FIGURE 292 K'ang rug, XIX century. Catalogue no. 218

diaper set at regular intervals with small decorated discs, either singly or in groups of two or three.

Buddhist emblems are especially associated with a series of eighteenth- and nineteenth-century rugs for enclosing columns in the temples of Lamaist Buddhism in Mongolia and Tibet, and Peking under the

FIGURE 293 Pillar rug for Lamaist market in China or Tibet, XIX century. Catalogue no. 219

Manchus. These rugs, ranging in quality from fine to coarse, are vertically oriented, and have a wave-and-mountain border across the bottom and an upper border simulating a valance from which tassels hang down into the field. The Eight Buddhist Emblems with clouds, flower sprays, spotted deer, precious jewels, and other auspicious objects may fill the field

in freely balanced arrangement, or they may form a setting for a half-life-size figure of a Lamaist priest calling the faithful to worship by blowing a conch shell (figure 293), for a series of seated priestly figures,[42] or for a big dragon disposed in such a way as to appear coiled around the pillar when it is enclosed by the rug.[43] Invocations in Chinese, Tibetan, Manchu, or Mongolian may be part of the decoration.

Lions were popular decorative motifs, though they were not native to China, and were thought of either as the austere guardians of Buddhism or as playful, fantastic creatures. A rug in a private collection in Edinburgh (unpublished), said to have been given by the Ming emperor Wan Li to his mother-in-law, has an enormous scowling lion with its cub on its back, as often represented by the Chinese, boldly drawn and nearly filling an unpatterned field with a shaded interlocking T-border. The exaggerated drawing of the lion, however, suggests a nineteenth-century date. Another boldly patterned rug[44] in blue, yellow, and brown, has a central lion with a cub on its back; smaller lions with Buddhist emblems and occasional clouds fill the corners and interspaces. The border is of shaded interlocking T's set off by two decorated inner borders recalling those on one of the lotus rugs in the University Museum, Philadelphia (figure 279). Such borders are associated with western Chinese and Turkestan taste, and the field of this rug may be early Ch'ing in style. An early Ch'ing rug in the Metropolitan has a central medallion (figure 282) in which lions play with auspicious objects, and stylized flames of creatures of fable spring at their shoulders and haunches. Another rug in the Metropolitan (figure 288) shows a lion in a roundel within a garden setting. A small round rug[45] is filled by two lions circling a brocade ball with long, decoratively fluttering ribbons.

A favorite Chinese subject, often used for end borders or reversed at the central axis to fill both halves of a small rectangular rug, is a Manchurian crane with spread wings, descending toward a spotted deer in a landscape setting. A charmingly stylized, early nineteenth-century version of this subject (figure 294, page 168) has carefully differentiated details and a balanced but unsymmetrical composition so that it indeed suggests a scene in the Taoist Paradise. Later versions often present such a simplified version of the crane flying over a startled deer that one is probably meant to see in it only a punning wish for longevity, happiness, and riches (the characters for *deer* and for *happiness and official pay* are both romanized as *lu*).

Other popular Ming and Ch'ing decorative sub-jects are used frequently on small rugs, as major elements in balanced arrangements, or as incidental detail. Goldfish of eccentric shape and size are among these, as are bats, symbolic of happiness because the romanization of the different characters for both *bat* and *happiness* is *fu*. Bats may appear in a roundel of five to signify the Five Blessings—old age, wealth, health, love of virtue, and a natural death. The Eight Trigrams, eight different combinations of whole or broken lines figuratively denoting the evolution of nature and its cyclic changes, are symbols from China's early days that appear occasionally on rugs. Semimythical Chou times are recalled by a popular nineteenth-century travel rug decoration—the Eight Horses of King Mu (figure 295). The Chinese fond-ness for all-embracing symbolism appears in one rather different Ch'ing rug decoration of unknown origin. Small discs, variously decorated, are sym-metrically placed in groups of one, two, or three in an unpatterned field, and handled similarly in the border. Filleted books, scrolls, seals, and other emblems of scholarly attainment, the Five Bats, the spotted deer, the longevity emblem, and every other possibly auspicious symbol may be clearly seen in miniature.[46] In later versions, where the discs are sometimes laid over fret borders (figure 292), the decoration on each disc is so stylized and simplified as to be, in some cases, unreadable. In a reversal of this treatment, probably dating from the early Ch'ing period, a single enormous disc with a yang-yin center fills the center of a small rectangular rug, and the animals of the Chinese zodiac, used to designate years or hours, are evenly spaced around it.[47]

The most important symbol in China, starting with her early history, is that of the cosmic power of the universe expressed as a dragon—a creature of many aspects, especially associated with rain-bearing clouds and water, equally at home in all parts of the universe, which is indicated by the heaven of clouds over a wave border symbolizing water, with rock moun-tains symbolizing land. The small round object often pursued or held by the dragon is variously read. It may be the sun, the moon, or the "night-shining pearl."[48] The dragon with five claws was officially the symbol of the emperor in the Ming and Ch'ing periods, and the court furnishings and robes of these periods depict it in several ways. An unusual example of an eighteenth-century carpet is a large square rug (figure 296) made for a palace or a temple under royal patronage. A slim, coiling, five-clawed dragon is centered in a field of small puffy clouds, with

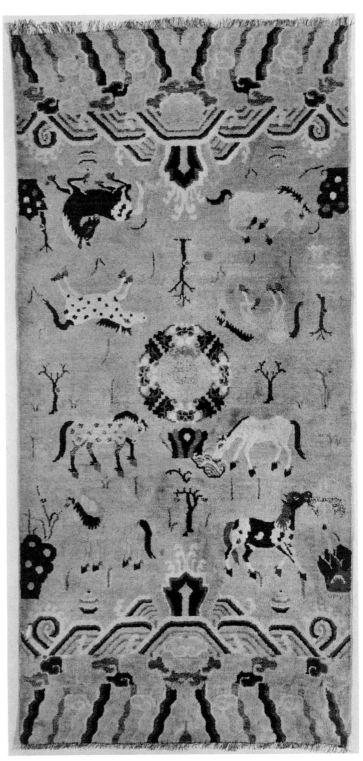

FIGURE 295   Saddle or traveler's rug, XIX century. Catalogue no. 221

FIGURE 296   Imperial dragon rug (detail), Ch'ien-lung period (1736–1795). Collection of Fred Mueller, New York.

FIGURE 297   Throne cushion cover, XIX century. Catalogue no. 223

slightly smaller dragons coiling—a differently colored one in each corner—over a deep wave border set with rocks and sprinkled with flowers. A wide fret border is set off from the field by a guard band with small, spaced lotuses. The rug has a slanting, coarsely set pile in a range of soft colors on a golden tan ground. A late nineteenth-century version of this symbolic universe is crowded into a square throne cushion cover (figure 297) with wave borders on four sides and five cartoonlike dragons. Its colors, hard and bright, are derived from coal tar dyes.

A problematical series of silk and metal carpets, with this symbolic universe in a central medallion and four quarter medallions, on a yellow field with an allover pattern of twining flowers, may have been made for palace use. They bear five-clawed dragons and a four- or five-character inscription specifying use in a certain hall or palace (figure 298). Though they echo in general layout the great Persian medallion rugs of the Safavid period, the Persian examples are infinitely finer, both aesthetically and technically.

FIGURE 298 "Palace carpet," possibly Khotan, Chinese Turkestan, late XIX century. Catalogue no. 224

FIGURE 299 K'ang rug, K'ang-hsi period (1662–1722). Catalogue no. 225

In the rugs under consideration, the metal threads introduced as a ground in the medallions and borders are not brocaded as in the Persian carpets, but are bunched and wrapped in the Sumak technique seen in certain Caucasian rugs. This technique is also seen as the metal ground for silk or wool pile designs in seventeenth- and eighteenth-century rugs from Chinese Turkestan; it is possible that figure 298 and the related rugs were produced in Khotan, Chinese Turkestan. Apparently several medallion rugs were woven from the same cartoon; ones almost identical with figure 298 are in the Warner Museum at the University of Oregon,[49] the collection of A. Stepanov, Quebec (unpublished), and elsewhere. An example with a much greater color range and an "upright water" and wave border belongs to the Tokyo National Museum.[50] Rugs in this technically distinct series are known with other types of design—landscapes within elaborately decorated borders, a seated bodhisattva in a silver field with a wide compartmented border, and a small panel with a mythical bird.[51] The drawing, design, and colors of the whole series suggest a date in the second half of the nineteenth century, if not later. Some of them may indeed have been made with Western travelers in mind. Occasionally wool pile rugs not in this category, but of late Ch'ing style, have metal Sumak areas as a ground for decorated medallions or for border detail. Examples (unpublished) are in the Musée des Arts Décoratifs, Lyons, and the E. B. Crocker Art Gallery, Sacramento, California.

Not all material intended for imperial use seems to have borne the five-clawed dragons, either alone or as part of the universe symbol. Actual palace carpets may be represented by existing large and small fragments in the City Museum, Halle, Germany, and in the William Rockhill Nelson Gallery, Kansas City (unpublished), with thick woven pile renderings of heavy scrolling stems, long curling leaves, and various exotic flowers. Their designs suggest those of Indian export material at the time of the East India Companies in the seventeenth and eighteenth centuries, the so-called "Chinese fashion." In the Cincinnati Museum is what appears to be the field of

FIGURE 300 Cushion cover or kneeling mat, K'ang-hsi style. Catalogue no. 226

such a rug.[52] It has more than a hint of the Louis XIV style in the big lobed curves of its cornerpieces and central medallions, which enclose unidentifiable exotic foliage and flowers of the "Chinese fashion." At the height of the activities of the East India Companies, Europeans were more welcome in China than in India, and they expounded the wonders of their curious Western civilizations to a fascinated imperial court. The Western style in painting became so popular that its leading exponent in China, Fra Castiglione, a Jesuit missionary, was given a Chinese name and stayed on for many years as court painter to the Emperor Ch'ien-lung. The international decorative style of this period, whatever its source—a blend of East and West—seems to have appeared in rugs, too, of which these fragments survive. Reports of their use as palace floor coverings came from Western visitors of the early twentieth century.

The dragon and its complement, the mythical dual bird, the *fêng-huang*, were widely used without the framing universe in the Ming and Ch'ing periods. The *kuei* dragons so frequent in K'ang-hsi decoration (an archaic form first seen in early bronzes) appear in bold simple profile and large scale in two horizontal rows in soft colors on a tan ground of a rectangular k'ang cover in the collection of Frank Michaelian (unpublished). In the same collection, a single,

muscular, coiling five-clawed dragon entwined in a sinuous flowering tendril effectively fills a banner with straight top and curving sides. Both pieces were perhaps for use in some part of the household or entourage of the emperor K'ang-hsi.

Numerous dragon forms decorated objects in general use with no indication of specific rank, though the five-clawed dragon as imperial insignia was never used under foot, according to many sinologists. Large roundels, each formed by a single deep blue foliage dragon, appear in horizontal rows on a tawny golden rug (unpublished) believed by its owner to date to the Wan-li period (1562–1620). This beautiful rug may actually be a little later, since K'ang-hsi decoration makes frequent use of this dragon form. On a small rectangular k'ang cover (figure 299) such foliage dragons form the central medallion, a balanced motif at either end of the rug, and corner fillings. A simpler form of the same dragon pattern, with a central medallion entirely of fretwork, appears on a small square cushion cover (figure 300). A more elaborate version with K'ang-hsi motifs, late in that period, or perhaps even later because of a certain lively delicacy, is used in the carefully preserved lower half of a large rectangular rug (figure 301). In Chinese families, a treasured rug was sometimes divided among several inheritors, as

FIGURE 301 Rug (lower half), late K'ang-hsi style. Catalogue no. 227

apparently happened here. The foliage dragons or birds in the corners and in the central medallion are smaller and more skittish than those on the rugs described above. In the border, mythical foliage birds alternate with lotus arabesques with the same delicate nervous quality. The salmon field has a fine allover pattern of small lotuses or Precious Image Flowers, with stems and leaves in paler salmon, skillfully balanced in mirror image on either side of the central axis, yet giving an artfully random appearance. The quality of this rug is exceptionally fine and its surface is carved with great skill. Ghiordes knotting is here and there found in the borders and in the field near them, possibly as the result of repair in a Turkish workshop.

An example of a distinctly Chinese usage is a "special occasion" rug (figure 302), with a field of scattered clouds in which a dragon confronts a *fêng-huang*, a flaming pearl set with precious jewels between them. The endless knot, one of the Eight Buddhist Emblems, symbolizing eternity, is supported between them by a bat. Four auspicious objects—a pair of cash, a *ju'i* scepter, peaches, and a swastika—are suspended by bats in each of the four corners. In the narrow border, set off by unpatterned guard bands, a lotus or Holy Image Flower, flanked by scrolling foliage, alternates with the character for conjugal happiness, the "double *hsi*." The combination of these particular auspicious objects, especially the dragon (*lung*), the masculine essence of the universe, facing the mythical bird (*fêng*), the feminine essence, indicates that the special occasion for which this rug was intended was a wedding. This is what the Chinese call a *lung-fêng* carpet. This one is knotted

FIGURE 302   Marriage rug (*lung-fêng*), XIX century, and reverse side, showing pattern. Catalogue no. 228

in long thick shaggy silk floss whose surface catches the light in such a way that it is difficult to make out the design (seen much more clearly in a photograph of the reverse, figure 302). The colors and the distorted drawing of the short-nosed dragon and the bird suggest a nineteenth-century date.

A large square rug in the Metropolitan (figure 303), with its strange interpretation of the T'ang decorative style, is problematical. It may be from either Mongolia or Japan. In both places, as well as in Tibet, the T'ang style was much admired and persisted long after the T'ang period in China. The Mongols embraced Buddhism after their conquest of China, and it appears that they adopted the T'ang style decoration of the great Buddhist centers of Chinese Turkestan as their empire declined. The large central roundel of the Metropolitan's rug is composed of two descending three-clawed dragons confronted on either side of a stylized tree. The roundel is circled at a distance by twelve small rosettes seen on other so-called Mongol rugs. The rug's narrow border and symmetrical corner ornaments with points reaching almost to the central roundel are formed of strangely distorted flowers, stems, leaves, and foliage dragons apparently closely adapted from the large interstitial rosettes on Shoso-in silks, or from such T'ang rosettes, in any case. Pairs of dragons in the same position on either side of a flaming pearl are to be seen in the tops of steles with Tibetan, Mongol, and Chinese inscriptions, as is a great deal more T'ang-style decorative detail all through the ruins around Karakorum from the thirteenth century on. The color scheme suggests that seen in so-called Mongol rugs—deep rusty red, rust, blackish brown, wood brown on grayish fawn.

FIGURE 303   Rug, Japan or Central Asia, XIX century. Catalogue no. 229

Chinese Turkestan

A few of the many rugs that combine Chinese, Central Asian, and Persian characteristics and taste in varying proportions are in the Metropolitan. These rugs must all have come from centers or tribes in the vast stretch of land between the western borders of Kansu and Szechuan in China and the eastern borders of Persia.

That rugs were produced here from very early times is witnessed by the wool pile fragments dating from the second to the sixth century found in the Tarim Basin in Chinese Turkestan, many of them apparently of local origin (page 303). The silk route running along the southern border of this basin had great oasis cities that were already ancient when Buddhist pilgrims of the T'ang period passed through on their way to India (see map, page 296). Kashgar, an important political and commercial city on the junction of the southern silk route and of trade routes from the Oxus Valley of India, was noted by these pilgrims: "Its manufactures are a fine kind of twilled haircloth, and carpets of a fine texture and skilfully woven."[53]

Khotan, further east, was a great religious center with a flourishing cult of Buddhism and temples with beautiful frescoes and sculpture. Here, "in old time," says a pilgrim's diary, a king sought marriage with a Chinese princess in order to obtain the closely guarded secret of sericulture. The princess brought with her to her new country, hidden in her headdress, silk worms and mulberry seeds, and it was in Khotan that sericulture took its first step toward the countries of the Near East. In the T'ang period the most famous product of Khotan was white and green jade,

but a pilgrim also lists "fine woven silken fabrics, hair cloth of fine quality, and carpets."[54]

After centuries under various Islamic tribes, the Mongols, and the Ch'ing emperors of China, in the early twentieth century Khotan was visited by European explorers. Albert von le Coq remarked on "carpets, many with very beautiful patterns, known as Samarkand" as a special product of Khotan and the surrounding oasis, whose manufacture was dying out in his time, and "felt with various colours stamped in to form exceedingly remarkable patterns," and "embroidery of a very artistic nature."[55] And Stein says: "I was struck by the thriving look of its villages, due largely to the flourishing carpet industry which is centered here. Its products, though unfortunately debased by the use of aniline dyes, are still much prized throughout Turkestan. There is little doubt that the manufacture of these famous silk carpets, and some other local industries connected with Khotan are an inheritance from ancient days."[56]

Traditionally attributed to Khotan is a group of rugs with characteristic stylized floral patterns in Senna-knotted pile of silk or wool on a ground of silver and gold threads bunched and wrapped in Sumak technique. These rugs have either silk or cotton warps and cotton ground wefts. A remote influence from Timurid decoration may well be reflected in these, since Chinese Turkestan formed one border of the Herat empire that, under the successors of Timur, stretched from the Tigris far into Central Asia. The somewhat rigid patterns of detached or interlocking floral sprays appear in rich shades of red, yellow, deep blue, with green stems outlined in black or dark brown (figure 304), or in shades of yellow, blue, brown, salmon, and blue green suggesting the pastel colors of the Safavid "Polish" rugs. Some of these Khotan rugs date at least as early as the eighteenth century, if one may judge from the colors and designs in relation to those of Chinese and Near Eastern rugs. The re-use of the same cartoon is suggested by the fact that a border fragment in the Metropolitan (figure 305) seems to

FIGURE 307   Rug, Chinese Turkestan, xvIII century.
Catalogue no. 232

FIGURE 308   Rug, Khotan, Chinese Turkestan,
xIX century. Catalogue no. 233

have the same design as the border of a rug in the
National Museum in Stockholm,[57] and the rug of
figure 304 is a close variant of one from the Benguiat
collection.[58]

A design believed to be from one or another of the
ancient neighbor cities on the southern silk route, and
probably used in all of them, appears in a group of
rugs with a vase and pomegranate field pattern and a
series of wide and narrow borders of frets, rosettes,
and pearls. The vase and pomegranate pattern

appears in early decoration in these oasis cities, perhaps borrowed from Gandhara or perhaps coming from the late classical world of the Near East through Turkish invasions. A version in wood-carving from a ceiling in Niya (near Khotan on the southern trade route) is dated to A.D. 300.[59] In the rugs of the eighteenth and nineteenth centuries, the vases with angular rising pomegranate trees are stylized into an allover treatment, often in shades of red, mulberry, and blue green on a deep, bright blue ground, with many borders in those and additional colors (figure

measure about fourteen by seven feet, or else half this size.

A local interpretation of the Chinese wave border is characteristic of many rugs from Chinese Turkestan. The central medallion, in this framework, stands for the cosmic mountain, according to some scholars. A rug of this type (figure 308) has an interesting field closely set with small discs, each marked with a cruciform flower reminiscent in general effect of Tibetan tie-dye patterns. The inner border on this rug is a stylized floral spray border similar to the

FIGURE 309 Rug, Khotan, Chinese Turkestan, XVIII century. Catalogue no. 234

306, page 170). Or the design may be interpreted in more muted shades of the same colors on a light ground (figure 307). Senna-knotted in wool or silk on cotton or occasionally wool warps, with a corresponding ground weft, the rugs are usually in the shapes and sizes demanded by the domestic architecture of the Tarim Basin. Here the main room for eating, sleeping, and receiving guests was a rectangular "atrium" with a raised platform running around the walls. For use on the platform and floor, the rugs

floral decoration on so-called Khotan rugs.

Another type of product from the rug-weavers of Khotan, or Koko-nor, east of Khotan in the Kuenlun Mountains, may be exemplified by three small rugs of Chinese silk, apparently for cushions for chairs or thrones. These have a short uncarved pile of Senna knots on silk warps with silk ground wefts. One (figure 309) has a field pattern somewhat crudely derived from Chinese seventeenth- and eighteenth-century satins with a repeat of dragon medallions and clouds. Such satins were made in great number and variety. Dragon and cloud satins with two-tailed

FIGURE 310 Detail of Lamaist temple hanging showing satin dragon and cloud border, Chinese for Tibetan market, perhaps XVII century. The Metropolitan Museum of Art, Kennedy Fund, 15.95.154

FIGURE 312 Chair or throne back, Khotan, Chinese Turkestan, XIX century. Catalogue no. 235

clouds[60] are preserved in Buddhist temple banners and Tibetan costumes, as in the border of a large Lamaist temple hanging in the Metropolitan (figure 310) showing Manjusri, the bodhisattva of wisdom. The color combination often seen in these dragon and cloud satins is also used in this little k'ang or seat cover. Yellow, orange, white, and pink silk in the

FIGURE 311 Embroidered satin cushion cover, Ch'ien-lung period (1736–1795). The Metropolitan Museum of Art, Bequest of William Christian Paul, 30.75.64

five-clawed dragons approximates the effect of the various wrapped gold threads almost always used for the dragons in the satins, on a deep blue ground. Separated by multiple guard stripes from this field, a fine swastika-fret diaper regularly set with tiny symmetrical bats fills the deep border.

The other two pieces, back and seat for throne or chair, have designs and colors suggesting a clumsy, slightly misunderstood approximation of the Ch'ienlung style seen in the decorative arts of that period (figure 311), with the angular fret entwined with graceful naturalistic flowers. One of these (figure 312) has a closely set, symmetrical allover pattern in both field and border of angular floral sprays and berries with occasional strangely rendered bats and small

orange fish—perhaps streat fish (*nien nien*), a punning wish for longevity and happiness. The pomegranate of Chinese Turkestan rugs is suggested in the large, central, cross-hatched, flattened disc framed in tendrils. What might be considered a "matching piece" (figure 313) comes perhaps from another such set since it is lighter in color and modified in detail. A close variant is in the Victoria and Albert Museum.[61]

FIGURE 313   Chair or throne seat, Khotan, Chinese Turkestan, XIX century. Catalogue no. 236

Notes to Chapter Eleven

1 Arthur Waley, trans., *The Book of Songs (Shih Ching)* (New York, 1960), p. 111.

2 Ibid., p. 283.

3 Ibid., p. 295.

4 David Hawkes, *Ch'u Tz'u: The Songs of the South: An Ancient Chinese Anthology* (Oxford, 1959), p. 36.

5 James Legge, trans., *The Sacred Books of China: The Texts of Confucianism*. Part 1. The Sacred Books of the East, vol. III (Oxford, 1899), p. 238.

6 Leah Kisselgoff, trans., "Miscellaneous Records of the Western Capital" (*Hsi-ching Tsa-chi*), p. 127.

7 Osaka, Japan Textile Color Design Center, *Textile Designs of Japan*, III, *Designs of Ryuku, Ainu and Foreign Textiles* (Osaka, 1961), p. 31.

8 Richard C. Rudolph, "Newly Discovered Chinese Painted Tombs," *Archaeology*, XVIII (Autumn, 1965), fig. 9.

9 Yoshito Harada, *Chinese Dress and Personal Ornaments in the Han and Six Dynasties* (Tokyo, 1937), pl. XXVIII.

10 Aurel Stein, *Serindia: Detailed Report of Explorations in Central Asia and Westernmost China*, IV (Oxford, 1921), pls. LX–LXX, LXXIX, CIV, CXXIV–CXXVI.

11 Edwin O. Reischauer, trans., *Ennin's Diary: The Record of a Pilgrimage to China in Search of the Law* (New York, 1955), p. 207.

12 Ibid., p. 228.

13 Ibid., p. 221.

14 Ibid., p. 233.

15 Ibid., pp. 180–82.

16 Hiuen Tsiang, *Si-Yu-Ki. Buddhist Records of the Western World*, I, trans. Samuel Beal (London, 1884), p. xci.

17 Hans Bidder, *Carpets from Eastern Turkestan*, p. 34.

18 Reischauer, *Ennin's Diary*, p. 48.

19 Edward H. Schafer, *The Golden Peaches of Samarkand: A Study of T'ang Exotics* (Berkeley and Los Angeles, 1963), p. 198.

20 Edward H. Schafer and Benjamin E. Wallacker, "Local Tribute Products of the T'ang Dynasty," *Journal of Oriental Studies*, IV (1957–58), pp. 230, 233.

21 S. I. Rudenko, *Kul'tura naseleniia Gornogo Altaia v skifskoe vremia*, p. 397, pl. LXXVI-3.

22 Aurel Stein, *Innermost Asia: Detailed Report of Explorations in Central Asia, Kan-su and Eastern Iran*, I (Oxford, 1928), p. 232.

23 Carl Johan Lamm, *Cotton in Medieval Textiles of the Near East* (Paris, 1937), p. 136.

24 R. Soame Jenyns, *Chinese Art: The Minor Arts*, II (New York, 1965), p. 44.

25 Folke Bergman, *Archaeological Researches in Sinkiang: Especially the Lop-nor Region*, VII. Archaeology 1, Reports from the Scientific Expedition to the Northwestern Provinces of China, Sino-Swedish Expedition (Stockholm, 1939), p. 128.

26 A. C. Moule and Paul Pelliot, *Marco Polo: The Description of the World*, I (London, 1938), p. 218.

27 *Nan-Ts'un Cho-Kêng Lu* (Peking, 1959), trans. Leah Kisselgoff for this chapter.

28 "Kuang-Ts'ang Hsüeh-Chun Ts'ung-Shu" (unpublished), trans. Leah Kisselgoff for this chapter. Aschwin Lippe brought this reference to my attention.

29 James Russell Hamilton, *Les Ouïghours à l'époque des Cinq Dynasties d'après les documents chinois* (Paris, 1955), pp. 90–91.

30 Information from Robert Hatfield Ellsworth.

31 *Chin P'ing Mei: The Adventurous History of Hsi Men and his Six Wives*, intro. Arthur Waley (New York, 1960), p. 418.

32 Information from Charles Grant Ellis.

33 Information from Schuyler Cammann.

34 Ying-hsing Sung, *T'ien-kung K'ai-wu: Chinese Technology in the Seventeenth Century*, trans. E-tu Zen Sun and Shiou-chuan Sun (University Park, Pa., 1966), pp. 69–70, 79.

35 Louis J. Gallagher, S. J., trans., *China in the Sixteenth Century: The Journals of Matthew Ricci, 1583–1610* (New York, 1953), p. 14.

36 Albert von Le Coq, *Chotscho* (Berlin, 1913), pls. 4, 5, 21.

37 American Art Galleries, *Antique Chinese Rugs: Thomas B. Clarke Collection*, no. 481; American Art Galleries, *Ancient Looms and Other Oriental Treasures*, no. 268. For further discussion of iconography, see Newark, *Catalogue of the Tibetan Collection and Other Lamaist Material in the Newark Museum*, IV, p. 17, pl. VI.

38 American Art Galleries, *Art of Ancient China: A. W. Bahr Collection*, no. 597.

39 Ibid., no. 595.

40 Ibid., no. 587.

41 Joseph V. McMullan, *Islamic Carpets*, no. 152.

42 "Mongolian Rugs of the Eighteenth Century," *Bulletin of the Pennsylvania Museum*, XVII (1920–1922), pp. 18–23.

43 American Art Association, *Rare and Beautiful Antique Chinese Productions, Yamanaka and Co.*, nos. 468, 514; American Art Galleries, *Clarke Collection*, no. 511; Newark, *Tibetan Collection*, pp. 23–25.

44 Galerie Georges Petit, Paris, *Liquidation des Biens Worch: Objets d'Art Anciens de la Chine*, Sale Catalogue, March, 1922, no. 377.

45 American Art Galleries, *Clarke Collection*, no. 472.

46 American Art Association, *Chinese Productions: Yamanaka and Co.*, no. 521.

47 American Art Galleries, *Clarke Collection*, no. 495.

48 Schafer, *Golden Peaches*, p. 237. See also M. W. DeVisser, *The Dragon in China and Japan* (Amsterdam, 1913), pp. 103–08, and bibliographies in both books.

49 John C. Ferguson, *Survey of Chinese Art* (Shanghai, 1939), no. 208.

50 Tokyo, *Chinese Arts of the Ming and Ch'ing Periods*, Tokyo National Museum Exhibition Catalogue (1963), no. 472.

51 London, *The Arts of the Ch'ing Dynasty*, Arts Council of Great Britain and the Oriental Ceramic Society Exhibition Catalogue (1964), no. 75; Jenyns, *Chinese Art*, no. 19.

52 Jenyns, *Chinese Art*, no. 56.

53 Hiuen Tsiang, *Si-Yu-Ki*, II, p. 306. Literally (trans. Leah Kisselgoff): "They export fine wool [hair] fabrics and fine wool woven rugs [weave fine wool rugs]."

54 Ibid., p. 306. Literally (trans. Leah Kisselgoff): "They export rugs and fine wool fabrics."

55 Albert von Le Coq, *Buried Treasures of Chinese Turkestan*, trans. Anna Barwell (London, 1928), p. 41.

56 Aurel Stein, *Sand-Buried Ruins of Khotan* (London, 1904), p. 422.

57 E. G. Folcker, "A Silk and Gold Carpet in the National Museum, Stockholm," *Burlington Magazine*, XXXV (1919), p. 61.

58 American Art Association, New York, *XV–XVIII Century Rugs: Vitall and Leopold Benguiat*, Sale Catalogue, 1925, no. 54.

59 Bidder, *Carpets from Eastern Turkestan*, p. 50, fig. 3.

60 According to Schuyler Cammann and other scholars, this motif represents a table supporting the Three Precious Jewels. The two-tailed cloud interpretation was suggested by David Stitt, and is supported by the tradition of more legible two-tailed clouds on a series of Chinese satins (see figure 310).

61 Jenyns, *Chinese Art*, no. 57.

195 a, b   FIGURE 264, AND BELOW

Pair of rugs or hangings, western China, XIX century

(a) 10′ 10½″ × 3′ 10″
(b) 10′ 10½″ × 3′ 9¾″

WARP: Cotton

WEFT: Wool or hair

TECHNIQUE: Tapestry (so-called Mongolian *k'o-ssu*), about 13 warp threads per inch; block-printed details and decoration on both sides.

COLORS: 10. *Ground*: orange. *Pattern*: pale gray, 2 tans, pale yellow, 2 pale oranges, pale celadon, dark blue, brown.

DECORATION: *Field*: Vases and flowers (probably the Hundred Antiques), block-printed in colors originally, now faded so that visible only in deeper tones of gray. Symmetrically spaced woven design of five wild geese, with block-printed detail. *Borders* (top and bottom): Multiple bands.

NOTE: Both printed and woven designs reversible. Selvage is single cord of bunched warps included in ground weave.

Rogers Fund
(a) 67. 66. 1
(b) 67. 66. 2

196   FIGURE 266

K'ang rug, XVII century style

5′ 8″ × 4′

WARP: Cotton

WEFT: Cotton; 2 shoots after each row of knots

KNOTTING: Wool. Senna knot, about 36 knots per square inch

COLORS: 6. *Ground*: tan, originally salmon (field), light salmon (border), light blue, dark blue (guard stripes). *Pattern*: yellow, light blue green, dark blue.

DECORATION: *Field*: Swastika diaper set at regular intervals with small symmetrical bat repeat. *Border*: Continuous swastika fret set off by guard stripes.

NOTE: Worn; trimmed on four sides.

PUBLISHED: Dilley, pl. LVII; Leitch, pl. 3; Tiffany Studios, 1908, p. 84, pl. IX.

Rogers Fund
08. 248. 3

197   NEXT PAGE

Kneeling mat or rug for stool, K'ang-hsi style

2′ 6″ × 2′ 6¾″

WARP: Cotton

WEFT: Cotton; 2 shoots after each row of knots

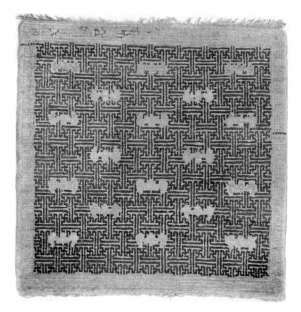

KNOTTING: Wool. Senna knot, about 42 knots per square inch

COLORS: 6. *Ground*: soft salmon (field), soft golden yellow (border). *Pattern*: yellow, salmon, blue, light brown.

DECORATION: *Field*: Swastika-fret diaper set with rows of stylized bats. *Border*: Continuous interlocking L-fret.

NOTE: Short even pile with quite a bit of lean. Twisted warp loops at one end, short worn warp fringe at the other. Tabby selvages at sides badly worn.

Bequest of Ellis Gray Seymour

49. 6. 1

198   FIGURE 267

K'ang rug, K'ang-hsi period (1662–1722)

3′ 10″ × 2′ 8″

WARP: Cotton

WEFT: Cotton; 2 shoots after each row of knots

KNOTTING: Wool. Senna knot, about 30 knots per square inch

COLORS: 9. *Ground*: light golden yellow, deeper golden yellow (field), rosy brown (border), dark blue (guard band). *Pattern*: white, light salmon, salmon, blue, dark blue, soft brown.

DECORATION: *Field*: Diagonal angular fret diaper set with symmetrically spaced repeats of two sizes of peony branch with single large stylized flower and bud. *Border*: Continuous interlocking T-fret. *Guard band*: Stylized four-petaled flowers. Guard stripes set off border and guard band; an unpatterned band edges whole rug.

NOTE: Shaggy pile with definite lean and effect of carving, latter perhaps because of age and wear of different dyes.

Gift of William N. Cohen

38. 109

199   FIGURE 268, PAGE 164

Rug, XVII century, Ming style

11′ 10″ × 11′ 2½″

WARP: Cotton

WEFT: Cotton; 2 shoots after each row of knots

KNOTTING: Wool. Senna knot, about 42 knots per square inch

COLORS: 7. *Ground*: soft salmon (field), soft golden tan (border). *Pattern*: soft golden tan, lemon yellow, golden yellow, soft green blue, dark blue, soft brown.

DECORATION: *Field*: Diaper of four-lobed cloud or *ju-i* medallions. The medallions in every other row enclose bats, those in alternating rows peach sprays; eight-pointed stars in the interspaces. *Border*: Continuous swastika fret. *Inner guard band*: A stylized running vine scroll. Unpatterned guard stripes enclose border and guard band; a wide unpatterned band edges the rug on two sides.

NOTE: Soft silky pile with flat continuous surface, marked lean. Very short warp fringe top and bottom, where much worn.

Gift of Mrs. Thorne W. Kissel

50. 234

200   FIGURE 278

K'ang rug, second half of XVII century

6′ 4″ × 4′ 4″

WARP: Cotton

WEFT: Cotton; 2 shoots after each row of knots

KNOTTING: Wool. Senna knot, about 42 knots per square inch

COLORS: 7. *Ground*: deep blue. *Pattern*: 2 yellows, 2 pale blues, 2 light browns, perhaps originally salmon.

DECORATION: *Field*: Allover pattern of twining tree-peony branches with large blooms symmetrically disposed in alternating rows of twos and threes, and small leaves spread flat and closely spaced

NOTE: Possibly originally had borders, now missing. Thick pile with carved effect of surface probably due to age and wear; trimmed on four sides.

PUBLISHED: Dilley, pl. LVII; Leitch, pl. 6.

Rogers Fund

16. 40

201   FIGURE 280

Cushion cover for seat, XVII century

3′ 6″ × 3′ 5″

WARP: Cotton

WEFT: Cotton; 3 shoots after each row of knots

KNOTTING: Wool. Senna knot, about 42 knots per square inch

COLORS: 2. *Ground*: dark blue. *Pattern*: pale lemon yellow.

DECORATION: *Field*: Allover pattern of more or less symmetrically arranged Precious Image Flowers with scrolling tendrils, leaves, and intertwining stems. *Border*: An unpatterned band set off by a stripe.

NOTE: Short pile. 4″ wide panel on each side to cover cushion, notched corners. Woven to this shape: narrow selvages on edges of each panel, except top and bottom. Warp fringe top, bottom, and at short ends of side panels, trimmed very short.

Rogers Fund

17. 125

202 FIGURE 281

K'ang, Buddhist temple, or altar rug, XVIII century

5′ 10″ × 3′ 8″

WARP: Cotton

WEFT: Cotton; 2 shoots after each row of knots

KNOTTING: Wool. Senna knot, about 25 knots per square inch

COLORS: 7. *Ground*: cream (field), light blue, blue (guard stripes), brown (outer band). *Pattern*: pale yellow, light blue, blue, soft brown, brown, chestnut.

DECORATION: *Field*: Symmetrical allover pattern formed by double row of rectangular repeats, each composed of a single Precious Image Flower or "western lotus." An unpatterned band edges whole rug, separated from field by three guard stripes.

NOTE: Twisted warp loops at one end, warp fringe at the other.

PUBLISHED: Tiffany Studios, 1908, p. 87, pl. XIII.

Rogers Fund

08. 248. 4

203 FIGURE 282

K'ang rug, XVII century

6′ 5″ × 4′ 3″

WARP: Cotton

WEFT: Cotton; 2 shoots after each row of knots

KNOTTING: Wool. Senna knot, about 36 knots per square inch

COLORS: 7. *Ground*: light tan, golden yellow (field), soft brown (central medallion), light golden yellow (inner border), dark brown (outer border). *Pattern*: light tan, tan, light golden yellow, golden yellow, turquoise blue.

DECORATION: *Field*: A large, slightly elongated central medallion containing two circling lions with auspicious objects, framed by a triple stripe. Around the medallion, a diaper of octagons linked by four-partite squares. *Inner border*: A continuous swastika fret. *Outer border*: Lotus serpentine. Guard stripes in groups of three enclose borders; an unpatterned band edges whole rug.

NOTE: Pile surface appears lightly carved, possibly due to age and wear on differently dyed wools. Worn warp fringe top and bottom with narrow tabby heading.

PUBLISHED: Tiffany Studios, 1908, p. 81, pl. IV.

Rogers Fund

08. 248. 2

204 FIGURE 283

Rug, early XVIII century

5′ 1″ × 2′ 5″

WARP: Cotton

WEFT: Cotton; 2 shoots after each row of knots

KNOTTING: Wool. Senna knot, about 49 knots per square inch

COLORS: 7. *Ground*: yellow tan, originally salmon (field), rose (border), cream, blue, dark blue (guard bands, guard stripes). *Pattern*: cream, yellow, rose, blue, dark blue, dark yellow green.

DECORATION: *Field*: Central medallion formed of two pairs of confronted, long-nosed, archaic dragons with some foliate detail, joined by a straight bar on either side of rosette center. Stylized profile flowers alternate with dragons; three tree-peony sprays fill each long end of field. Elaborated swastika frets are cornerpieces. *Border*: Continuous swastika fret emphasized at intervals by deepening colors, giving shaded, three-dimensional effect. *Inner guard bands*: One pearled, the other a row of endless knots. Guard stripes set off guard bands and border, and a narrow unpatterned band edges rug on three sides.

NOTE: Flat surface, short warp fringe top and bottom.

PUBLISHED: Breck-Morris, no. 124.

Gift of James F. Ballard, the James F. Ballard Collection

22. 100. 34

205 NEXT PAGE

Rug, XVIII century

10′ × 3′ 10¾″

WARP: Cotton

WEFT: Cotton; 2 shoots after each row of knots

KNOTTING: Wool. Senna knot, about 49 knots per square inch

COLORS: 6. *Ground*: light golden yellow (field, outer border), dark yellow (inner border), light blue, dark blue (guard stripes). *Pattern*: white, salmon pink, light blue, dark blue.

DECORATION: *Field:* Central floral medallion with symmetrically arranged detail; symbols of the Four Elegant Accomplishments spaced around medallion. A spreading stylized lotus spray centered at each end, and various flower sprays disposed over the field in freely

206 FIGURE 284

Rug, early XVIII century

12′ 8″ × 6′ 7″

WARP: Cotton

WEFT: Cotton; 2 shoots after each row of knots

KNOTTING: Wool. Senna knot, about 24 knots per square inch

COLORS: 8. *Ground*: light yellow (field), coral (inner border), salmon (outer border), white, 2 blues (guard stripes). *Pattern*: white, light yellow, salmon, 3 blues.

DECORATION: *Field*: Allover "cash" diaper; a central lobed medallion formed of a fretwork disc framed in a wreath of four symmetrical tree-peony scrolls. Four smaller peony medallions are placed above and below the central roundel. Symmetrical lobed cornerpieces are intertwined stylized tendrils. *Inner border*: Continuous interlocking T-fret. *Outer border*: Scrolling tree-peonies. Guard stripes in groups of three edge borders; a wide unpatterned band edges whole rug.

NOTE: Worn. Short warp fringe at one end; tabby strip of four shoots and warp fringe at other end.

Gift of F. Huntington Babcock

67. 86

207 FIGURE 285, PAGE 166

Rug, Ch'ien-lung period (1736–1795)

8′ 1″ × 5′ 1″

WARP: Cotton

WEFT: Cotton; 2 shoots after each row of knots

KNOTTING: Wool. Senna knot, about 52 knots per square inch

COLORS: 8. *Ground*: soft golden yellow (field), salmon (border), white, 2 blues (guard band, stripes). *Pattern*: white, tan, salmon, 2 blues, green, brown.

DECORATION: *Field*: Eight large floral medallions symmetrically spaced, with butterflies and flower sprays closely set in balanced arrangement over rest of the field. Stylized floral cornerpieces. *Border*: Continuous row of S-shaped floral scrolls. *Inner guard band*: Pearled; set off by grouped guard stripes.

NOTE: Surface appears slightly carved. Warp fringe at each end.

PUBLISHED: Breck-Morris, no. 119; Leitch, pl. 24.

Gift of James F. Ballard, the James F. Ballard Collection

22. 100. 36

208 FACING PAGE

Rug, Ch'ien-lung period (1736–1796)

3′ 5″ × 1′ 11″

WARP: Cotton

WEFT: Cotton; 2 shoots after each row of knots

balanced arrangement. Cornerpieces of swastika frets set with dragon heads. *Inner border*: Continuous angular S-scroll. *Outer border*: Continuous swastika fret. Guard stripes edge borders; an unpatterned band edges whole rug.

NOTE: Flat continuous surface, shaggy leaning pile. Tabby band and twisted warp loops at one end, warp fringe at other.

Gift of J. T. Keresy and Company

10. 72

209 FIGURE 286

Cushion cover for chair, late XVIII century

2′ 6″ × 2′ 8″

WARP: Cotton

WEFT: Cotton; 2 shoots after each row of knots

KNOTTING: Wool. Senna knot, about 45 knots per square inch

COLORS: 9. *Ground*: buff, originally lighter (field), brown (border, guard bands), golden yellow (side pieces). *Pattern*: buff, light yellow, yellow, light salmon, salmon, blue, dark blue, brown.

DECORATION: *Field*; Central floral medallion of interlocking tree-peony sprays; symmetrical floral cornerpieces. *Border*: Wide swastika fret set with three rosette-discs at each corner, two in the center of each side. *Inner guard bands*: One pearled, the other a row of interlocking T's. *Side pieces* (three, continuous with seat): Lozenge diaper.

NOTE: Swastika border is deeply worn on one side; short twisted warp fringe on opposite side. Surface appears carved.

PUBLISHED: Breck-Morris, no. 120.

Gift of James F. Ballard, the James F. Ballard Collection 22. 100. 29

210 BELOW

Oval rug or cushion cover, XVIII century

3′ 2″ × 1′ 11″

KNOTTING: Wool. Senna knot, about 72 knots per square inch

COLORS: 10. *Ground*: rosy tan, originally salmon (field), light yellow (border), white, light blue, dark blue (guard band and stripes). *Pattern*: white, 2 yellows, 2 salmons, 2 blues, 2 soft browns.

DECORATION: *Field*: Central medallion of various flowers with fruit, flower sprays, and butterflies filling the rest of the field in balanced arrangement. In each corner, a stylized lotus spray. *Border*: Symmetrical lotus scrolls in each corner and centered on each long side, alternating with filleted Buddhist emblems. *Guard band*: Pearled. Guard stripes edge borders and guard band; an unpatterned band edges whole rug.

NOTE: Surface appears finely carved. Narrow tabby band, twisted warp loops at one end; short warp fringe at other.

PUBLISHED: Breck-Morris, no. 121.

Gift of James F. Ballard, the James F. Ballard Collection 22. 100. 31

WARP: Cotton

WEFT: Cotton; 2 shoots after each row of knots

KNOTTING: Wool. Senna knot, about 56 knots per square inch

COLORS: 8. *Ground*: warm light brown, originally salmon (field), golden yellow (border). *Pattern*: white, cream, originally sage green, light golden yellow, 3 blues.

DECORATION: *Field*: Central floral medallion surrounded by four floral sprays; allover ground pattern of small symmetrical stylized flowers. *Border*: Deep continuous fret set at intervals with a peony flower. *Inner guard band*: Pearled. Guard stripes edge border; an unpatterned band edges whole rug.

NOTE: Pile surface appears lightly carved with definite lean. Warp fringe top and bottom, very worn at one end. Bound in dark blue cotton rep (twentieth century?).

EX COLL. Tiffany Studios

Rogers Fund

08. 248. 7

211   BELOW

Cushion cover or kneeling mat, XVIII–XIX century

2′ 8″ × 2′ 4¾″

WARP: Cotton

WEFT: Cotton; 2 shoots after each row of knots

KNOTTING: Wool. Senna knot, about 63 knots per square inch

COLORS: 6. *Ground*: buff (field, borders), blue (guard band). *Pattern*: 2 tans, 2 blues, brown.

DECORATION: *Field*: Central medallion containing lotus framed by other flower sprays; four Endless Knots spaced around medallion. Cornerpieces of angular scrolls enclosing swastikas. *Inner border*: Broad swastika fret. *Outer border*: Symmetrical floral scrolls. *Inner guard band*: Pearled. Guard stripes edge border and guard band.

NOTE: Outer border worn, top and bottom. Re-edging on sides.

Rogers Fund

18. 34

212   FIGURE 287

Rug, XIX century, Ch'ien-lung style

8′ 9″ × 5′ 8″

WARP: Cotton

WEFT: Cotton; 2 shoots after each row of knots

KNOTTING: Wool. Senna knot, about 36 knots per square inch

COLORS: 6. *Ground*: golden yellow. *Pattern*: lemon yellow, gray tan, bright pink orange, blue, dark blue.

DECORATION: *Field*: Central medallion of stylized flowers framed in clouds. Four smaller medallions, above and below, each with a different subject: two pairs of confronted lions or dragons, a spotted deer and a flying crane in a garden, two lions and a brocade ball, a spotted deer and a bird in a garden. Flower and fruit sprays and butterflies are spaced in balanced arrangement over the field, with stylized flower sprays in the corners, a spray of lotus and orchids at the bottom, a spray of poppies at the top. *Border*: Lotus scrolls alternating with filleted Buddhist emblems. *Inner guard band*: Pearled. Guard stripes edge border and guard band; an unpatterned band edges whole rug.

NOTE: Silky pile with marked lean. Twisted warp loops at one end, warp fringe at other. Somewhat worn, especially around edges.

PUBLISHED: Hawley, pl. 64; Leitch, pl. 25; Tiffany Studios, 1908, p. 91, pl. XXIV.

Rogers Fund

08. 248. 9

213   FIGURE 288

Rug, XIX century

7′ 8″ × 5′ 8″

WARP: Cotton

WEFT: Cotton; 2 shoots after each row of knots

KNOTTING: Wool. Senna knot, about 45 knots per square inch

COLORS: 6. *Ground*: dark blue (field, border), white, blue (border). *Pattern*: white, yellow, salmon, blue, soft gray brown.

DECORATION: *Field*: Central medallion with lion and cub in landscape setting, framed with wide band of stylized flowers and leaves; flower and fruit sprays and butter-flies set in balanced arrangement over rest of field. *Border*: Simple form of "upright water stripe" extend-ing from central point on each side of rug. Guard stripes separate border from field.

NOTE: Surface appears slightly carved. Very short twisted warp loops at top, warp fringe at bottom.

PUBLISHED. Breck-Morris, no. 123.

Gift of James F. Ballard, the James F. Ballard Collection
22. 100. 48

214   BELOW

Cushion cover or kneeling mat, western China, XVIII–XIX century

2′ 6″ × 2′ 7″

WARP: Cotton

WEFT: Cotton; 2–3 shoots after each row of knots

KNOTTING: Wool. Senna knot, about 45 knots per square inch

COLORS: 4. *Ground*: dark beige (field), light orange (border). *Pattern*: dark orange, dark blue.

DECORATION: *Field*: Stylized floral medallion in the center, stylized fruit or flower sprays, or butterflies, in the corners. *Border*: Broad continuous swastika fret. Guard stripes edge border.

NOTE: Coarse leaning pile. Short warp fringe top and bottom; sides finished with thick cord tightly wound with wool. A band of blue wefts (6–8″) top and bottom.

215   FIGURE 289

Saddle rug, XIX century

4′ 5″ × 2′ 3″

WARP: Cotton

WEFT: Cotton; 2 shoots after each row of knots

KNOTTING: Sheep or goat hair. Senna knot, about 56 knots per square inch

COLORS: 7. *Ground*: deep blue (field), tan, originally salmon (border). *Pattern*: white, 2 tans, originally salmon, yellow, light blue, mixture of white and yellow.

DECORATION: *Field*: Symmetrically patterned with lobed convention on either side of central seam, coinciding with horse's spine. On each side, a large medallion of flowers with butterfly and flower sprays above, wave-and-mountain pattern below. *Border*: Tree-peony sprays and *wan* and *shou* longevity medallions. *Inner guard band*: Pearled. Unpatterned guard stripes set off various parts of border and form outer edge of rug.

NOTE: Lightly carved surface with lean of pile extending downward on either side of seam. Long sides finished by natural wool in chevron effect around two bunches of warps. Warp fringe top and bottom, worn very short.

PUBLISHED: Breck-Morris, no. 122.

Gift of James F. Ballard, the James F. Ballard Collection
22. 100. 30

216   FIGURE 290

Rug, late XIX or early XX century, Ch'ien-lung style

6′ 4″ × 4′ 3″

WARP: Cotton

WEFT: Cotton; 2 shoots after each row of knots

KNOTTING: Wool. Senna knot, about 90 knots per square inch

COLORS: 13. *Ground*: brown (field), yellow (borders), 3 blues (guard stripes). *Pattern*: cream, light yellow, golden yellow, light salmon, salmon, deep salmon, 3 blues, light brown, brown, mixture of pale blue and white.

DECORATION: *Field*: Central medallion of stylized peonies, surrounded by sprays of various flowers; symmetrical cornerpieces of archaic dragon frets twined with flowers. *Inner border*: Decorated lozenge diaper. *Outer border*: Wide continuous swastika fret shaded with various colors. Guard stripes enclose borders; a wide unpatterned band edges whole rug.

NOTE: Lightly carved pile; twisted warp loops at one end, short warp fringe at the other. Yarns may be machine-spun.

Gift of Mrs. Frederick Vaughan Lowe

64. 23. 4

217   FIGURE 291

Rug, XIX century, Ch'ien-lung style

6′ 11″ × 4′ 3″

WARP: Cotton

WEFT: Cotton; 2 shoots after each row of knots

KNOTTING: Wool. Senna knot, about 49 knots per square inch

COLORS: 10. *Ground*: off-white (field, outer border), dark blue (inner border, outer band). *Pattern*: yellow, light orange, vivid orange, 2 salmons, light blue, dark blue, 2 browns.

DECORATION: *Field*: Objects from various auspicious categories—the symbols of the Four Elegant Accomplishments in the center, surrounded by the Hundred Antiques and the Eight Immortals—interspersed with sprays of fruit and flowers, spaced in three rows extending from the center toward either end of the field. *Inner border*: Continuous angular fret. *Outer border*: Buddhist emblems filleted with scalloped ribbons. Guard stripes edge borders; a wide unpatterned band edges whole rug.

NOTE: Surface appears slightly carved. Bound with dark brown leather on four sides and border lining of blue cotton tabby, 6″ deep. Both appear old.

PUBLISHED: Breck-Morris, no. 118; Leitch, pl. 14.

Gift of James F. Ballard, the James F. Ballard Collection

22. 100. 35

218   FIGURE 292

K'ang rug, XIX century

4′ 3″ × 2′ 3″

WARP: Cotton

WEFT: Cotton; 2 shoots after each row of knots

KNOTTING: Wool. Senna knot, about 56 knots per square inch

COLORS: 7. *Ground*: buff, originally white (field), salmon (border). *Pattern*: yellow, 3 blues, soft brown.

DECORATION: *Field*: A double row of the Eight Buddhist Emblems of Happy Augury, filleted with scalloped bands. *Border*: Swastika-fret diaper on a diagonal axis overlaid by groups of variously ornamented discs alternating with longevity symbols. *Inner guard bands*: One pearled, the other a zigzag. Guard stripes edge border and guard bands; an unpatterned band edges whole rug.

NOTE: Flat surface; short warp fringe top and bottom.

PUBLISHED: Breck-Morris, no. 126.

Gift of James F. Ballard, the James F. Ballard Collection

22. 100. 33

219   FIGURE 293

Pillar rug (for Lamaist market in China or Tibet), XIX century

6′ 10″ × 4′ 6″

WARP: Cotton

WEFT: Cotton; 2 shoots after each row of knots

KNOTTING: Wool. Senna knot, about 35 knots per square inch

COLORS: 13. *Ground*: apricot (field), dark blue (border). *Pattern*: white, tan, light yellow, light orange, orange, light salmon, light pink, vivid pink, pink red, blue green, blue, dark blue.

DECORATION: *Field*: Standing figure of priest in three-quarter profile, wearing Lamaist crown and blowing conch to summon worshipers. Two confronted five-clawed dragons above, and the Eight Buddhist Emblems filleted and spaced regularly around him, interspersed with clouds. A row of tassels is suspended from stripe edging top of field. *Upper border*: Shaded continuous swastika fret. *Lower border*: Deep wave-and-mountain pattern. *Top guard bands*: Upper: unpatterned; lower: rose petals. Guard stripes edge guard bands.

NOTE: Shaggy uneven pile with definite lean; appears lightly carved in main outlines only. Narrow side edges in tabby; Ghiordes knots along left side. Warp fringe top and bottom. Pinks and reds have run in cleaning; probably some aniline dyes.

Gift of Mr. and Mrs. Francis Keally

63. 192

220   FIGURE 294, PAGE 168

End border of rug, early XIX century

1′ 11″ × 5′ 4″

WARP: Cotton

WEFT: Cotton; 2 shoots after each row of knots

KNOTTING: Wool. Senna knot, about 50–60 knots per square inch

COLORS: 10. *Ground*: light cinnamon brown, originally salmon (field), white, deep blue (borders). *Pattern*: white, lemon yellow, beige, tan, 2 deep blues, gray, mixture of blue and white, mixture of blue, yellow, and white.

DECORATION: *Field*: Freely balanced, stylized landscape with stag and doe under swooping Manchurian crane, between stylized mountain slope at either side formed of stepped diagonal bands set with small rectangles. *Borders*: Three narrow unpatterned bands.

NOTE: Firm close pile with slight lean; lightly carved surface. Top border is later re-weaving to complete panel, which was probably originally the end of a much larger rug. Narrow tabby band, top and bottom. Short warp fringe at top, short plied warp loops at bottom.

Rogers Fund

64.231

221   FIGURE 295

Saddle or traveler's rug, XIX century

5′ 2″ × 2′ 5½″

WARP: Cotton

WEFT: Cotton; 2 shoots after each row of knots

KNOTTING: Wool. Senna knot, about 68 knots per square inch

COLORS: 9. *Ground*: golden yellow. *Pattern*: off-white, golden yellow, lemon yellow, 2 salmons, 2 blues, 2 browns.

DECORATION: *Field*: Small central wreath framing longevity (*shou*) emblem, with the Eight Horses of Wang Mu, placed four in each half of the rug, among stylized rocks and trees. *Borders* (top and bottom): Deep wave-and-mountain pattern.

NOTE: Warp fringe top and bottom. Some knotting restored; colors faded.

PUBLISHED: American Art Galleries, *Clarke Collection*, no. 508.

Bequest of Florance Waterbury

68.149.8

222   ABOVE RIGHT

Rug for low stool, XIX century

3′ 11″ × 2′ 2″

WARP: Cotton

WEFT: Cotton; 2 shoots after each row of knots

KNOTTING: Wool. Senna knot, about 64 knots per square inch

COLORS: 8. *Ground*: dark tan, originally deep rose (field), buff, originally white (border). *Pattern*: white, 3 tans, originally rose, yellow, 2 blues.

DECORATION: *Field*: Variously ornamented discs, singly or in groups of two or three, symmetrically disposed against unpatterned ground. *Border*: Similar discs. *Inner guard bands*: One a zigzag, the other pearled. An unpatterned band edges whole rug.

NOTE: Flat surface. Short warp fringe top and bottom, where quite worn.

PUBLISHED: Breck-Morris, no. 125.

Gift of James F. Ballard, the James F. Ballard Collection

22.100.32

223   FIGURE 297

Throne cushion cover, XIX century

2′ 6¼″ × 2′ 6½″

WARP: Cotton

WEFT: Cotton; 2 shoots after each row of knots

KNOTTING: Wool. Senna knot, about 72 knots per square inch

COLORS: 10. *Ground*: warm red brown. *Pattern*: white, lemon yellow, golden yellow, blue, dark blue, blue green, olive green, 2 light cinnamon browns.

DECORATION: *Field*: Rampant frontal dragon with flaming pearl above and below, surrounded by four profile running dragons, all set in clouds. *Border*: Wave-and-mountain pattern.

NOTE: Thick, lightly carved pile with slight lean. Very short warp fringe at one end, longer warp fringe at other.

Bequest of Gilbert H. Montague, in memory of Amy Angell Collier Montague

61.93.6

224   FIGURE 298

"Palace carpet," possibly Khotan, Chinese Turkestan, late xix century

12′ 8″ × 9′ 3″

WARP: Cotton

WEFT: Cotton; 2 shoots after each row of knots or double row of wrapping

KNOTTING: Silk. Senna knot, about 60 knots per square inch, with Sumak detail in bunched yarns made of silvered copper strips wound around a silk core

COLORS: 13. *Ground*: golden yellow (field, border, swastika- and T-fret guard bands), silvered copper (medallion, quarter medallions), white, 2 blues (pearled guard band). *Pattern*: white, beige, 2 soft pinks, light purple blue, deep purple blue, soft brown, gray, golden yellow mixed with beige.

DECORATION: *Field*: A scalloped circular central medallion enclosing a frontally coiled, five-clawed dragon with raised front feet and flaming pearl. Matching quarter medallions in each corner with a coiled profile dragon and flaming pearl. The rest of the field has an allover scrolling pattern of flowers, leaves, and narrow stems ending in numerous double curls, in balanced arrangement. *Border*: Balanced pattern of scrolling summer flowers and bats, with filleted lotus (or Buddhist umbrella) in center top and bottom, and filleted Buddhist emblems regularly spaced on all sides. *Inner guard bands*: One pearled, the other a swastika fret. *Outer guard band*: Shaded continuous T-fret. An unpatterned band edges whole rug.

INSCRIPTION (inlaid in tabby at top): In Chinese characters, *Yung pei kung shou ning* ("Use made for palace longevity peace" or the Palace of Tranquil Longevity).

NOTE: Tabby band top and bottom; short warp fringe.

Gift of William M. Emery

63.58

225   FIGURE 299

K'ang rug, K'ang-hsi period (1662–1722)

5′ 9″ × 4′ 6″

WARP: Cotton

WEFT: Cotton; 2 shoots after each row of knots

KNOTTING: Wool. Senna knot, about 30 knots per square inch

COLORS: 5. *Ground*: cream (field), golden yellow (borders), soft brown (outer band). *Pattern*: light blue, dark blue.

DECORATION: *Field*: Large central medallion of two interlocking foliage dragons, enclosed at a distance by four fret-arabesque cornerpieces. Foliage dragons centered above and below the central group and in each corner of the field. *Inner border*: Continuous interlocking tendril scroll. *Outer border*: Wide continuous swastika fret. Guard stripes set off borders; wide unpatterned band on each long side of rug.

NOTE: Short twisted warp loops at one end, short warp fringe at other.

PUBLISHED: Hackmack, pl. xx; Hawley, pl. 63; Oskar Münsterberg, *Chinesische Kunstgeschichte*, II (Esslingen, 1924), p. 409, no. 586; Tiffany Studios, 1908, p. 80, pl. III; W. V., "Chinese Rugs," *Metropolitan Museum of Art Bulletin*, IV (Feb., 1909), pp. 20–21.

Rogers Fund

08.248.1

226   FIGURE 300

Cushion cover or kneeling mat, K'ang-hsi style

2′ 1″ × 2′ 3″

WARP: Cotton

WEFT: Cotton; 2 shoots after each row of knots

KNOTTING: Wool. Senna knot, about 36 knots per square inch

COLORS: 6. *Ground*: apricot shading to brick (field), deeper shade of same (border). *Pattern*: very light and light apricot, blue, dark blue.

DECORATION: *Field*: Central medallion formed of angular scrolls with square of T's in center; foliage dragon cornerpieces. *Border*: Elongated angular C-scrolls, two on each side.

NOTE: Lower and upper edges not completed or missing. Coarse shaggy pile with definite lean, effect of light carving. Short warp fringe top and bottom.

EX COLL. Tiffany Studios

Rogers Fund

08.248.6

227   FIGURE 301

Rug (lower half), late K'ang-hsi style

6′ 4″ × 7′ 4″

WARP: Cotton

WEFT: Cotton; 2 shoots after each row of knots

KNOTTING: Wool. Senna knot, about 70 knots per square inch

COLORS: 6. *Ground*: salmon (field), pale golden yellow (border), 2 blues (guard stripes), dark blue (outer band). *Pattern*: white, pale golden yellow, pale salmon, light blue, dark blue.

DECORATION: *Field*: Half of vertical panel with lower half of small central medallion of foliage dragons, and a finely drawn allover symmetrical pattern of scrolling lotuses, leaves, and stems. Foliage dragon cornerpieces. *Border*: Foliage birds or bird dragons alternating with symmetrical floral sprays. Four guard stripes set off border; a wide unpatterned band edges rug.

NOTE: Top border and small part of top of field added after original rug was cut in half. Surface appears carved. Scattered Ghiordes knots found in field and border (Turkish repairs?). Short warp fringe at top, narrow band of tabby and twisted warp loops at bottom.

Bequest of George D. Pratt

45.174.47

228   FIGURE 302

Marriage rug (*lung-fêng*), XIX century

8′ 11″ × 7′ 1″

WARP: Cotton

WEFT: Cotton; 2 shoots after each row of knots

KNOTTING: Silk floss. Senna knot, about 80 knots per square inch

COLORS: 5. *Ground*: tawny yellow. *Pattern*: pale yellow, pale pink, pale red, pale blue.

DECORATION: *Field*: Large rampant five-clawed dragon (*lung*) confronting standing mythological bird (*fêng*) with flaming pearl between, against background of clouds. From bats in the corners and center are suspended filleted auspicious objects ("cash," *ju-i* scepter, swastika, peaches). *Border*: Scrolling lotus spray alternating with character for conjugal happiness (the "double *hsi*"). Guard stripes edge border.

NOTE: Long thick pile, flat surface, short warp fringe top and bottom.

Bequest of Mrs. H. O. Havemeyer, The H. O. Havemeyer Collection

29.100.158

229   FIGURE 303

Rug, Japan or Central Asia, XIX century

9′ 7″ × 9′ 7″

WARP: Cotton

WEFT: Bast fiber; 1 shoot after each row of knots

KNOTTING: Tussah silk. Senna knot, about 45 knots per square inch

COLORS: 6. *Ground*: gray fawn. *Pattern*: yellow, orange, deep rusty red, wood brown, black brown.

DECORATION: *Field*: Large central medallion formed by two descending three-clawed dragons on either side of stylized tree, encircled at a distance by twelve small, twelve-petaled rosettes. Along all four sides of rug, and extending from the corners almost to the central medallion, is a design formed of decorative details combining flowers, leaves, and foliage dragons.

NOTE: Thick, medium long pile; continuous flat surface Tabby edge top and bottom with bunched cotton wefts, warp selvage at top, warp fringe at bottom.

PUBLISHED: Tiffany Studios, *Notable Rugs*, p. 35, no. 4770; W. V., "Chinese Rugs," *Metropolitan Museum of Art Bulletin*, IV (Feb., 1909), p. 20.

Rogers Fund

08.248.10

230   FIGURE 304

Rug, Khotan, Chinese Turkestan, XVIII century

9′ × 5′ 10″

WARP: Silk

WEFT: Silk; 3 shoots after each row of knots

KNOTTING: Silk. Senna knot, about 81 knots per square inch, with Sumak detail in silver and gold foil wound around a silk core.

COLORS: 8. *Ground*: silver. *Pattern*: cream, yellow, rose, deep blue, pale green, dark brown or black, gold.

DECORATION: *Field*: Stylized symmetrical floral patterns in ogival framework formed of stems and leaves. *Border*: Similar stylized symmetrical floral patterns. *Guard bands*: A stylized vine. Hatched and unpatterned guard stripes edge guard bands.

NOTE: Very short warp fringe top and bottom, somewhat worn.

PUBLISHED: Breck-Morris, no. 117.

Gift of James F. Ballard, the James F. Ballard Collection

22.100.49

231   FIGURE 306, PAGE 170

Rug, Chinese Turkestan, late XVIII–early XIX century

13′ 11″ × 6′ 10″

WARP: Cotton

WEFT: Blue cotton; 2 shoots after each row of knots

KNOTTING: Silk. Senna knot, about 90 knots per square inch

COLORS: 8. *Ground*: deep bright blue (field), light red (inner border), light green blue (outer border). *Pattern*: pink, light red, mulberry, deep blue, blue green, black.

DECORATION: *Field*: Entirely filled by four stylized pomegranate trees, each growing out of vase centered at lower end of each quarter of field. *Inner border*: Various kinds of rosettes, widely spaced. *Outer border*: Closely set rosettes alternating with smaller rosettes in octagonal frames. The borders are edged by unpatterned guard bands and stripes; an unpatterned band edges whole rug.

NOTE: Top and bottom fringe of warps knotted in bunches; band of tabby above fringe.

PUBLISHED: Breck-Morris, no. 116; Dimand, *Peasant and Nomad Rugs*, no. 34.

Gift of James F. Ballard, the James F. Ballard Collection

22.100.28

232   FIGURE 307

Rug, Chinese Turkestan, XVIII century

6′ × 3′ 4″

WARP: Cotton

WEFT: Wool; 3 shoots after each row of knots

KNOTTING: Wool. Senna knot, about 52 knots per square inch

COLORS: 8. *Ground*: off-white (field), rust red (border), yellow, rust red, brown (guard band and stripes). *Pattern*: golden yellow, lemon yellow, rust red, light blue, blue.

DECORATION: *Field*: Stylized pomegranate tree growing out of vase centered at one end, fruit and leaves symmetrically arranged to fill field. *Border*: Large rosettes, each formed of four heart shapes. *Outer guard band*: A string of small lozenges. Pearled guard stripes edge border and guard band; an unpatterned band edges whole rug.

NOTE: Twisted warp loops at bottom with torn area in middle (about 20″) ending in longer warp fringe; warp fringe at top. Narrow tabby band across bottom, above warp loops.

EX COLL. Tiffany Studios

Rogers Fund

08. 122

233   FIGURE 308

Rug, Khotan, Chinese Turkestan, XIX century

13′ 9″ × 5′

WARP: Bast fiber

WEFT: Cotton; 3 shoots after each row of knots

KNOTTING: Wool. Senna knot, about 35 knots per square inch

COLORS: 8. *Ground*: blue (field), rust red (central medallion, borders), dark brown (guard stripes). *Pattern*: white, pale yellow, pale salmon, light blue, blue, light blue green.

DECORATION: *Field*: Central circular medallion with elaborate floral rosette framed in stylized wreath of carnations and marigolds; quarter medallion with related floral pattern in each corner. Remainder of field closely set with small discs, each containing cruciform flower based on Tibetan tie-dye pattern. *Inner border*: Stylized floral spray closely set at alternately opposing diagonals. *Outer border:* Typical Turkestan version of Chinese wave border. Pearled and unpatterned guard stripes edge borders.

Gift of Mrs. Bernard Reis

69. 248

234   FIGURE 309

Rug, Khotan, Chinese Turkestan, XVIII century

4′ 8″ × 3′

WARP: Silk

WEFT: Silk; 3 shoots after each row of knots

KNOTTING: Silk. Senna knot, about 156 knots per square inch

COLORS: 7. *Ground*: deep blue (field), yellow (border). *Pattern*: white, golden yellow, salmon, rose, blue.

DECORATION: *Field*: Closely set rows of a small five-clawed dragon medallion alternating with a double-tailed cloud. *Border*: Swastika-fret diaper, set off from field by three guard stripes.

NOTE: Warp threads run horizontally across piece in color bands: reddish, blue green, lemon (undyed?). Tabby band on bottom and incomplete top.

PUBLISHED: Alan Priest, "Two Chinese Rugs," *Metropolitan Museum of Art Bulletin*, XXXII (May, 1937), p. 132.

Gift of Baroness Clemens von Ketteler

08. 248. 8

235   FIGURE 312

Chair or throne back, Khotan, Chinese Turkestan, XIX century

2′ 1½″ × 2′ 2¼″

WARP: Silk

WEFT: Silk; 1–2 shoots after each row of knots

KNOTTING: Silk. Senna knot, about 320 knots per square inch

COLORS: 10. *Ground*: golden yellow (field), pale orange (border). *Pattern*: white, pale orange, pale pink, salmon, light blue, bright blue, yellow green, green, black.

DECORATION: *Field*: Central panel with square lower corners and scalloped upper corners, containing central pomegranatelike form surrounded by floral and berry or grape sprays, bats, and fish, symmetrically and densely arranged. *Border*: Deep and similarly decorated, with narrow fret cornerpieces. *Guard bands*: An angular running scroll.

NOTE: Warp fringe top and bottom. Similar to catalogue no. 236, but not from same set.

PUBLISHED: Alan Priest, "Two Chinese Rugs," *Metropolitan Museum of Art Bulletin*, XXXII (May, 1937), p. 132.

Gift of Baroness Clemens von Ketteler

36. 153. 2

236   FIGURE 313

Chair or throne seat, Khotan, Chinese Turkestan, XIX century

4′ 2″ × 3′ 2¾″

WARP: Silk

WEFT: Silk; 2 shoots after each row of knots

KNOTTING: Silk. Senna knot, about 160 knots per square inch

COLORS: 7. *Ground*: golden yellow. *Pattern*: tan, originally salmon, rose, blue, light green, gray lavender, black.

DECORATION: *Field*: Rectangular field with rounded corners, containing central pomegranatelike motif, surrounded by closely set, small, stylized floral sprays, bats, vases, and orange fish; fret cornerpieces. *Border*: Deep and similarly decorated. *Inner guard band*: An angular running scroll.

NOTE: Warp fringe top and bottom, with narrow tabby band. Similar to catalogue no. 235, but not from same set.

PUBLISHED: Alan Priest, "Two Chinese Rugs," *Metropolitan Museum of Art Bulletin*, XXXII (May, 1937), p. 132.

Gift of Baroness Clemens von Ketteler

36.153.1

BIBLIOGRAPHY

Chapters One through Ten

Aga-Oglu, Mehmet. *Safawid Rugs and Textiles. The Collection of the Shrine of Imam Ali at Al-Najaf.* New York, 1941.

Ali Ibrahim Pasha. "Early Islamic Rugs of Egypt or Fostat Rugs," *Bulletin de l'institut d'Égypte*, XVII, 1934–35, pp. 123–127.

Aslanapa, Oktay. *Turkish Arts.* Istanbul [1961], pp. 13–83.

Barnett, R. D., and Watson, W. "The World's Oldest Persian Carpet, Preserved for 2400 Years in Perpetual Ice in Central Siberia," *The Illustrated London News*, July 11, 1953, pp. 69–71.

Bellinger, Louisa. "Textile Analysis: Pile Techniques in Egypt and the Near East," Part 4, *The Textile Museum: Workshop Notes*, Paper No. 12, December, 1955.

Bode, Wilhelm. *Altpersische Knüpfteppiche.* Berlin, 1904.

Bode, Wilhelm, and Kühnel, Ernst. *Antique Rugs from the Near East.* 4th rev. ed. Translated by Charles Grant Ellis. Brunswick, 1958.

Bogolubov, A. *Tapis de l'Asie Centrale.* St. Petersburg, 1908.

Breck, Joseph, and Morris, Frances. *The James F. Ballard Collection of Oriental Rugs.* New York, 1923.

Briggs, Amy. "Timurid Carpets," *Ars Islamica*, VII, 1940, pp. 20–54.
   "Timurid Carpets," *Ars Islamica*, XI–XII, 1946, pp. 146–158.

Campana, P. Michele, *Il Tappeto Orientale.* Milan, 1945.

Chicago, The Art Institute. *An Exhibition of Antique Oriental Rugs.* Chicago, 1947.

Dilley, Arthur Urbane. *Oriental Rugs and Carpets.* Revised by Maurice S. Dimand. New York, 1959.

Dimand, Maurice S. *Loan Exhibition of Persian Rugs of the So-Called Polish Type.* The Metropolitan Museum of Art. New York, 1930.
   "An Early Cut-pile Rug from Egypt," *Metropolitan Museum Studies*, IV, 1932–33, pp. 151–162.
   The Ballard Collection of Oriental Rugs in the City Art Museum of St. Louis. St. Louis, 1935.
   A Guide to an Exhibition of Oriental Rugs and Textiles. The Metropolitan Museum of Art. New York, 1935.
   "A Persian Garden Carpet in the Jaipur Museum," *Ars Islamica*, VII, 1940, pp. 93–96.

A Handbook of Muhammadan Art. 3rd ed., rev. New York, 1958, pp. 279–323.
   Peasant and Nomad Rugs of Asia. Exhibition catalogue: Asia House Gallery. New York, 1961.
   "Two Fifteenth-Century Hispano-Moresque Rugs," *The Metropolitan Museum of Art Bulletin*, June, 1964, pp. 341–352.
   The Kevorkian Foundation: Collection of Rare and Magnificent Oriental Carpets. Special Loan Exhibition. New York, 1966.
   "An Unpublished 17th Century Compartment Vase Carpet," in *Forschungen zur Kunst Asiens. In Memoriam Kurt Erdmann.* Edited by Oktay Aslanapa and Rudolf Naumann. Istanbul, 1969, pp. 190–193.
   "The Seventeenth-Century Isfahan School of Rug Weaving," in *Islamic Art in The Metropolitan Museum of Art.* Edited by Richard Ettinghausen. New York, 1972, pp. 255–267.

Emery, Irene. *The Primary Structures of Fabrics.* Washington, D.C., 1966.

Erdmann, Kurt. "Orientalische Tierteppiche auf Bildern des XIV. und XV. Jahrhunderts," *Jahrbuch der Preuszischen Kunstsammlungen*, 50, 1929, pp. 261–298.
   "Kairener Teppiche. Teil I: Europäische und islamische Quellen des 15.–18. Jahrhunderts," *Ars Islamaica*, V, pt. 2, 1938, pp. 179–206.
   "Kairener Teppiche. Teil II: Mamluken und osmanenteppiche," *Ars Islamica*, VII, 1940, pp. 55–81.
   "Zu einem anatolischen Teppichfragment aus Fostat," *Istanbuler Mitteilungen*, 6, 1955, pp. 42–52.
   "Die kleinen Seidenteppiche Kaschans," *Pantheon*, XIX, 1961, pp. 159–163.
   Europa und der Orientteppich. Berlin, 1962.
   Oriental Carpets. Translated by Charles Grant Ellis. 2nd ed. New York, 1962.
   Seven Hundred Years of Oriental Carpets. Translated by May H. Beattie and Hildegard Herzog. Berkeley, California, 1970.

Ettinghausen, Richard. "New Light on Early Animal Carpets" in *Aus der Welt der islamischen Kunst. Festschrift für Ernst Kühnel.* Berlin, 1957.

Ferrandis-Torres, José. *Exposicion de Alfombras Antiguas Españolas.* Exhibition catalogue: Sociedad Española de Amigos del Arte. Madrid, 1933.
   "Alfombras Hispano-Moriscas 'Tipo Holbein,'" *Archivo Español de Arte*, XV, 1942, pp. 103–111.

Grote-Hasenbalg, Werner. *Der Orientteppich.* 3 vols. Berlin, 1922.

Hawley, Walter A. *Oriental Rugs.* New York, 1913.

Hendley, T. H. *Asian Carpets, XVI and XVII Century Designs from the Jaipur Palaces.* London, 1905.

Jacoby, Heinrich. *Eine Sammlung Orientalischer Teppiche.* Berlin, 1923.

"Materials Used in the Making of Carpets," in *A Survey of Persian Art.* Vol. III. Edited by Alexander U. Pope. New York, 1938, pp. 2459–2462.

Kendrick, A. F., and Tattersall, C. E. C. *Hand-Woven Carpets: Oriental and European.* 2 vols. London, 1922.

Kerimov, L. *Carpets of Azerbaijan.* 2 vols. (in Russian). Baku/Leningrad, 1961.

Kühnel, Ernst. "Maurische Teppiche aus Alcaraz," *Pantheon,* VI, 1930, pp. 416–420.

"The Rug Tiraz of Akhmin," *The Textile Museum: Workshop Notes,* Paper No. 22, October, 1960.

Kühnel, Ernst, and Bellinger, Louisa. *Catalogue of Spanish Rugs.* The Textile Museum, Washington, D.C., 1953.

Cairene Rugs. The Textile Museum, Washington, D.C., 1957.

Lamm, Carl Johan. "The Marby Rug and Some Fragments of Carpets Found in Egypt," *Svenska Orientsällskapets Årsbok,* 1937.

Lisbon, Museu Nacional de Arte Antiqa. *Oriental Islamic Art: Collection of the Calouste Gulbenkian Foundation.* Exhibition catalogue. Lisbon, 1963.

McMullan, Joseph V. *Islamic Carpets.* New York, 1965.

Martin, F. R. *A History of Oriental Carpets before 1800.* Vienna, 1908.

May, Florence Lewis. "Hispano-Moresque Rugs," *Notes Hispanic,* V, 1945, pp. 31–69.

Mohamed Mostafa. "Neuerwerbungen des Museums für Islamische Kunst in Kairo," in *Aus der Welt der Islamischen Kunst. Festschrift für Ernst Kühnel.* Berlin, 1959.

Mumford, John Kimberly. *The Yerkes Collection of Oriental Carpets.* London, 1910.

Pfister, R., and Bellinger, Louisa. Yale University. *The Excavations at Dura-Europos Conducted by Yale University and the French Academy of Inscriptions and Letters. Final Report IV. Part II. The Textiles.* New Haven, 1945.

Pope, Arthur Upham. "The Myth of the Armenian Dragon Carpets." *Jahrbuch der Asiatischen Kunst,* II, 1925, pp. 147–158.

Catalogue of a Loan Exhibition of Early Oriental Carpets from Persia, Asia Minor, The Caucasus, Egypt and Spain. The Arts Club of Chicago. Chicago, 1926.

A Survey of Persian Art from Prehistoric Times to the Present. Vol. III, pp. 2257–2430, 2437–2455. Vol. VI, pls. 1107–1275. London/New York, 1938–39.

"The Technique of Persian Carpet Weaving," in *A Survey of Persian Art,* III. London/New York, 1939, pp. 2437–2455.

Riefstahl, Rudolf M. "Primitive Rugs of the 'Konya' Type in the Mosque of Beyshehir," *The Art Bulletin,* June, 1931, pp. 177–220.

Rudenko, S. I. *Kul'tura naseleniia Gornogo Altaia v skifskoe vremia* (The Culture of People of the Gorny-Altai during the Period of the Scyths). Moscow, 1953.

Sakisian, Arménag. "Les Tapis à dragons et leur origine arménienne," *Syria,* IX, 1928, pp. 238–256.

Sarre, Friedrich. "Die Ägyptischen Teppiche," *Jahrbuch der Asiatischen Kunst,* I, 1924, pp. 19–23.

Sarre, Friedrich, and Falkenberg, Th. "Eines frühes Knüpfteppich-fragment aus Chinesisch-Turkistan," *Berliner Museen,* XLII, 1921, pp. 110–114.

Sarre, Friedrich, and Trenkwald, Hermann. *Old Oriental Carpets.* Translated by A. F. Kendrick. 2 vols. Vienna/Leipzig, 1926–29.

Schmutzler, Emil. *Altorientalische Teppiche in Siebenbürgen.* Leipzig, 1933.

Schürmann, Ulrich. *Central-Asian Rugs.* Translated by Alan Grainge. Frankfurt am Main, 1969.

Tattersall, C. E. C. *Notes on Carpet-Knotting and Weaving.* London, 1961.

Thacher, Amos Bateman. *Turkoman Rugs.* New York, 1940.

Valentiner, Wilhelm R. *Catalogue of a Loan Exhibition of Early Oriental Rugs.* The Metropolitan Museum of Art. New York, 1910.

Wilson, Lillian M. *Ancient Textiles from Egypt in the University of Michigan Collection.* Ann Arbor, 1933.

For additional bibliography, see Erdmann, *Oriental Carpets,* pp. 59–69.

Chapter Eleven

American Art Association, New York. *Rare and Beautiful Chinese Productions: Yamanaka and Co.* Sale catalogue. January 5–7, 1911.

American Art Galleries, New York. *Ancient Looms and Other Oriental Treasures*. Sale catalogue. January 6–9, 1914.

Antique Chinese Rugs: Thomas B. Clarke Collection. Sale catalogue. January 6–9, 1915.

Art of Ancient China: A. W. Bahr Collection. Sale catalogue. January 17–19, 1916.

Chinese Rugs and Carpets: Tiffany Studios Collection. Sale catalogue. April 28–29, 1916.

Oriental Art Treasures from the Chinese Imperial Palace: Yamanaka and Co. Sale catalogue. January 26–27, 1917.

Anderson Galleries, New York. *Old Chinese Rugs: Frederick Moore and John Kimberly Mumford Collections*. Sale catalogue. March 2–4, 1916.

Old Chinese Rugs, Brocades, and Embroideries: Frederick Moore Collection. Sale catalogue. February 23–24, 1917.

Bidder, Hans. *Carpets from Eastern Turkestan*. New York, 1964.

Breck, Joseph, and Morris, Frances. *The James F. Ballard Collection of Oriental Rugs*. New York, 1923.

Dilley, Arthur Urbane. *Oriental Rugs and Carpets*. Revised by Maurice S. Dimand. New York, 1959.

Dimand, Maurice S. *Peasant and Nomad Rugs of Asia*. Exhibition catalogue: Asia House Gallery. New York, 1961.

Galerie George Petit, Paris. *Liquidation des Biens Worch: Objets d'Art Anciens de la Chine*. Sale catalogue. March, 1922.

Hackmack, Adolf. *Der Chinesische Teppich*. Hamburg, 1921.

Hawley, Walter A. *Oriental Rugs*. New York, 1913.

Japan, Imperial Treasury (Shosoin). *Shosoin Homotsu Someori*. 2 vols. Tokyo, 1963–64.

Jenyns, R. Soame. *Chinese Art: The Minor Arts*. Vol. II. New York, 1965.

Larkin, T. J. *Collection of Antique Chinese Rugs*. Sale catalogue. London, April–May, 1910.

Leitch, Gordon B. *Chinese Rugs*. New York, 1935.

Lorentz, H. A. *A View of Chinese Rugs*. London, 1972.

Newark, New Jersey. Newark Museum. *Catalogue of the Tibetan Collection and other Lamaist Material in the Newark Museum*. Vol. IV. Newark, 1961.

Parke-Bernet Galleries, Inc., New York. *Chinese Art . . . Rugs Belonging to China Institute in America*. Sale catalogue. December 1, 1962.

Schürmann, Ulrich. *Central-Asian Rugs*. Translated by Alan Grainge. Frankfurt am Main, 1969.

Society of the Four Arts, Palm Beach, Florida. *Antique Rugs Lent by The Metropolitan Museum of Art*. Palm Beach, 1966.

Tiffany Foundation, Louis Comfort. *Catalogue of Oriental and Chinese Rugs*. New York, 1920.

Tiffany Studios. *The Tiffany Studios Collection of Notable Antique Oriental Rugs*. New York, 1906.

The Tiffany Studios Collection of Notable Antique Rugs. New York, 1907.

The Tiffany Studios Collection of Antique Chinese Rugs. New York, 1908.

Washington, D.C. The Textile Museum. *East of Turkestan: An Exhibition of Chinese Rugs and Textiles*. Washington, D.C., 1967.